The Diabetes Comfort Food Cookbook

The Diabetes Comfort Food Cookbook

More Than 250 Soul-Satisfying Dishes from Breakfast to Dessert

JOHANNA BURKHARD AND JUDITH FINLAYSON

with Barbara Selley, BA, RD, Nutrition Editor

RODALE

This book is intended as a reference volume only, not as a medical manual. The information given here is designed to help you make informed decisions about your health. It is not intended as a substitute for any treatment that may have been prescribed by your doctor. If you suspect that you have a medical problem, we urge you to seek competent medical help.

Mention of specific companies, organizations, or authorities in this book does not imply endorsement by the author or publisher, nor does mention of specific companies, organizations, or authorities imply that they endorse this book, its author, or the publisher.

Internet addresses and telephone numbers given in this book were accurate at the time it went to press.

Printed in the United States of America

Rodale Inc. makes every effort to use acid-free ⊗, recycled paper ♲.

Parts of this book have been previously published as *Diabetes Comfort Food* (Robert Rose Inc., Toronto, Canada, 2006), and *The Best Diabetes Slow Cooker Recipes* (Robert Rose Inc., Toronto, Canada, 2007)

Photographs © 2006, 2007 Robert Rose Inc.

Cover and interior design by Christina Gaugler

Library of Congress Cataloging-in-Publication Data is on file with the publisher.

ISBN 13 978–1–60529–953–2

ISBN 10 1–60529–953–7

2   4   6   8   10   9   7   5   hardcover

LIVE YOUR WHOLE LIFE™

We inspire and enable people to improve their lives and the world around them

For more of our products visit **rodalestore.com** or call 800-848-4735

CONTENTS

FOREWORD

We've all overheard this conversation. Janice says to her friend, "The Johnsons are coming to dinner and I have no idea what to serve. Helen has diabetes so we can't have anything with sugar, and she shouldn't have pasta or potatoes. I just don't know where to begin." Does Janice really have a problem, or would some up-to-date information help her with her menu-planning dilemma?

Sharing meals with family and friends is one of life's greatest pleasures. Over the past eighteen years, I've had the opportunity to work with the authors of more than twenty cookbooks to develop healthier versions of traditional recipes, calculate nutrient values and diabetic food exchanges for recipes, and write nutrition advice and tips. I was delighted to work with Johanna Burkhard and Judith Finlayson, the authors of this cookbook, along with dietitian reviewers from a leading diabetes association, to bring you all these delicious recipes (including more than 100 time-saving dishes for the slow cooker!) that people with diabetes can enjoy without guilt or worry.

Sometimes, especially when faced with a health challenge such as diabetes, planning and serving healthy meals may seem overwhelming. Can you still eat your favorite foods? Do you need special foods or recipes? Can everyone in the family eat the same meals? Your health-care providers probably give you advice; well-meaning friends might contradict that advice; and on television or the Internet you'd inevitably find additional conflicting information. How do you sort it all out?

The Diabetes Comfort Food Cookbook gives you answers to those questions—whether you have diabetes and are cooking for yourself, or for a family member with diabetes, or for a circle of friends. The book is full of wholesome recipes—including such favorites as Shepherd's Pie (page 76), Easy One-Pot Macaroni and Cheese (page 193), and Zesty Barbecued Spareribs (page 112)—that will help you control your blood sugar without feeling deprived.

As you thumb through this book, you'll find chapters starting with breakfast and ending with dessert! Yes, dessert. The book features dozens of tempting favorites including Frozen Strawberry Cake (page 320), Fudgy Chocolate Brownies (page 336), and Peach Almond Crumble (page 318)—all perfect endings to the healthy meals you'll be making. And as you share the recipes with your family and friends, you'll feel comfort in knowing that they are eating healthful foods that taste just like good old-fashioned favorites.

But let's not forget Janice (who really should have this book!) and her dinner menu. Does she have to serve a meal containing no sugar, pasta, or potatoes? Does she have to give up the delicious comfort foods she loves? The short answer is "no," yet the idea that people with diabetes must severely restrict or avoid these foods altogether persists. The happy truth is that almost everyone with diabetes can eat an appropriate serving of almost any food. And you'll find no shortage of great ideas in the pages that follow. As you might suspect, many of the recipes in this book are already favorites in my household.

Bon appétit!

Barbara Selley, RD

RECIPES FOR EVERYONE

Each of us has our own favorite comfort foods—whether they are special-occasion meals that bring back memories of time spent with family and friends, or cherished recipes that inspire raves when you serve them. People with diabetes (and those planning and cooking meals for them) sometimes assume they will no longer be able to enjoy their favorite comfort foods. Not true. This book will help you prepare healthy, soul-satisfying meals using familiar recipes that every member of the family, including those with diabetes, will enjoy. These meals include a variety of breads and other grain products; vegetables and fruit; lean meat, poultry, and fish; and lower-fat dairy products. Furthermore, the book offers an analysis of calories, carbohydrate, fiber, protein, total fat, saturated fat, sodium, and cholesterol, as well as dietary exchanges per serving for each recipe. Time-saving shortcuts and techniques abound to foolproof your results and help you effortlessly manage your diabetes while pleasing your tastebuds at the same time.

It's not an exaggeration to say there's something in this book for everyone. As you walk down the street, 7 of every 100 people you encounter have diabetes. It's hard to fathom, but approximately 20.8 million American adults and children are living with diabetes—and this number has risen steadily in recent years. Whether you have diabetes yourself, know someone who does, or are simply interested in healthy eating, you will enjoy the flavorful, easy-to-prepare recipes in this book.

WHAT IS DIABETES?

Diabetes is a serious disease. The best-known early signs are high blood glucose (sugar) levels and glucose in the urine. Normally, insulin, a hormone produced by the pancreas, allows the body to remove glucose (sugar) from the blood and use it as fuel. In diabetes, blood glucose rises to unhealthy levels because it isn't removed from the blood at all, or not quickly enough. When glucose reaches a certain level, it "spills over" into the urine.

Untreated, diabetes can lead to a wide variety of debilitating and sometimes life-threatening complications involving the heart, eyes, kidneys, nerves, and circulatory system.

There are three main types of diabetes:

Type 1 diabetes most often appears in childhood, but can occur later in life. The pancreas does not produce any insulin. About 10 percent of people with diabetes have the type 1 form. There is no cure for type 1 diabetes at present, so people with type 1 need to receive insulin by injection.

Type 2 diabetes is much more prevalent, affecting about 90 percent of people with diabetes. It occurs when the pancreas produces insufficient insulin, or when the body doesn't use it properly, a condition known as insulin resistance. Until recently, type 2 diabetes was considered a condition of middle age, but, alarmingly, it is now occurring in children and teenagers. It is almost always associated with being overweight or obese.

Gestational diabetes occurs in about 4 percent of pregnant women. It usually disappears after the baby is born, but both mother and child face a higher risk of type 2 diabetes later in life.

In addition to those with known diabetes, millions of Americans of all ages have what is called *prediabetes*. These people have blood glucose readings that are above normal but not high enough for a diagnosis of diabetes (the terms *impaired fasting glucose* (IFG) and *impaired glucose tolerance* (IGT) are used to describe the test findings in prediabetes). While prediabetes can develop into type 2 diabetes, we now know it's possible in most cases to prevent this progression with healthy eating habits and physical activity.

HOW IS DIABETES MANAGED?

The most important person in the diabetes management team is the person with diabetes. The more that is known about diabetes, the easier it is to work with a physician, dietitian, pharmacist, and other members of a health-care team.

Whether you have type 1 or 2 diabetes, gestational diabetes, or prediabetes, you need to:

- manage your food intake to control blood glucose
- increase your physical activity
- achieve or maintain a healthy weight
- monitor your blood glucose
- take medication (insulin or oral medications) if required
- keep your blood pressure in a healthy range.

For information on all aspects of diabetes, its prevention, and treatment, contact your health-care providers and the American Diabetes Association: http://www.diabetes.org.

WHAT SHOULD PEOPLE WITH DIABETES EAT?

As this book shows, healthy eating recommendations for people with diabetes are very similar to those for the general population. Separate meals, special foods, and recipes are unnecessary in the management of this disease. The following information is general. Your doctor's and/or dietitian's recommendations for you may differ in some ways.

Energy (Calories) Food energy is measured in calories, which are derived from the carbohydrate, protein, fat, and alcohol in what we eat and drink.

The amount of energy you need is determined by your age, sex, body size, activity level, and whether you're currently at a healthy weight. A dietitian will help you determine the right number of calories to maintain your weight if it's at a healthy level, or to reduce it if necessary.

Carbohydrate You should get about 50 percent of your daily calories from the carbohydrate in whole-grain products, vegetables, legumes (dried peas and beans), fruit, and low-fat dairy products. You may be surprised to learn that people with diabetes can also consume moderate amounts of added sugars (another form of carbohydrate). See "Is It Really Okay to Eat Sugar?" opposite.

Fiber You should aim for a daily fiber intake of 25 to 30 grams. Start the day with a high-fiber breakfast cereal, favor whole-grain breads over ones made with white flour, choose legumes for some of your protein choices, and fill up on non-starchy vegetables.

Fat No more than 30 percent of your calories should come from fat. At 2,000 calories per day, this is equivalent to 65 grams, including fat from visible and invisible sources in meat, fish, poultry, eggs, oils and spreads, nuts and seeds, dairy products, and baked goods.

When it comes to fat, keep the following pointers in mind:

- **Keep an eye on saturated fats** (found mainly in dairy fat and meat). Saturated fat should make up less than 25 percent of your fat intake, or 16 grams or fewer.
- **Avoid trans fats.** These very bad fats are found in the partially hydrogenated vegetable oils in many packaged foods, fried fast foods, shortening, some cooking oils, solid margarines, and some tub margarines. Carefully check the Nutrition Facts panels on the products you buy.
- **Use monounsaturated vegetable oils** (olive, canola, or soybean). In addition, replace butter, shortening, stick margarine, and other trans

IS IT REALLY OKAY TO EAT SUGAR?

There is a common misperception that people with diabetes should avoid all refined sugars, such as white or brown sugar, honey, or syrups, whether used as ingredients in manufactured foods or in recipes or added to beverages and other foods at the table.

Varying amounts of different sugars occur naturally in many foods (for example, you'll find lactose in milk and glucose, fructose, and sucrose in fruit and vegetables). This is why you will find fruit, milk, and vegetable Exchange lists in the Carbohydrate Group (see page xiv). Furthermore, in the Carbohydrate Group you will also see Other Carbohydrates, which include refined sugars, and foods that are high in them.

No one should eat unlimited amounts of these Other Carbohydrates. That's because they provide carbohydrate and calories but none of the fiber, vitamins, and minerals found in other carbohydrate-containing foods.

Because added sugars are low in these vital nutrients, they should replace only small amounts of carbohydrate from other sources. The key word is "replace." Eating added sugars, or any other food in excess of what you need, will lead to weight gain and/or elevated blood glucose levels.

Current guidelines allow for up to 10 percent of total daily energy (calories) as added sugars from all sources (including processed foods). If you eat 2,000 calories per day, this translates into 50 grams of carbohydrate—about 3 Other Carbohydrate Exchanges, or about 10 teaspoons of sugar. Remember that this 50 grams includes both sugar you can see (added to your coffee, for example) and hidden sugar in sweet foods such as baked goods and carbonated beverages.

---

fat–containing margarine with *non-hydrogenated trans-free margarine.*

- **Get plenty of healthy omega-3 fats.** These are found in *fish*, especially those from cold waters, such as salmon, king mackerel, sardines, and trout. Aim to have at least two servings per week prepared with no fat or a small amount of monounsaturated fat (a teaspoon of olive oil). Avoid commercial fried fish items.
- **Watch for cholesterol in foods.** The American Diabetes Association recommends limiting *cholesterol* to no more than 200 mg per day.

Protein Found mainly in meat, fish, poultry, eggs, dairy products, and legumes, protein should make up approximately 15 to 20 percent of your calories. At an intake of 2,000 calories per day, this is equivalent to 75 to 100 grams of protein. Higher amounts are not recommended, as they may increase the work of the kidneys.

Sodium People with diabetes should follow the sodium recommendation for the general population: a maximum of 2,300 mg per day (the amount in 1 teaspoon of salt). To achieve this level, you will likely need to modify some of your food choices and change some long-established habits.

Keep the following in mind when it comes to sodium:

- Overall, the American food supply contains far more sodium than we need. As a result, many people are accustomed to levels several times higher than the 2,300-mg recommendation.
- The most familiar source of sodium is the salt that

Here are a some tips to help you reduce the sodium in your diet:

- Skip the fast food and pack a lunch for work.
- When choosing between brands at the grocery store, compare sodium values on the Nutrition Facts panels.
- Be especially careful when buying salad dressings. Quite often, reduced-fat or fat-free dressings are higher in sodium than the regular ones they replace. It's easy to make your own salad dressing with small amounts of oil.
- Use only small quantities of salted meats and processed meats, such as bologna.
- Do not routinely add salt to the cooking water for vegetables, pasta, and rice.
- Always taste food before adding salt.
- Use other seasonings such as black pepper, chilies, and sodium-free mixtures of herbs and spices to heighten the flavor of dishes.

---

we add in cooking and at the table, but for most people it supplies only about 25 percent of the sodium we consume. The remainder comes from processed grocery products and fast foods.

Alcohol If you have diabetes, you should discuss your alcohol intake with your health-care team, especially if you are prone to episodes of low blood glucose.

The general advice regarding alcohol consumption is the same for the general population and for those with diabetes: one drink per day for women and two for men. Pregnant women should not drink alcoholic beverages.

How much is one drink? One drink is defined as 15 grams of pure alcohol, which is equivalent to 12 ounces of beer, 5 ounces of wine, or 1½ ounces of spirits.

MANAGING WHAT YOU EAT

When planning meals and preparing and serving the diabetes-friendly recipes in this book, consider the following:

Plan ahead Whether you have diabetes or not, you will enjoy your meals more if you plan, shop, and

prepare ahead. Depending on your schedule, plan meals either a few days or a week ahead, and buy the ingredients you will need in advance. Try to get the family to sit down to dinner together at least one evening per week. For the other evenings, plan menu items that can be kept hot on the stove or in a slow cooker so family members can help themselves. Or, prepare and refrigerate or freeze individual servings ahead of time to reheat in the microwave. To make life less hectic for the family in the morning, prepare bag lunches and organize breakfasts the night before.

Pay attention to serving size In this era of ever-larger dinner plates, food packages, and restaurant meals, it's easy to lose sight of what a reasonable serving size looks like. You may therefore find that some portions in this book may be smaller than what you or your guests are accustomed to. Remember, these are healthy portions designed to help keep blood sugar under control.

- Pay attention to the number of servings specified in the recipes. If a recipe makes 4 servings, be sure you serve yourself one-fourth of what the recipe makes—not half! Save leftovers for the next day or freeze for later use.

- To make it easier to quickly and accurately determine portion size, use a measuring cup to check the volume of your usual cups, bowls, and serving utensils. In other words, check to see if the bowls you typically serve your soups and stews in hold 1 cup or 1½ cups. Once you've got this down, you'll be able to figure proper servings visually.

- A recipe for a liquid or semi-liquid dish (for example, a soup or stew) may state that it makes 4 servings, but how much, exactly, is a serving? This is not easy to determine, especially if others have already been served. For help in determining portion sizes for these foods, see the Portion Calculator (page xviii).

Measure accurately Be sure to use standard measuring cups and spoons to measure recipe ingredients.

- The nutrient values and exchanges on the recipes are based on the ingredient quantities and number of servings stated. If you change ingredient amounts (or the portion size), the exchanges and nutrients will not be correct for your serving.

- If ingredient amounts are incorrect, baked goods may not rise properly. So measure carefully.

- Using the wrong amount of liquid in a slow cooker recipe may make it too dry or runny. (We have included special instructions for slow cooker use on pages xv–xx.)

Utilize the Nutrients per Serving box Each recipe includes Nutrients per Serving, a nutritional analysis that breaks down calories, carbohydrate, fiber, protein, total fat, saturated fat, sodium, and cholesterol per serving. It's a great asset in planning your meals. In doing the calculations, the smaller ingredient amount was calculated when there is a range, and the first ingredient listed was used when there is a choice. Optional ingredients and those in unspecified amounts, or "to taste," were not calculated.

Utilize the Exchanges per Serving box You will find Exchanges per Serving with every recipe. The calculations are based on the American Diabetes Association food exchange values (page xiv).

ADVICE FROM YOUR DIETITIAN

Meal plans for people with diabetes are generally based on the overall proportions of carbohydrate, protein, and fat described above. To determine the right number of daily calories and the distribution of food throughout the day, your dietitian will take into account the following factors:

- the type of diabetes you have: type 1, type 2, gestational diabetes, or prediabetes
- your weight: just right, overweight, or underweight
- prescribed insulin or oral medication
- your schedule (9 to 5, the night shift, or perhaps rotating shifts?)
- your activity level

For additional information about diet and diabetes, visit www.diabetes.org.

THREE REAL-LIFE PROFILES

We've included the following profiles of John, Marilyn, and Melissa to show that you can use the recipes and information in this book no matter what type of diabetes you have. As it happens, the dietitians for all three prescribed them each 2,000 calories per day. Following the recommendations noted on pages x–xi, this would be made up of 250 grams of carbohydrate, 65 grams of fat, and 100 grams of protein.

- **John** has type 2 diabetes, which he controls with diet and physical activity alone. His dietitian has advised him to spread his 250 grams of carbohydrate evenly over his three meals, which means getting approximately 80 grams at breakfast, lunch, and dinner. He does not have snacks (they are not usually recommended for those with type 2 diabetes).

- **Marilyn** is a busy teacher and mother who also has type 2 diabetes. Unlike John, she takes an oral medication to lower her blood sugar. Her dietitian initially advised her to divide her 250 grams of carbohydrate evenly throughout the day, but it became necessary to adjust this distribution when testing showed that her blood glucose was falling too low at certain times.
- **Melissa** is an 18-year-old student athlete with type 1 diabetes. She must take insulin and uses the Exchange system to plan what she eats. Her daily meals and snacks usually include the following exchanges: Starch (5), Fruit (4), Non-Starchy Vegetable (5), Fat-free/Low-fat Milk (3), Other Carbohydrate (4), Lean Meat (6), and Fat (7). Because her activity level varies from day to day, she often needs to adjust the food quantities in her meals and snacks (and the amount of insulin she takes).

John, Marilyn, and Melissa each have different diabetes issues and consequent meal patterns, but they can all use the recipes in this book. John and Marilyn will find the calorie and carbohydrate per serving information they need in the Nutrients per Serving box accompanying each recipe. For Jennifer, there are the Exchanges per Serving counts.

You too can use the information found with each recipe to help you plan and serve healthy meals for your family and friends. All of the nutrient values have been rounded to the nearest whole number, and Exchanges to the nearest half.

EXCHANGES PER SERVING

Calculations of the Exchanges per Serving were based on the American Diabetes Association food exchange values in the table below. In these calculations, fiber is included in the carbohydrate value.

GROUPS/LISTS	NUTRIENTS PER EXCHANGE		
	Carbohydrate (g)	Protein (g)	Fat (g)
Carbohydrate Group			
Starch	15	3	0–1
Fruit	15	–	–
Milk			
Fat-free, low-fat	12	8	0–3
Reduced-fat	12	8	5
Whole	12	8	8
Other Carbohydrates	15	v*	v*
Vegetables	5	2	–
Meat and Meat Substitutes Group			
Very lean	–	7	0–1
Lean	–	7	3
Medium-fat	–	7	5
High-fat	–	7	8
Fat Group	–	–	5

* v = variable

Source: Adapted from **Exchange Lists for Meal Planning**, *American Diabetes Association and American Dietetic Association, 2003.*

A SLOW COOKER PRIMER

In this book, you'll find more than 100 recipes for the slow cooker, from wholesome breakfasts, soups, and stews, to chilies for all occasions, and even some desserts. Having a slow cooker makes it much easier to plan and prepare meals in advance and to have them on the table on time. And to help you take further advantage of the convenience provided by this helpful appliance, most of the slow cooker recipes are accompanied by Make Ahead information.

There's no question that less is better when it comes to slow cooking. And in many ways, this is the secret to its success. The appliance does its work by cooking foods very slowly—from about 200°F on the Low setting to 300°F on High. This slow, moist cooking environment enables the appliance to produce mouthwatering braised foods, chilies, and many other kinds of soups and stews, as well as delicious breakfast cereals and desserts.

AN EFFECTIVE TIME MANAGER

In addition to producing great-tasting food, a slow cooker is one of the most effective time-management tools available. Most recipes can be at least partially prepared up to two days before you intend to finish the recipe. (For detailed instructions, look for the Make Ahead that accompanies appropriate recipes.) Once the ingredients have been assembled in the stoneware and the appliance is turned on, you can pretty much forget about it. The slow cooker performs unattended while you carry on with your workday life. You can be away from the kitchen all day and return to a hot, delicious meal.

A LOW-TECH APPLIANCE

Slow cookers are amazingly low-tech. The appliance usually consists of a metal casing and a stoneware insert with a tight-fitting lid. For convenience, this insert should be removable from the metal casing, making it easier to clean and increasing its versatility as a serving dish. The casing contains the heat source: electric coils that usually surround the stoneware insert. These coils do their work using the energy it takes to power a 100-watt lightbulb. Because the slow cooker operates on such a small amount of energy, you can safely leave it turned on while you are away from home.

SLOW COOKER BASICS

Slow cookers are generally round or oval and range in size from 1 to 7 quarts. We feel there is a benefit to having two: a smaller (3- to 4-quart) one, which is ideal for making recipes with smaller yields, such as breakfast cereals and some desserts; and a larger (6-quart) oval one, which is necessary for cooking larger quantities, as well as making recipes that call for setting a baking dish or pan inside the stoneware. Because the heating coils usually surround the stoneware, most slow cookers cook from the sides, rather than the bottom, which means you'll produce better results if the stoneware is at least half full. Some manufacturers sell a "slow cooker" that is actually a multi-cooker. It has a heating element at the bottom and, in our experience, it cooks faster than a traditional slow cooker. Also, since the heat source is at the bottom, it is likely that the food will scorch during the long cooking time unless it is stirred.

Your slow cooker should come with a booklet that explains how to use the appliance. We recommend that you read this carefully and/or visit the manufacturer's Web site for specific information on the model you purchased. We've cooked with a variety of slow cookers and have found that cooking times can vary substantially from one to another. Although it may not seem particularly helpful if you're just starting out, the only firm advice we can give is: *Know your slow cooker*. After trying a few of these recipes, you will get a sense of whether your slow cooker is faster or slower than the ones we used to create the recipes in this book, and you will be able to adjust the cooking times accordingly.

Other variables that can affect cooking time are extreme humidity, power fluctuations, and high altitudes. Be extra vigilant if any of these circumstances affect you.

SLOW COOKER TIPS

Like all appliances, the slow cooker has a unique way of doing things and, as a result, you need to understand how it works and adapt your cooking style accordingly. Success with the slow cooker, like success with oven or stovetop cooking, depends on using proper cooking techniques. The slow cooker saves you time because it allows you to forget about the food once it is in the stoneware. But you must still pay attention to the advance preparation. To ensure slow cooker success:

Soften vegetables Although it requires using an extra pan, we are committed to softening most vegetables before adding them to the slow cooker. In our experience, this is not the most time-consuming part of preparing a slow cooker dish—it usually takes longer to peel and chop the vegetables, which you have to do anyway. But softening vegetables, such as onions and carrots, dramatically improves the quality of the dish for two reasons: It adds color and begins the process of caramelization, which breaks down the vegetables' natural sugars and releases their flavor. And it extracts the fat-soluble components of foods, which further enriches the taste. Moreover, tossing herbs and spices with the softened vegetables emulsifies their flavor, helping to produce a sauce in which the flavors are better integrated into the dish than they would have been if this step had been skipped.

Reduce liquid As you use your slow cooker, one of the first things you will notice is that it generates a tremendous amount of liquid. Because slow cookers cook at a low heat, tightly covered, the liquid doesn't evaporate as it would in the oven or on the stovetop. As a result, food made from traditional recipes will be watery. So the second rule of successful slow cooking is to reduce the amount of liquid. Naturally, you don't want to reduce the flavor, so we suggest using lower-sodium broth or homemade salt-free stock rather than water to cook most of the dishes. The other potential problem with liquid generation is that it can affect the results of starch dishes, such as cakes and some grains. One technique that works well with such dishes is to place folded tea towels over the top of the stoneware before covering with the lid. This prevents accumulated moisture from dripping onto the food.

Cut root vegetables into thin slices or small pieces Not surprisingly, root vegetables—carrots, parsnips, turnips and, particularly, potatoes—cook very slowly in the slow cooker. As a result, root vegetables should be thinly sliced or cut into small pieces no larger than 1-inch cubes.

Pay attention to cooking temperature Many desserts, such as those containing milk, cream, or some leavening agents, need to be cooked on High. In these recipes, a Low setting is not suggested as an option. For recipes that aren't dependent upon cooking at a particular temperature, the rule of thumb is that 1 hour of cooking on High equals 2 to 2½ hours on Low.

Don't overcook Although slow cooking reduces your chances of overcooking food, it is still not a "one size fits all" solution to meal preparation. Many vegetables, such as beans, lentils, and root vegetables, need a good 8-hour cooking span and may even benefit from a longer cooking time. But others, such as green beans and cauliflower, are usually cooked within 6 hours on Low and will be overcooked and unappetizing if left for longer. One solution (which, because of food safety concerns, is not possible if you are cooking meat) is to extend the cooking time by assembling the dish ahead, then refrigerating it overnight in the stoneware. Because the mixture and the stoneware are chilled, the vegetables will take longer to cook. This is a useful technique if you are cooking tender vegetables and need to be away from the house all day.

Use ingredients appropriately Some ingredients do not respond well to long, slow cooking at all, and should be added during the last 30 minutes of cooking, after the temperature has been increased to High. These include zucchini, peas, snow peas, fish and shellfish, and milk and cream (which will curdle if cooked too long).

Although we love to cook with peppers, we've learned that most peppers become bitter if cooked for too long. The same holds true for cayenne pepper, hot pepper sauces (such as Tabasco), and large quantities of spicy curry powder (small quantities of mild curry powder seem to fare well, possibly because natural sugars in the vegetables counter any bitterness). The solution to this problem is to add fresh green or red bell peppers to recipes during the last 30 minutes of cooking, use cayenne pepper in small quantities, if at all, and add hot pepper sauce after the dish is cooked. All of the recipes in this book address these concerns in the instructions.

Use whole-leaf herbs and coarsely ground spices Cumin seeds and other spices that have been toasted and coarsely ground and whole-leaf dried herbs (such as dried thyme and oregano leaves) release their flavors slowly throughout the long cooking period. Finely ground spices and herbs, on the other hand, tend to lose flavor during slow cooking. If you're using fresh herbs, finely chop them—unless you're using the whole stem (which works best with thyme and rosemary)—and add during the last hour of cooking.

We recommend the use of cracked black peppercorns rather than ground pepper in many of the recipes because they release flavor slowly during the long cooking process. "Cracked pepper" can be purchased in the spice section of most supermarkets, but you can make your own using a mortar and pestle. If you prefer to use ground black pepper, use one-fourth to one-half the amount of cracked black peppercorns called for in the recipe.

Find dishes and pans that fit into your stoneware Some recipes, notably breads, need to be cooked in an extra dish placed inside the slow cooker stoneware. Not only will you need a large oval slow cooker for this purpose, but finding a dish or pan that fits into the stoneware can be a challenge. I've found several kinds of dishes that suit this purpose well: standard 7-inch-square baking pans; 4-cup and 6-cup ovenproof baking dishes; 6-cup soufflé dishes; and 8- by 4-inch loaf pans.

Before you decide to make a recipe that requires a baking dish, make sure you have a container that will fit into your stoneware. We've noted the size and dimensions of the containers used in all relevant recipes. Be aware that varying the size and shape of the dish is likely to affect the cooking time.

MAXIMIZE SLOW COOKER CONVENIENCE

In addition to producing mouthwatering food, a slow cooker's great strength is convenience. Where appropriate, the recipes feature a Make Ahead tip that will help you maximize this attribute. To get the most out of your slow cooker and to keep work to a minimum, prepare ingredients up to the cooking stage the night before you intend to cook them rather than in the morning. You can also cook an entire recipe overnight in the slow cooker and refrigerate until ready to serve. (Do not reheat in the slow cooker, however.) And here's a tip: If you are making a slow cooker soup, chili, or a similar mixed dish for a much later meal, measure out single-serving amounts into individual storage containers and freeze.

SERVING SIZE MATTERS

In the 1970s, a typical pasta serving in a restaurant was 1 cup; now, it's not unusual to see a serving size of 3 cups. Bagels weighing 5 ounces or more dwarf those of 30 years ago, which were 2 to 3 ounces.

We all encounter this "portion distortion" or "portion creep" everywhere we turn. And it's easy to start choosing larger amounts of food than we need, often without realizing it. So you may find that some of the serving sizes in this book are smaller than what you're accustomed to. The Portion Calculator below will help you serve the right amount.

FOOD SAFETY IN THE SLOW COOKER

Because food cooks in a slow cooker at a very low temperature for long periods of time, this type of cooking requires a bit more vigilance about food safety than does cooking at higher temperatures. There's a delicate balance between cooking the food slowly enough to ensure that it doesn't require your attention and fast enough to ensure that food reaches temperatures that are appropriate to inhibit bacterial growth. Bacteria grow rapidly at temperatures higher than 40°F and lower than 140°F. Once the temperature reaches 165°F, bacteria are killed. Slow cooker manufacturers have designed the appliance to ensure that bacterial growth is not a concern. As long as the lid is left on and the food is cooked for the appropriate length of time, that temperature will be reached quickly enough to ensure food safety.

Unless you have made part of the recipe ahead and refrigerated it, most of the ingredients in these recipes

PORTION CALCULATOR

Delicious aromas are wafting from your slow cooker, and dinner is ready. You know the recipe makes 8 servings, but how much is 1 serving?

Dishing up the right size serving from a large quantity in a slow cooker can be a challenge. But with a little one-time-only "homework," you'll always be able to determine how much food is in your slow cooker—and thus your serving size. You'll need a measuring cup for liquids and a ruler, preferably plastic or metal.

How to Measure

1. Count the number of measuring cups of water needed to fill the slow cooker stoneware one-half to three-quarters full.

2. Measure the depth of the water to the nearest quarter inch.

3. Divide the number of cups by the depth of the water in inches to calculate the number of cups per inch.

   #### Example
   You've poured 12 cups of water into the stoneware of a 6-quart slow cooker, and measured the depth of the water as 2¾ inches (or 2.75 inches).

   12 (cups) ÷ 2.75 (inches) = 4.4 (cups per inch)

4. Use the value you obtained in Step 3 to calculate a table of volumes for various depths (rounding to the nearest cup), as follows:

are warm when added to the slow cooker (the meat has been browned and the sauce has been thickened on the stovetop), which adds a cushion of comfort to any potential concerns about food safety.

The following tips will help to ensure that food safety standards are met:

- Keep food refrigerated until you are ready to cook it. Bacteria multiply quickly at room temperature. Do not allow ingredients to get to room temperature before cooking.
- Take care when partially cooking meat or poultry. Refrigerate immediately after cooking. If you're browning meat before adding it to the slow cooker, do so just before placing it in the slow cooker. When cooking meat, try to get it to a high temperature as quickly as possible.

- If cooking a large cut of meat, such as a pot roast, which has been added to the stoneware without being browned, set the temperature on High for at least 1 hour to accelerate the cooking process.
- If preparing ingredients in advance of cooking, refrigerate precooked meat, such as ground beef or sausage, in a container separate from any vegetables. Assemble the ingredients when ready to cook.
- Pay attention to the Make Ahead instructions for those recipes that can be partially prepared in advance of cooking—they have been developed to address food safety issues.
- Do not put frozen meat, fish, or poultry into a slow cooker. Unless otherwise instructed, thaw frozen food before adding it to the slow cooker. Frozen

Example

Depth × 4.4 = Volume
2.25 inches = 10 cups
2.5 inches = 11 cups

2.75 inches = 12 cups
3 inches = 13 cups
3.25 inches = 14 cups

Keep this table handy for quick reference when you are preparing meals in your slow cooker.

5. After you have prepared a meal in your slow cooker, measure the depth of the food, then refer to your table of volumes to determine how many cups of food you have. Divide this number by the number of servings stated in the recipe to determine the size of a serving.

Example

You've prepared chili, and the recipe states that it makes 10 servings. You measure the depth of the chili and find that it is 3 inches deep. Referring to your handy table of volumes, you see that you have 13 cups of chili. You divide the number of cups (13) by the number of servings (10), and learn that each serving will be 1.3 cups (roughly 1⅓ cups). This 1⅓-cup serving will provide the Nutrients per Serving and Exchanges per Serving stated in the recipe.

Tip

This calculator can also be used to calculate portion size for any recipe cooked in a container that has more or less vertical sides.

fruits and vegetables should usually be thawed under cold running water to separate the pieces before adding them to a recipe.

- Don't lift the lid while food is cooking. Each time the lid is removed, it takes about 20 minutes for the slow cooker to recover the lost heat. This increases the time it takes for the food to reach the "safe zone."

- If you are away and the power goes out, discard the food if it has not finished cooking. If the food has cooked completely, it should be safe for up to 2 hours.

Refrigerate leftovers as quickly as possible.

TESTING FOR SAFE TEMPERATURES

If you are concerned that your slow cooker isn't cooking quickly enough to ensure food safety, try this simple test. Fill the stoneware insert with 8 cups of cold water and set the temperature to Low for 8 hours. Using an accurate thermometer (and checking quickly, because the temperature drops when the lid is removed), ensure that the temperature of the water is 185°. If the water has not reached that temperature, the slow cooker is not heating food fast enough to avoid food safety problems. If the temperature is significantly higher than that, the appliance is not cooking slowly enough to be used as a slow cooker.

LEFTOVERS

Cooked food can be kept warm in the slow cooker for up to 2 hours. At that point, it should be transferred to small containers so that it cools as rapidly as possible, and then should be refrigerated or frozen. Because the appliance heats up so slowly, food should never be reheated in a slow cooker.

BREAKFASTS, BREADS & MUFFINS

Oven French Toast

Makes 10 slices (1 slice per serving)

NUTRIENTS PER SERVING

Calories	168
Carbohydrate	19 g
Fiber	1 g
Protein	6 g
Fat, total	8 g
Fat, saturated	4 g
Sodium	245 mg
Cholesterol	88 mg

EXCHANGES PER SERVING

1	Starch
½	Medium-fat Meat
1	Fat

Expecting company and want to get a head start on the cooking? Here's a great breakfast dish that can be assembled a day ahead or frozen. Ten minutes before serving, arrange the toasts on baking sheets lightly coated with cooking spray and pop them in the oven while you make the coffee.

4 large eggs	¼ cup melted butter
1 cup low-fat milk	¾ teaspoon ground cinnamon
3 tablespoons sugar	No-sugar-added syrup (optional)
1 teaspoon vanilla extract	
10 slices day-old French bread, cut ¾" thick on the diagonal	

1. Preheat the oven to 425°F. Coat a baking sheet with cooking spray.

2. In a medium bowl, whisk together eggs, milk, 1 tablespoon of the sugar, and the vanilla. Arrange bread slices in a single layer in a 13" × 9" baking dish. Pour egg mixture over bread. Turn bread over and let stand until egg mixture is absorbed. Cover and refrigerate until ready to bake. (Recipe can be prepared up to this point the night before.)

3. Arrange bread in a single layer on the prepared baking sheet and brush tops with 2 tablespoons of the butter.

4. Bake for 10 minutes. Turn slices over and brush tops with remaining butter. Bake for 8 minutes longer, or until puffed and golden.

5. In a shallow bowl, combine cinnamon and remaining 2 tablespoons sugar. Dip both sides of baked toasts in sugar mixture to lightly coat. Serve with syrup, if using, and accompany with fruit kebabs (see box, below), if desired.

FRUIT KEBABS

Colorful fruit kebabs really dress up the breakfast plate. Thread 5 or 6 chunks of assorted fresh fruits, such as apple, banana, strawberry, kiwifruit, pear, or pineapple, onto small 4" bamboo skewers. (Trim or cut the skewers in half, if necessary, to get the right length.) One of these kebabs is a Free Food.

Buttermilk Pancakes

**Makes 18 pancakes
(2 pancakes per serving)**

TIPS

● To keep the pancakes warm, place them on a rack in a warm oven.

● Extra pancakes can be wrapped and frozen, then popped in the toaster for a quick breakfast.

● To get a head start on a weekend breakfast, measure out the dry ingredients for several batches of pancakes in advance, place in plastic bags, and store in the cupboard. Beat in the liquid ingredients and the batter is ready for the griddle.

If you want to make a breakfast that will bring the kids out from under their down comforters on a lazy weekend morning, this is it.

1¾ cups all-purpose flour	½ teaspoon salt
1 tablespoon sugar	2 large eggs
2 teaspoons baking powder	2 cups buttermilk
½ teaspoon baking soda	2 tablespoons melted butter

1. In a large bowl, combine flour, sugar, baking powder, baking soda, and salt.

2. In a medium bowl, beat eggs; add buttermilk and butter. Whisk into flour mixture to make a smooth, thick batter.

3. On an oiled, preheated griddle or in a large nonstick skillet over medium heat, drop ¼ cup of batter for each pancake and spread into 4" circles. Cook until bubbles appear on top, about 1½ minutes; turn and cook until browned on the other side.

NUTRIENTS PER SERVING

Calories	156
Carbohydrate	23 g
Fiber	1 g
Protein	6 g
Fat, total	4 g
Fat, saturated	2 g
Sodium	355 mg
Cholesterol	50 mg

EXCHANGES PER SERVING

1½	Starch
½	Fat

Creamy Morning Millet with Apples

Makes 8 servings

TIPS

● If you are cooking this cereal in a large oval slow cooker, reduce the cooking time by half.

● Use plain or vanilla-flavored rice milk, varying the quantity to suit your preference. Three cups produces a firmer result. If you like a creamier cereal, use up to 4 cups.

● Like lentils, some millet may contain bits of dirt or discolored grains. If your millet looks grimy, rinse it thoroughly in a pot of water before using. Swish it around and remove any offending particles, then rinse under cold running water.

VARIATION

Use half millet and half short-grain brown rice.

If you're tired of the same old breakfast, perk up your tastebuds by enjoying millet as a cereal. You can refrigerate leftovers for up to 2 days and reheat portions in the microwave.

● **Works best in a small (3½-quart) slow cooker (see Tips, left)**

3 to 4 cups enriched rice milk (see Tips, left)	3 apples, peeled, cored, and chopped
1 cup millet (see Tips, left)	¼ teaspoon salt

1. Coat the slow cooker stoneware with cooking spray.

2. In the prepared slow cooker, combine rice milk, millet, apples, and salt. Cover and cook on High for 4 hours or on Low for 8 hours or overnight. Stir well and spoon into bowls.

NUTRIENTS PER SERVING

Calories	171
Carbohydrate	36 g
Fiber	5 g
Protein	3 g
Fat, total	2 g
Fat, saturated	0 g
Sodium	104 mg
Cholesterol	0 mg

EXCHANGES PER SERVING

1½	Starch
1	Other Carbohydrate

Multigrain Cereal with Fruit

Makes 8 servings

TIPS

● If you are cooking this cereal in a large oval slow cooker, reduce the cooking time by half.

● This cereal tends to get dry and brown around the edges if cooked for more than 8 hours. If you need to cook it for longer, add an additional ½ cup of water.

● If you're not using Medjool dates, which are naturally soft, place the chopped dates in a micro-wave-safe dish, cover with water, and microwave on High for 30 seconds to soften before adding to the cereal.

A steaming bowl of this tasty cereal will get you off to a good start in the morning.

● **Works best in a small (3½-quart) slow cooker (see Tips, left)**

½ cup brown rice
½ cup millet (see Tips, page 4)
½ cup wheat berries
2 apples, peeled, cored, and thinly sliced
4 cups water (see Tips, left)

½ teaspoon vanilla extract
½ cup chopped pitted soft dates, preferably Medjool (see Tips, left)
Wheat germ (optional)

1. Coat the slow cooker stoneware with cooking spray.

2. In the prepared slow cooker, combine rice, millet, wheat berries, and apples. Add water and vanilla. Cover and cook on Low for up to 8 hours or overnight. Add dates and stir well. Serve sprinkled with wheat germ, if using.

NUTRIENTS PER SERVING

Calories	232
Carbohydrate	52 g
Fiber	6 g
Protein	5 g
Fat, total	1 g
Fat, saturated	0 g
Sodium	9 mg
Cholesterol	0 mg

EXCHANGES PER SERVING

2	Starch
1½	Fruit

Irish Oatmeal

Makes 4 servings

TIPS

• If you are cooking this cereal in a large oval slow cooker, reduce the cooking time by half.

• If you prefer a creamier version, use half fat-free or 2% evaporated milk and half water. This will add 1 Low-fat Milk Exchange per serving.

Although rolled oats are very tasty, steel-cut oats (often sold under the name "Irish oatmeal") are even better. They have more flavor than rolled oats and an appealing, crunchy texture.

• **Works best in a small (3½-quart) slow cooker (see Tips, left)**

1 cup steel-cut oats	4 cups water
½ teaspoon salt	

1. Coat the slow cooker stoneware with cooking spray.

2. In the prepared slow cooker, combine oats and salt. Add water. Cover and cook on High for 4 hours or on Low for 8 hours or overnight. Stir well before serving.

MINDFUL MORSELS

Many people enjoy a cup of coffee at breakfast and more throughout the day. Coffee contains caffeine—as do tea, chocolate, and many soft drinks. Experts recommend that healthy adults consume no more than 400 to 450 milligrams of caffeine per day, the amount in approximately 3 (8-ounce) cups of coffee. (Pregnant women should consume no more than 300 milligrams daily.) In addition to its well-known ability to make you jittery if you have too much, caffeine can also decrease bone density and increase the risk of fractures. Studies indicate that people who drink coffee are less prone to these effects if they have enough calcium in their diets.

NUTRIENTS PER SERVING

Calories	90
Carbohydrate	16 g
Fiber	2 g
Protein	4 g
Fat, total	2 g
Fat, saturated	1 g
Sodium	296 mg
Cholesterol	0 mg

EXCHANGES PER SERVING

1	Starch

Breakfast Rice

Makes 10 servings

Simple yet delicious, this tasty combination couldn't be easier to make.

TIPS

- If you are cooking this cereal in a large oval slow cooker, reduce the cooking time by half.

- Made with this quantity of liquid, the rice will be a bit crunchy around the edges. If you prefer a softer version or will be cooking it longer than 8 hours, add ½ cup of water or rice milk to the recipe.

VARIATION

Use half rice and half wheat berries.

- **Works best in a small (3½-quart) slow cooker (see Tips, left)**

1 cup brown rice	½ cup dried cherries or cranberries
4 cups vanilla-flavored enriched rice milk	

1. Coat the slow cooker stoneware with cooking spray.

2. In the prepared slow cooker, combine rice, rice milk, and cherries. Place a clean tea towel, folded in half (so you will have 2 layers), over the top of the stoneware to absorb moisture. Cover and cook on High for 4 hours or on Low for up to 8 hours or overnight. Stir well and serve.

MINDFUL MORSELS

Few foods are more ubiquitous than rice, which is eaten around the world. Although many people consume white rice, brown rice is far more nutritious. A complex carbohydrate, it contains much more fiber than white rice, as well as B vitamins and minerals such as manganese, selenium, and magnesium. Because it also contains essential oils, which become rancid at room temperature, brown rice should be stored in an airtight container in the refrigerator.

NUTRIENTS PER SERVING

Calories	145
Carbohydrate	31 g
Fiber	3 g
Protein	2 g
Fat, total	2 g
Fat, saturated	0 g
Sodium	37 mg
Cholesterol	0 mg

EXCHANGES PER SERVING

1	Starch
½	Fruit
½	Other Carbohydrate

Banana Nut Bread

Makes 14 servings

Most cooks have a recipe for banana bread in their files. This delicious, easy version relies simply on the flavors of banana and walnut, with honey lending extra moistness.

1¾ cups all-purpose flour
1 teaspoon baking soda
½ teaspoon salt
2 large eggs
1 cup mashed ripe bananas (about 3 bananas)

⅓ cup vegetable oil
½ cup honey
⅓ cup packed brown sugar
½ cup chopped walnuts

1. Preheat the oven to 325°F. Coat a 9" × 5" loaf pan with cooking spray.

2. In a medium bowl, sift together flour, baking soda, and salt.

3. In a large bowl, beat eggs. Stir in bananas, oil, honey, and sugar. Stir dry ingredients into banana mixture until combined. Fold in walnuts.

4. Pour batter into the prepared loaf pan. Bake for 75 minutes, or until a tester inserted in the center comes out clean. Let the pan cool on a rack for 15 minutes. Run a knife around the edges; turn out loaf, and let cool completely on the rack.

NUTRIENTS PER SERVING

Calories	211
Carbohydrate	31 g
Fiber	1 g
Protein	3 g
Fat, total	9 g
Fat, saturated	1 g
Sodium	185 mg
Cholesterol	27 mg

EXCHANGES PER SERVING

1	Starch
1	Other Carbohydrate
1½	Fat

Banana-Walnut Oat Bread

Makes 10 servings

● This bread, like the others in this book, can be made in almost any kind of baking dish that will fit into your slow cooker. A variety of baking pans work well: A small loaf pan (about 8" × 4") makes a traditionally shaped bread; a round (6-cup) soufflé dish or square (7") baking dish produces slices of different shapes. All taste equally good.

● To ease cleanup, mix the dry ingredients on a sheet of waxed paper instead of in a bowl.

NUTRIENTS PER SERVING

Calories	262
Carbohydrate	35 g
Fiber	2 g
Protein	5 g
Fat, total	12 g
Fat, saturated	5 g
Sodium	278 mg
Cholesterol	57 mg

EXCHANGES PER SERVING

1½	Starch
½	Fruit
½	Other Carbohydrate
2	Fat

Serve this moist and flavorful bread for a delicious breakfast—or even for dessert.

● **Large (minimum 5-quart) oval slow cooker**

⅔ cup brown sugar	2 tablespoons milled flaxseed
⅓ cup butter, softened	2 teaspoons baking powder
2 large eggs	½ teaspoon salt
1¼ cups mashed ripe bananas (about 3 bananas)	¼ teaspoon baking soda
¾ cup all-purpose flour	½ cup finely chopped walnuts
¾ cup old-fashioned rolled oats	

1. Coat an 8" × 4" loaf pan or a 6-cup soufflé dish or 7"-square baking dish with cooking spray (see Tips, left).

2. In a large bowl, beat sugar and butter until light and creamy. Add eggs one at a time, beating until incorporated. Beat in bananas.

3. In a separate large bowl (see Tips, left), combine flour, oats, flaxseed, baking powder, salt, and baking soda. Add to banana mixture, stirring just until combined; do not overmix. Fold in walnuts.

4. Spoon batter into the prepared pan. Cover tightly with foil and secure with a string. Place the pan in the slow cooker and pour in enough boiling water to come 1" up the sides. Cover and cook on High for 3 hours, or until a tester inserted in the center comes out clean. Unmold and serve warm or let cool.

Carrot Bread

Makes 12 servings

● This bread, like the others in this book, can be made in almost any kind of baking dish that will fit into your slow cooker. A variety of baking pans work well: A small loaf pan (about 8" × 4") makes a traditionally shaped bread; a round (6-cup) soufflé dish or square (7") baking dish produces slices of different shapes. All taste equally good.

● Whole wheat flour quickly becomes rancid at room temperature and should be stored in the freezer. It will keep for up to a year and can be used directly from the freezer.

Serve this tasty bread as a snack or for a healthy breakfast.

● **Large (minimum 5-quart) oval slow cooker**

1½ cups all-purpose flour	½ cup packed brown sugar
½ cup whole wheat flour (see Tips, left)	¼ cup granulated sugar
2 teaspoons baking powder	3 tablespoons olive oil
1 teaspoon ground cinnamon	1 large egg, beaten
½ teaspoon ground cloves	1½ cups peeled shredded carrots
½ teaspoon salt	⅓ cup chopped pecans
¾ cup low-fat plain yogurt	

1. Coat an 8" × 4" loaf pan or a 6-cup round soufflé or 7"-square baking dish with cooking spray (see Tips, left).

2. In a large bowl, combine the all-purpose flour, whole wheat flour, baking powder, cinnamon, cloves, and salt.

3. In a medium bowl, beat together yogurt, sugars, oil, and egg. Add to flour mixture, stirring just until combined; do not overmix. Fold in carrots and pecans.

4. Spoon batter into the prepared pan. Cover tightly with foil and secure with a string. Place the pan in the slow cooker and pour in enough boiling water to come 1" up the sides of the dish. Cover and cook on High for 4 hours, or until a tester inserted in the center of loaf comes out clean. Unmold and serve warm or let cool.

NUTRIENTS PER SERVING

Calories	199
Carbohydrate	32 g
Fiber	2 g
Protein	4 g
Fat, total	6 g
Fat, saturated	1 g
Sodium	169 mg
Cholesterol	16 mg

EXCHANGES PER SERVING

1	Starch
1	Other Carbohydrate
1	Fat

Lemon-Yogurt Loaf

● Double this recipe to keep an extra loaf handy in the freezer. Wrap it in plastic wrap, then in foil, and freeze for up to 1 month.

VARIATION

Lemon Poppy Seed Loaf
Stir 2 tablespoons poppy seeds into the flour mixture before combining with the yogurt mixture.

NUTRIENTS PER SERVING

Calories	170
Carbohydrate	26 g
Fiber	1 g
Protein	3 g
Fat, total	6 g
Fat, saturated	1 g
Sodium	125 mg
Cholesterol	27 mg

EXCHANGES PER SERVING

1	Starch
½	Other Carbohydrate
1½	Fat

Here's a lemon-flavored loaf that stays moist for days—if it lasts that long.

LEMON-YOGURT LOAF

1¾ cups all-purpose flour
1 teaspoon baking powder
½ teaspoon baking soda
¼ teaspoon salt
2 large eggs
¾ cup sugar
¾ cup plain low-fat yogurt
⅓ cup vegetable oil
1 tablespoon grated lemon zest

TOPPING

2 tablespoons fresh lemon juice
2 tablespoons granulated sugar

1. Preheat the oven to 350°F. Coat a 9" × 5" loaf pan with cooking spray.

2. **Make the loaf:** In a large bowl, combine flour, baking powder, baking soda, and salt.

3. In another large bowl, beat eggs. Stir in sugar, yogurt, oil, and zest. Fold in flour mixture to make a smooth batter.

4. Spoon into the prepared pan; bake for 50 to 60 minutes, or until a tester inserted in the center comes out clean. Transfer the pan to a rack; do not remove loaf from the pan.

5. **Make the topping:** As soon as the loaf comes out of the oven, in a small saucepan, heat lemon juice and sugar; bring to a boil. Cook, stirring, until sugar is dissolved. (Or place in a microwaveable glass bowl and microwave on High for 1 minute, stirring once.) Pour topping over hot loaf in the pan; let cool completely before turning loaf out of the pan.

Orange-Pumpkin Loaf

Makes 14 servings

This bread is so much easier to bake than pumpkin pie but still loaded with the spice-scented flavors we all love.

1 cup all-purpose flour	¼ teaspoon ground cloves or allspice
¾ cup whole wheat or all-purpose flour	1¼ cups packed brown sugar
2 teaspoons baking powder	2 large eggs
½ teaspoon baking soda	1 cup canned pumpkin purée (not pie filling)
½ teaspoon salt	⅓ cup vegetable oil
1½ teaspoons ground cinnamon	¼ cup orange juice
½ teaspoon freshly grated nutmeg	2 teaspoons grated orange zest

1. Preheat the oven to 350°F. Coat a 9" × 5" loaf pan with cooking spray.

2. In a large bowl, combine all-purpose flour, whole wheat flour, baking powder, baking soda, and salt.

3. In another large bowl, combine cinnamon, nutmeg, and cloves. Transfer 1 teaspoon of the spice mixture to a small bowl; add 2 tablespoons of the brown sugar. Set aside for topping.

4. Add remaining brown sugar to the large bowl with the spices. Add eggs and beat well. Stir in pumpkin, oil, juice, and zest. Add dry ingredients to pumpkin mixture and stir until just combined.

5. Spoon batter into the prepared loaf pan. Sprinkle top with reserved spice-sugar mixture. Bake for 50 to 55 minutes, or until a tester inserted in the center comes out clean. Let the pan cool on a rack for 15 minutes; turn loaf out and let cool completely.

NUTRIENTS PER SERVING

Calories	195
Carbohydrate	33 g
Fiber	2 g
Protein	3 g
Fat, total	6 g
Fat, saturated	1 g
Sodium	185 mg
Cholesterol	27 mg

EXCHANGES PER SERVING

1	Starch
1	Other Carbohydrate
1	Fat

Cheddar Drop Biscuits

Makes 15 servings

● To assemble the recipe ahead of time, place the dry ingredients in a bowl. Cut in the butter, add the cheese, cover, and refrigerate. While the oven is preheating, stir in the milk and continue with the recipe.

● If you (or your children) aren't a fan of chives, simply leave them out.

Serve these wonderful biscuits straight from the oven. Consider baking a double batch if you're expecting a hungry crowd.

2 cups all-purpose flour	2 tablespoons chopped fresh chives plus additional for topping
1 tablespoon baking powder	1 cup low-fat milk
½ teaspoon salt	
⅓ cup room-temperature butter, cut into pieces	
1 cup coarsely shredded light Cheddar cheese	

1. Preheat the oven to 400°F. Coat a baking sheet with cooking spray.

2. In a large bowl, combine flour, baking powder, and salt. Cut in butter using a pastry blender or 2 knives to make coarse crumbs. Add cheese and 2 tablespoons of the chives. Stir in milk to make a soft, sticky dough. Use a ¼-cup measure to drop 15 portions onto the prepared baking sheet. Sprinkle tops with remaining chopped chives.

3. Bake on the middle rack of the oven for 18 to 20 minutes, or until edges are golden. Transfer biscuits to a rack and serve warm.

NUTRIENTS PER SERVING

Calories	129
Carbohydrate	14 g
Fiber	1 g
Protein	4 g
Fat, total	6 g
Fat, saturated	4 g
Sodium	245 mg
Cholesterol	17 mg

EXCHANGES PER SERVING

1	Starch
1	Fat

Teatime Scones

Apricot and Candied Ginger Scones Substitute ¼ cup chopped dried apricots for the currants, and add 2 tablespoons finely chopped candied ginger to the flour mixture.

Brew a steaming pot of tea, invite some good friends over, and spoil them with these tender, light scones.

2 cups all-purpose flour
¼ cup plus 2 teaspoons sugar
1 tablespoon baking powder
½ teaspoon baking soda
½ teaspoon salt
½ cup cold butter, cut into pieces

½ cup dried currants or raisins
½ cup plus 1 tablespoon buttermilk
1 large egg

1. Preheat the oven to 400°F. Coat a large baking sheet with cooking spray.

2. In a large bowl, stir together flour, ¼ cup of the sugar, baking powder, baking soda, and salt. Cut in butter using a pastry blender or 2 knives to make coarse crumbs. Stir in currants.

3. In a medium bowl, beat ½ cup of the buttermilk and egg; stir into dry ingredients to make a soft dough.

4. Turn dough out onto a floured board and knead gently 3 or 4 times. Using a floured rolling pin, pat or roll out dough into a circular shape about ¾" thick. Cut out 18 rounds using a 2" floured cutter; arrange on the prepared baking sheet.

5. Brush rounds with remaining 1 tablespoon buttermilk and sprinkle with remaining 2 teaspoons sugar.

6. Bake for 16 to 20 minutes, or until golden. Transfer to a rack and serve warm or at room temperature.

NUTRIENTS PER SERVING

Calories	128
Carbohydrate	17 g
Fiber	1 g
Protein	2 g
Fat, total	6 g
Fat, saturated	3 g
Sodium	210 mg
Cholesterol	24 mg

EXCHANGES PER SERVING

½	Starch
½	Other Carbohydrate
1	Fat

Whole Wheat Soda Bread

Makes 8 servings

This homey bread is easy to make and a delicious accompaniment to many main course dishes. Try it with Irish Stew (page 115).

● **Large (minimum 5-quart) oval slow cooker**

1 cup all-purpose flour	¾ teaspoon salt
1 cup whole wheat flour (see Tips, left)	1¼ cups buttermilk
¾ teaspoon baking soda	

1. Lightly coat an 8" × 4" loaf pan or a 6-cup soufflé dish or 7" square baking dish with cooking spray (see Tips, left).

2. In a large bowl, stir together flours, baking soda, and salt. Make a well in the center, pour buttermilk into the well, and mix just until combined; do not overmix. Spread into the prepared pan.

3. Cover the pan tightly with foil and secure with a string. Place the pan in the slow cooker and pour in enough boiling water to come 1" up the sides of the dish. Cover and cook on High for 2½ to 3 hours, or until bread springs back when touched lightly in the center. Unmold and serve warm.

TIPS

● This bread, like the others in this book, can be made in almost any kind of baking dish that will fit into your slow cooker. A variety of baking pans work well: A small loaf pan (about 8" × 4") makes a traditionally shaped bread; a round (6-cup) soufflé dish or square 7" baking dish produces slices of different shapes. All taste equally good.

● Whole wheat flour quickly becomes rancid at room temperature and should be stored in the freezer. It will keep for up to a year and can be used directly from the freezer.

MINDFUL MORSELS

Substituting whole wheat flour for some or all of the white flour in any recipe is a healthful strategy. Whole wheat flour includes all three nutrient-rich parts of the wheat berry: the bran, germ, and endosperm (all-purpose flour uses only the endosperm). Whole wheat flour has more protein, fiber, niacin, pantothenic acid, and vitamins E and B_6 than white flour. It is also much higher in magnesium and zinc. The fiber in whole wheat flour is one of its most valuable attributes.

NUTRIENTS PER SERVING

Calories	123
Carbohydrate	25 g
Fiber	2 g
Protein	5 g
Fat, total	1 g
Fat, saturated	0 g
Sodium	379 mg
Cholesterol	1 mg

EXCHANGES PER SERVING

1½	Starch

Whole Grain Irish Soda Bread

Makes 12 servings

Old-fashioned soda bread is a wonderful accompaniment to a hearty soup or stew. Any leftovers are delicious toasted.

2 cups whole wheat flour
1²⁄₃ cups all-purpose flour
²⁄₃ cup plus 1 tablespoon old-fashioned rolled oats
1 tablespoon sugar

1½ teaspoons baking soda
½ teaspoon salt
2 cups plus 1 tablespoon buttermilk

1. Preheat the oven to 375°F. Coat a baking sheet with cooking spray.

2. In a large bowl, combine whole wheat flour, all-purpose flour, ²⁄₃ cup of the oats, sugar, baking soda, and salt. Stir well. Make a well in the center and add 2 cups of the buttermilk. Stir until a soft dough forms.

3. Turn dough out onto a lightly floured board and knead 5 or 6 times until smooth. Shape into a ball, then pat into an 8" round. Place on the prepared baking sheet. With a sharp knife dipped in flour, cut a large ½"-deep cross on top of loaf.

4. Brush loaf with remaining 1 tablespoon buttermilk and sprinkle with remaining 1 tablespoon oats.

5. Bake for 50 to 60 minutes, or until well risen and golden; loaf should sound hollow when tapped on base. Immediately wrap in a clean dry dish towel; set aside to cool. This prevents the crust from becoming too hard.

NUTRIENTS PER SERVING

Calories	166
Carbohydrate	33 g
Fiber	3 g
Protein	6 g
Fat, total	1 g
Fat, saturated	0 g
Sodium	300 mg
Cholesterol	1 mg

EXCHANGES PER SERVING

2	Starch

Blueberry Cornmeal Muffins

Makes 12 servings

TIP

● To minimize the problem of frozen blueberries tinting the batter blue, place them in a sieve and quickly rinse under cold water to get rid of any ice crystals. Blot dry with paper towels. Place the berries in a bowl and toss with 2 tablespoons of the flour mixture. Use immediately, folding them into the batter with a few quick strokes.

When it comes to celebrating the pleasures of summer fruits, nothing beats juicy blueberries—especially when teamed with lemon in these deliciously moist muffins.

1½ cups all-purpose flour	¾ cup low-fat milk
½ cup sugar	¼ cup butter, melted
⅓ cup cornmeal	1 teaspoon grated lemon zest
2½ teaspoons baking powder	1 cup fresh or frozen blueberries
¼ teaspoon salt	
1 large egg	

1. Preheat the oven to 400°F. Line a 12-cup muffin pan with paper liners.

2. In a large bowl, stir together flour, sugar, cornmeal, baking powder, and salt.

3. In a medium bowl, beat egg. Stir in milk, butter, and zest. Add to dry ingredients and stir just until combined. Gently fold in blueberries.

4. Spoon batter into 12 prepared muffin cups, filling three-quarters full.

5. Bake for 20 to 24 minutes, or until tops are firm to the touch and lightly browned. Let muffins cool in the pans for 5 minutes, then transfer to a rack and cool completely.

NUTRIENTS PER SERVING

Calories	157
Carbohydrate	26 g
Fiber	1 g
Protein	3 g
Fat, total	5 g
Fat, saturated	3 g
Sodium	155 mg
Cholesterol	26 mg

EXCHANGES PER SERVING

1	Starch
½	Other Carbohydrate
1	Fat

Carrot-Raisin Muffins

Makes 16 servings

TIP

● Have only 1 muffin pan? Place muffin paper liners in 6-ounce glass custard cups or small ramekins, and fill them with extra batter. Place the ramekins in the oven and bake alongside the muffin pan.

Packed with fruit and carrots, these scrumptious muffins are perfect for breakfast. But they're just as tasty for afternoon snacks or stowed away in a lunch box.

2 cups all-purpose flour
¾ cup sugar
1½ teaspoons ground cinnamon
1 teaspoon baking powder
1 teaspoon baking soda
½ teaspoon freshly grated nutmeg
½ teaspoon salt
1½ cups grated carrots (about 3 medium)

1 cup peeled grated apples
½ cup sweetened shredded coconut
½ cup raisins
2 large eggs
⅔ cup plain low-fat yogurt
⅓ cup vegetable oil

1. Preheat the oven to 375°F. Line two muffin pans with paper liners (16 cups).

2. In a large bowl, stir together flour, sugar, cinnamon, baking powder, baking soda, nutmeg, and salt. Stir in carrots, apples, coconut, and raisins.

3. In another large bowl, beat eggs; add yogurt and oil. Stir into flour mixture until just combined; do not overmix. (Batter will be very thick.)

4. Spoon batter into 16 prepared muffin cups, filling almost to the top.

5. Bake for 25 to 30 minutes, or until tops spring back when lightly touched. Let muffins cool in the pans for 5 minutes, then transfer to a rack to cool completely.

NUTRIENTS PER SERVING

Calories	189
Carbohydrate	30 g
Fiber	1 g
Protein	3 g
Fat, total	7 g
Fat, saturated	2 g
Sodium	200 mg
Cholesterol	24 mg

EXCHANGES PER SERVING

1	Starch
½	Fruit
½	Other Carbohydrate
1	Fat

Maple Walnut–Apple Muffins

Makes 12 servings

These wholesome muffins have great appeal. For best results, use the light-colored California walnuts.

1¼ cups all-purpose flour	1 cup coarsely grated apple
2½ teaspoons baking powder	1 cup quick-cooking rolled oats
½ teaspoon baking soda	⅔ cup pure maple syrup
¼ teaspoon salt	½ cup low-fat plain yogurt
⅓ cup finely chopped walnuts	¼ cup vegetable oil
1 large egg	

1. Preheat the oven to 400°F. Line a 12-cup muffin pan with paper liners.

2. In a large bowl, combine flour, baking powder, baking soda, and salt. Stir in walnuts.

3. In another large bowl, beat egg. Stir in apple, oats, syrup, yogurt, and oil. Add to flour mixture and stir just until combined; do not overmix.

4. Spoon batter into 12 prepared muffin cups, filling three-quarters full.

5. Bake for 20 minutes, or until tops are springy to the touch. Let muffins cool in the pan for 5 minutes, then transfer to a rack to cool completely.

NUTRIENTS PER SERVING

Calories	206
Carbohydrate	30 g
Fiber	2 g
Protein	4 g
Fat, total	8 g
Fat, saturated	1 g
Sodium	170 mg
Cholesterol	16 mg

EXCHANGES PER SERVING

1	Starch
1	Other Carbohydrate
1½	Fat

Bran Muffins

● Always measure the oil before measuring sticky sweeteners such as molasses or honey. (For recipes that don't call for oil, coat the cup measure with cooking spray or lightly coat with oil. You'll find every last drop of sweetener will easily pour out.)

Bran muffins never go out of style. Nicely moistened with molasses, these muffins will become a morning favorite.

2 large eggs	1 cup wheat bran
1 cup buttermilk	1 teaspoon baking soda
⅓ cup packed brown sugar	½ teaspoon baking powder
¼ cup vegetable oil	¼ teaspoon salt
¼ cup molasses	½ cup raisins or chopped apricots
1¼ cups whole wheat flour	

1. Preheat the oven to 400°F. Line a 12-cup muffin pan with paper liners.

2. In a large bowl, beat eggs. Add buttermilk, sugar, oil, and molasses.

3. In another large bowl, stir together flour, bran, baking soda, baking powder, and salt. Add to liquid ingredients and stir to make a smooth batter; fold in raisins.

4. Spoon into 12 prepared muffin cups, filling three-quarters full.

5. Bake for 20 to 24 minutes, or until tops spring back when lightly touched. Let muffins cool in the pan for 10 minutes, then transfer to a rack to cool completely.

NUTRIENTS PER SERVING

Calories	175
Carbohydrate	29 g
Fiber	4 g
Protein	4 g
Fat, total	6 g
Fat, saturated	1 g
Sodium	205 mg
Cholesterol	32 mg

EXCHANGES PER SERVING

1	Starch
1	Other Carbohydrate
1	Fat

APPETIZING
APPETIZERS

Always Popular Layered Bean Dip

Makes 16 servings (¼ cup per serving)

Variations on this popular bean dip always make the party circuit. This one has an oregano-bean base, a creamy jalapeño-cheese layer, and a fresh, vibrant topping of tomatoes, olives, and cilantro.

1 can (19 ounces) red kidney beans or black beans, drained and rinsed

1 clove garlic, minced

1 teaspoon dried oregano

½ teaspoon ground cumin

1 tablespoon water

1 cup shredded light Cheddar cheese

¾ cup light sour cream

1 tablespoon minced pickled jalapeño pepper (see Tips, left)

2 tomatoes, seeded and finely diced

2 scallions, finely chopped

⅓ cup sliced black olives

⅓ cup chopped fresh cilantro or parsley (see Tips, left)

1. In a food processor, combine beans, garlic, oregano, cumin, and water; process until smooth. Spread in a shallow serving dish or pie plate.

2. In a medium bowl, combine cheese, sour cream, and jalapeño. Spread over bean layer. (The dip can be assembled to this point earlier in the day; cover and refrigerate until ready to serve.)

3. Just before serving, sprinkle with tomatoes, scallions, olives, and cilantro. Serve with baked tortilla chips or pita crisps (see box, below).

NUTRIENTS PER SERVING

Calories	74
Carbohydrate	8 g
Fiber	3 g
Protein	5 g
Fat, total	3 g
Fat, saturated	1 g
Sodium	185 mg
Cholesterol	5 mg

EXCHANGES PER SERVING

½	Other Carbohydrate
½	Medium-fat Meat

PITA CRISPS

For a lower-fat alternative to tortilla chips, try pita crisps. To make them, separate three 7" pitas into rounds and cut each into 8 wedges. Place them in a single layer on baking sheets; bake at 350°F for 8 to 10 minutes, or until crisp and lightly toasted. Let cool, then store in a covered container. Pita crisps can be made 1 day ahead.

Black Bean and Salsa Dip

This tasty Cuban-inspired dip is a welcome treat any time. Serve it with tortilla chips, tostadas, crisp crackers, or with fresh vegetables cut for dipping (crudités)—a Free Food.

● **Works best in a small (maximum 3½-quart) slow cooker**

2 teaspoons cumin seeds	1 teaspoon chili powder
1 can (19 ounces) canned black beans, drained and rinsed, or 2 cups cooked dried black beans (see Basic Beans Variation, page 236)	1 teaspoon cracked black peppercorns
	1 jalapeño pepper, finely chopped, optional (see Tips, left)
8 ounces light cream cheese, cubed	Finely chopped scallions (optional)
½ cup tomato salsa (see Tips, left)	Finely chopped cilantro (optional)
¼ cup light sour cream	

1. In a dry medium skillet over medium heat, toast cumin seeds, stirring, until fragrant and just beginning to brown, about 3 minutes. Immediately transfer to a mortar or spice grinder and grind. Set aside.

2. In the slow cooker stoneware, combine beans, cream cheese, salsa, sour cream, reserved cumin, chili powder, peppercorns, and jalapeño, if using. Cover and cook on High for 1 hour. Stir again and cook on High for 30 minutes longer, or until mixture is hot and bubbly. Serve immediately or set temperature to Low until ready to serve. Garnish with scallions and cilantro, if desired.

MINDFUL MORSELS

Look for low-fat baked varieties of "dippers" (no more than 3 grams of fat per 50 grams), and estimate the weight of 1 piece from the Nutrition Facts on the package. Twenty grams of low-fat baked tortilla chips is equivalent to a Starch Exchange. Because they are usually high in sodium, dippers should be consumed in small quantities.

NUTRIENTS PER SERVING

Calories	42
Carbohydrate	9 g
Fiber	2 g
Protein	4 g
Fat, total	2 g
Fat, saturated	0 g
Sodium	145 mg
Cholesterol	0 mg

EXCHANGES PER SERVING

½	Starch
½	Lean Meat

Creamy Spinach Dip

Makes 24 servings (2 tablespoons per serving)

TIPS

● To defrost spinach, remove packaging and place the spinach in a 4-cup casserole dish. Cover and microwave on High, stirring once, for 6 to 8 minutes, or until defrosted. Place in a strainer to press out excess moisture.

● To grate lemon zest, use a Microplane grater, which looks like a carpenter's rasp. When lemons are bargain-priced, stock up for the future. Grate the zest and squeeze the juice; place in separate containers and freeze.

Note: *The suggested accompaniments for this recipe are not included in the nutrients or exchanges per serving. Whether you keep track of exchanges or count carbohydrates, remember to account for what these additional foods contribute.*

Here's a dip that's so much tastier than the ones made with salty soup mixes. Serve with vegetable dippers, such as carrot, bell pepper, cucumber, celery, broccoli, fennel, or cauliflower. Use any leftovers as a dressing for pasta or potato salads or as a spread for sandwiches.

1 package (10 ounces) fresh or frozen spinach	1 clove garlic, minced
1 cup crumbed light feta cheese (about 4 ounces)	1 teaspoon grated lemon zest (see Tips, left)
⅓ cup chopped scallions	1½ cups light sour cream
¼ cup chopped fresh dill	½ cup light mayonnaise

1. Remove tough stem ends from fresh spinach, if using; wash leaves in cold water. Place spinach with moisture clinging to leaves in a large saucepan. Cook over high heat, stirring, until just wilted. (If using frozen spinach, see Tips, left.) Transfer spinach to a colander to drain. Squeeze out moisture by hand; wrap in a clean, dry towel, and squeeze out any excess moisture.

2. In a food processor, combine spinach, cheese, scallions, dill, garlic, and zest. Process until very finely chopped.

3. Add sour cream and mayonnaise; process, pulsing, just until combined. Transfer to a serving bowl, cover, and refrigerate until ready to serve. Serve in a bread bowl (see box, below), if desired, and accompany with vegetable dippers.

BREAD BOWL FOR SERVING DIP

Using a serrated knife, slice 2" off the top of a small (1-pound), unsliced round loaf of whole wheat or sourdough bread. Hollow out the loaf, reserving the contents and leaving a shell about 1" thick. Spoon the dip into the bread bowl. Cut the reserved bread into strips or cubes and serve along with vegetable dippers.

NUTRIENTS PER SERVING

Calories	45
Carbohydrate	3 g
Fiber	0 g
Protein	2 g
Fat, total	3 g
Fat, saturated	1 g
Sodium	105 mg
Cholesterol	3 mg

EXCHANGES PER SERVING

1	Fat

Sumptuous Spinach and Artichoke Dip

Makes 12 servings (⅓ cup per serving)

TIPS

• If you prefer a smoother dip, place the spinach and artichokes in a food processor in separate batches, and pulse until desired the degree of smoothness is achieved. Then combine with the remaining ingredients in the slow cooker.

Note: *The suggested accompaniments for this recipe are not included in the nutrients or exchanges per serving. Whether you keep track of exchanges or count carbohydrates, remember to account for what these additional foods contribute.*

This classic dip has its roots in Provençal cuisine, where vegetables are baked with cheese and served as a gratin. Serve with crudités (bite-size vegetable dippers)—a Free Food—or with low-fat baked tortilla chips.

• **Works best in a small (maximum 3½-quart) slow cooker**

1 cup shredded part-skim mozzarella cheese	1 can (14 ounces) artichokes, drained and finely chopped
8 ounces light cream cheese, cubed	1 pound fresh spinach, stems removed, or 1 package (10 ounces) frozen spinach, thawed if frozen (see Tip, p. 24)
¼ cup freshly grated Parmesan cheese	
1 clove garlic, minced	
¼ teaspoon freshly ground black pepper	

In the slow cooker stoneware, combine mozzarella, cream cheese, Parmesan, garlic, pepper, artichokes, and spinach. Cover and cook on High for 2 hours, or until hot and bubbly. Stir well before serving.

MINDFUL MORSELS

One-half cup of cooked spinach or another dark green leafy vegetable is an excellent source of folate, a B vitamin that is required for the proper development of all the cells in the body.

NUTRIENTS PER SERVING

Calories	97
Carbohydrate	5 g
Fiber	2 g
Protein	7 g
Fat, total	6 g
Fat, saturated	4 g
Sodium	311 mg
Cholesterol	20 mg

EXCHANGES PER SERVING

1	Vegetable
½	High-fat Meat

Do-Ahead Herb Dip

Makes 16 servings (2 tablespoons per serving)

● Other fresh herbs, including basil, can be added according to what you have in the fridge or growing in your garden. If you're fond of fresh dill, increase the amount to 2 tablespoons.

● This dip also makes a great dressing for pasta and potato salads. Store it in a covered container in the refrigerator for up to 1 week.

Note: *The suggested accompaniments for this recipe are not included in the nutrients or exchanges per serving. Whether you keep track of exchanges or count carbohydrates, remember to account for what these additional foods contribute.*

This creamy dip relies on lower-fat dairy products and zesty herbs, so it clocks in with a lot less fat and calories than you might imagine. Make it at least a day ahead to let the flavors develop. Serve with fresh veggie dippers.

1 cup 1% cottage cheese	1 tablespoon chopped fresh dill
½ cup light mayonnaise	1½ teaspoons Dijon mustard
½ cup low-fat plain yogurt or light sour cream	1 teaspoon red wine vinegar or lemon juice
⅓ cup finely chopped fresh parsley	Hot pepper sauce
2 tablespoons finely chopped fresh chives or minced scallions	

1. In a food processor, purée cottage cheese, mayonnaise, and yogurt until very smooth and creamy.

2. Transfer to a serving bowl. Stir in parsley, chives, dill, mustard, vinegar, and pepper sauce to taste. Cover and refrigerate until ready to serve.

NUTRIENTS PER SERVING

Calories	40
Carbohydrate	2 g
Fiber	0 g
Protein	2 g
Fat, total	3 g
Fat, saturated	1 g
Sodium	130 mg
Cholesterol	4 mg

EXCHANGES PER SERVING

½	Medium-fat Meat

5-Minute Crab Dip

Makes 8 servings (¼ cup per serving)

● Serve with melba toast rounds or crisp vegetable dippers.

5-Minute Clam Dip
Substitute 1 can (5 ounces) drained chopped clams for the crabmeat. Stir in 1 minced garlic clove, if desired.

Note: *The suggested accompaniments for this recipe are not included in the nutrients or exchanges per serving. Whether you keep track of exchanges or count carbohydrates, remember to account for what these additional foods contribute.*

With a can of crabmeat in the pantry and cream cheese in the fridge, you're all set to whip up a dip in 5 minutes flat. You can make it in the microwave or just as easily on the stove top over medium heat.

8 ounces light cream cheese

1 can (6 ounces) crabmeat, drained, liquid reserved

¼ cup finely chopped scallions

2 teaspoons fresh lemon juice

½ teaspoon Worcestershire sauce

¼ teaspoon paprika

Hot pepper sauce

1. Place cream cheese in a medium microwaveable bowl. Microwave on Medium for 2 minutes, or until softened. Stir until smooth.

2. Stir in crabmeat, scallions, 2 tablespoons of the reserved crab liquid, the lemon juice, Worcestershire sauce, paprika, and pepper sauce to taste. Microwave on Medium-High for 2 minutes, or until piping hot. Serve warm.

NUTRIENTS PER SERVING

Calories	83
Carbohydrate	2 g
Fiber	0 g
Protein	5 g
Fat, total	6 g
Fat, saturated	3 g
Sodium	345 mg
Cholesterol	20 mg

EXCHANGES PER SERVING

½	Medium-fat Meat
1	Fat

Italian White Bean Spread

Makes 16 servings (2 tablespoons per serving)

TIP

● The spread can be made up to 3 days ahead.

VARIATION

Instead using fresh basil, increase the chopped parsley to 2 tablespoons and add ½ teaspoon dried basil to the onions when cooking.

Note: The suggested accompaniments for this recipe are not included in the nutrients or exchanges per serving. Whether you keep track of exchanges or count carbohydrates, remember to account for what these additional foods contribute.

Serve this tasty, easy-to-make spread with warm squares of focaccia or pita crisps (see page 22).

2 tablespoons olive oil
1 small onion, finely chopped
2 large cloves garlic, finely chopped
1 tablespoon red wine vinegar
1 can (19 ounces) white kidney beans, drained and rinsed
2 tablespoons finely chopped oil-packed sun-dried tomatoes
1 tablespoon chopped fresh basil
1 tablespoon chopped fresh parsley
Freshly ground black pepper

1. In a small saucepan, heat oil over medium-low heat. Add onion and garlic; cook, stirring occasionally, until onion is softened (do not brown), about 5 minutes. Stir in vinegar and remove from the heat.

2. Transfer onion mixture to a food processor. Add beans and purée until smooth.

3. Transfer to a bowl. Stir in tomatoes, basil, and parsley; season with pepper to taste. Cover and refrigerate until ready to serve.

NUTRIENTS PER SERVING

Calories	51
Carbohydrate	6 g
Fiber	2 g
Protein	2 g
Fat, total	2 g
Fat, saturated	0 g
Sodium	75 mg
Cholesterol	0 mg

EXCHANGES PER SERVING

½	Other Carbohydrate
½	Lean Meat

Artichoke, Sun-Dried Tomato, and Goat Cheese Spread

Makes 16 servings (2 tablespoons per serving)

Serve this sophisticated spread on leaves of Belgian endive. Or spoon it into a pottery bowl and surround with pieces of flatbread.

● **Works best in a small (maximum 3½-quart) slow cooker**

1 can (14 ounces) artichokes, drained and finely chopped	¼ teaspoon freshly ground black pepper
4 sun-dried tomatoes, packed in olive oil, drained and finely chopped	8 ounces low-fat goat cheese, crumbled
2 cloves garlic, crushed	Belgian endive (optional)
¼ teaspoon salt	¼ cup toasted pine nuts, optional (see Tip, left)

1. In the slow cooker stoneware, combine artichokes, tomatoes, garlic, salt, and pepper. Cover and cook on High for 1 hour.

2. Add cheese and stir to combine. Cover and cook on High for 1 hour, or until hot and bubbly. Stir well. Spoon into a bowl or spread on leaves of endive and top with toasted pine nuts, if using.

NUTRIENTS PER SERVING

Calories	49
Carbohydrate	2 g
Fiber	1 g
Protein	3 g
Fat, total	3 g
Fat, saturated	2 g
Sodium	148 mg
Cholesterol	7 mg

EXCHANGES PER SERVING

½	High-fat Meat

Cheddar Jalapeño Toasts

Makes 36 pieces (3 per serving)

TIPS

● To freeze, spread the bread slices with the cheese mixture; arrange them in a single layer on baking sheets and freeze. Transfer to a freezer-proof container, separating layers with waxed paper. Freeze for up to 1 month. There's no need to defrost before baking.

● When handling hot peppers, wear rubber gloves to avoid skin irritation.

Get a head start on your party preparations with these tasty appetizers designed to be stored in the freezer (see Tips, left). When the festivities are about to begin, just pop the toasts into a hot oven.

8 ounces light Cheddar cheese, shredded	2 tablespoons finely chopped fresh parsley
4 ounces light cream cheese, cubed	36 baguette slices cut ⅓" thick
2 tablespoons finely diced red bell pepper	
2 tablespoons minced jalapeño pepper or 1 tablespoon minced pickled jalapeño (see Tips, left)	

1. Preheat the oven to 375°F.

2. In a food processor, purée Cheddar and cream cheese until very smooth. Transfer to a medium bowl; stir in bell pepper, jalapeño, and parsley.

3. Spread each bread slice with a generous teaspoonful of cheese mixture; arrange on baking sheets.

4. Bake for 10 to 12 minutes (or up to 15 minutes, if frozen), or until tops are puffed and edges toasted. Serve warm.

NUTRIENTS PER SERVING

Calories	123
Carbohydrate	9 g
Fiber	0 g
Protein	7 g
Fat, total	6 g
Fat, saturated	4 g
Sodium	320 mg
Cholesterol	20 mg

EXCHANGES PER SERVING

½	Starch
1	Medium-fat Meat

Creamy Mushroom-Walnut Toasts

Makes 40 toasts (2 per serving)

Want a great start to a meal? Begin here. It's so handy to have containers of this delicious mushroom spread in your freezer ready to defrost in the microwave when friends or family drop by. The same applies for the bread, which you can slice, pack into plastic bags, and freeze.

1 pound fresh mushrooms (an assortment of white, oyster, and portobello), coarsely chopped

2 teaspoons butter

⅓ cup finely chopped scallions

2 cloves garlic, minced

½ teaspoon dried thyme

4 ounces light cream cheese or goat cheese, cubed

¼ cup freshly grated Parmesan cheese, plus extra for topping

¼ cup finely chopped walnuts

2 tablespoons finely chopped fresh parsley

Freshly ground black pepper

40 crostini (see box, below)

1. Preheat the oven to 375°F.

2. In a food processor, finely chop mushrooms in batches, pulsing on and off.

3. In a large nonstick skillet, heat butter over medium-high heat. Add mushrooms, scallions, garlic, and thyme; cook until mushrooms are softened, 5 to 7 minutes. Cook 1 to 2 minutes longer, if necessary, or until all moisture has evaporated. (Mixture should be dry and almost crumbly.) Remove the pan from the heat.

4. Add cream cheese, stirring until smooth. Add Parmesan, walnuts, and parsley. Season with pepper to taste. Transfer to a bowl, cover, and let cool.

5. Spread each crostini with a generous teaspoonful of mushroom mixture. Arrange on a baking sheet. Sprinkle tops with additional Parmesan. Bake for 8 to 10 minutes, or until edges are toasted.

NUTRIENTS PER SERVING

Calories	71
Carbohydrate	7 g
Fiber	1 g
Protein	3 g
Fat, total	4 g
Fat, saturated	2 g
Sodium	135 mg
Cholesterol	8 mg

EXCHANGES PER SERVING

½	Other Carbohydrate
½	Fat

CROSTINI (TOASTED BAGUETTE SLICES)

Cut a thin baguette into ⅓"-thick slices. Arrange the slices on a baking sheet. Bake in a 375°F oven for 5 minutes, or until the edges are lightly toasted. Spread the toasts with the mushroom mixture just before baking to prevent them from becoming soggy.

Hummus

Makes 9 servings (¼ cup per serving)

Note: *The suggested accompaniment for this recipe is not included in the nutrients or exchanges per serving. Whether you keep track of exchanges or count carbohydrates, remember to account for what these additional foods contribute.*

You can buy hummus, the classic spread from the Middle East, in most supermarkets, but it is really easy to make in your own kitchen. Serve it as a dip with pita wedges or use as a sandwich spread.

1 can (19 ounces) chickpeas, rinsed and drained

⅓ cup kalamata olives, pitted (about 12)

¼ cup water

3 tablespoons fresh lemon juice

2 tablespoons olive oil

2 tablespoons tahini

2 cloves garlic, chopped

¼ teaspoon ground cumin (optional)

2 tablespoons finely chopped fresh parsley

1. In a food processor, purée chickpeas, olives, water, lemon juice, oil, tahini, garlic, and cumin, if using, until smooth.

2. Transfer to a serving bowl; stir in parsley. Cover and refrigerate until ready to serve.

NUTRIENTS PER SERVING

Calories	120
Carbohydrate	12 g
Fiber	3 g
Protein	4 g
Fat, total	7 g
Fat, saturated	1 g
Sodium	225 mg
Cholesterol	0 mg

EXCHANGES PER SERVING

½	Other Carbohydrate
½	Lean Meat
1	Fat

Hummus Pita Bites

Makes 24 pita bites (2 per serving)

These bites make a great appetizer or take-along snack. Carry them whole and cut just before eating.

2 (7") thin soft pitas, split
1 cup hummus (page 32)
½ small seedless cucumber
½ small red bell pepper, cut into thin strips

1. Spread the rough sides of each pita generously with hummus, leaving a small border.

2. Cut cucumber into 5"-long strips, each ¼" thick. Place a few cucumber and red pepper strips along edge of each pita half and roll into a tight bundle. Wrap each in plastic wrap and refrigerate until ready to serve.

3. To serve, trim ends and slice into 1" pieces. Place cut side up on a serving plate.

NUTRIENTS PER SERVING

Calories	71
Carbohydrate	11 g
Fiber	2 g
Protein	2 g
Fat, total	3 g
Fat, saturated	0 g
Sodium	130 mg
Cholesterol	0 mg

EXCHANGES PER SERVING

½	Starch
½	Fat

Caponata

Makes 16 servings (¼ cup per serving)

This robust spread is a treat from Sicily. Serve it on crostini (page 31) or with crackers, pitas, or crudités such as celery sticks. It keeps, covered, in the refrigerator for up to 1 week.

● **Works best in a small (maximum 3½-quart) slow cooker**

● To cut the basil into chiffonade, stack the leaves, 4 at a time, roll them into a cigar shape, and slice as thinly as you can.

You'll achieve the best flavor if you make the caponata a day ahead and chill it overnight in the refrigerator.

Note: *The suggested accompaniments for this recipe are not included in the nutrients or exchanges per serving. Whether you keep track of exchanges or count carbohydrates, remember to account for what these additional foods contribute.*

2 tablespoons balsamic vinegar	1 can (14.5 ounces) diced tomatoes, including juice
1 teaspoon packed brown sugar	½ cup chopped pitted black olives
3 tablespoons olive oil	1 tablespoon drained capers
1 eggplant, peeled, cut into 1" cubes, and drained of excess moisture	2 tablespoons toasted pine nuts (see Tip, page 29)
1 onion, finely chopped	2 tablespoons chiffonade of basil leaves, optional (see Tip, left)
2 stalks celery, finely chopped	
4 cloves garlic, minced	
1 teaspoon dried oregano	
½ teaspoon cracked black peppercorns	

1. In a small bowl, combine vinegar and brown sugar. Stir until sugar dissolves. Set aside.

2. In a large skillet, heat 2 tablespoons of the oil over medium-high heat for 30 seconds. Add eggplant in batches and cook, stirring and tossing, until it begins to brown, about 3 minutes per batch. Transfer to the slow cooker stoneware.

3. In the same skillet, over medium heat (adding more of the remaining oil if necessary), cook onion and celery, stirring, until softened, about 5 minutes. Add garlic, oregano, and peppercorns; cook, stirring, for 1 minute. Add tomatoes and their juice and balsamic mixture. Bring to a boil and cook for 1 minute to reduce liquid. Transfer to the slow cooker and stir thoroughly.

4. Cover and cook on Low for 7 to 8 hours or on High for 4 hours, or until eggplant is tender. Stir in olives and capers. Transfer to a serving bowl. Cover and refrigerate for 2 hours or overnight. Garnish with pine nuts and basil, if using.

NUTRIENTS PER SERVING

Calories	54
Carbohydrate	5 g
Fiber	1 g
Protein	1 g
Fat, total	4 g
Fat, saturated	1 g
Sodium	100 mg
Cholesterol	0 mg

EXCHANGES PER SERVING

1	Vegetable
1	Fat

Smoked Salmon Mousse

Makes 11 servings (¼ cup per serving)

TIPS

● Use canned sockeye salmon (instead of the pink variety) for its superior color and flavor.

● The mousse can be prepared up to 4 days ahead for easy entertaining.

● To get more juice out of a lemon, roll it on a countertop or microwave it on High for 20 seconds before squeezing.

Note: *The suggested accompaniments for this recipe are not included in the nutrients or exchanges per serving. Whether you keep track of exchanges or count carbohydrates, remember to account for what these additional foods contribute.*

This recipe delivers a wonderful smoked salmon flavor but uses relatively little of that expensive ingredient. The secret? A can of salmon. It keeps the cost down so you can serve this appetizer more often. Serve with melba toast or pumpernickel rounds.

1 can (7½ ounces) sockeye salmon	4 ounces smoked salmon, finely chopped
1 package (¼ ounce) unflavored gelatin	2 tablespoons finely chopped fresh dill
1 tablespoon fresh lemon juice	2 tablespoons minced scallions
½ teaspoon grated lemon zest	Hot pepper sauce
¼ teaspoon salt	Dill sprigs and lemon zest for garnish
1½ cups light sour cream	

1. Drain salmon and place juice in a small microwaveable measuring cup. Add enough water to make ¼ cup. Sprinkle gelatin over the salmon liquid. Let stand for 1 to 2 minutes to soften. Microwave on Medium for 45 to 60 seconds, or until gelatin is dissolved.

2. Remove any skin from salmon and discard. Place salmon in a food processor with gelatin mixture, lemon juice, zest, and salt. Process until smooth. Transfer mixture to a large bowl. Stir in sour cream, smoked salmon, dill, and scallions. Season with hot pepper sauce to taste.

3. Spoon mixture into a serving dish. Cover loosely with plastic wrap (it should not touch the surface of the mousse); refrigerate for 4 hours or overnight. When ready to serve, garnish top with dill sprigs and lemon zest.

NUTRIENTS PER SERVING

Calories	85
Carbohydrate	3 g
Fiber	0 g
Protein	8 g
Fat, total	4 g
Fat, saturated	1 g
Sodium	225 mg
Cholesterol	7 mg

EXCHANGES PER SERVING

1½	Lean Meat

Appetizer Meatballs

Makes 72 meatballs (3 per serving)

TIP

● The cooked meatballs can be made up to 1 day ahead and kept covered in the refrigerator or frozen for up to 2 months. To freeze, place the meatballs in a single layer on trays; when frozen, transfer to covered containers. To defrost quickly, place the meatballs in a microwaveable casserole dish and microwave on High, stirring once, for 4 to 5 minutes, or until just warmed through.

Who doesn't love meatballs as an appetizer? As fast as you fill the serving bowl with them, they disappear.

1 tablespoon vegetable oil	2 teaspoons Worcestershire sauce
1 onion, finely chopped	2 pounds lean ground beef
2 cloves garlic, minced	1 cup soft bread crumbs (see Tips, page 253)
¾ teaspoon salt	2 tablespoons finely chopped fresh parsley
½ teaspoon freshly ground black pepper	1 large egg, lightly beaten
½ teaspoon dried thyme	
½ cup reduced-sodium beef broth	

1. Preheat the oven to 400°F. Coat a baking sheet with cooking spray.

2. In a medium nonstick skillet, heat oil over medium heat. Add onion, garlic, salt, pepper, and thyme; cook, stirring often, until softened, about 5 minutes. Stir in broth and Worcestershire sauce; remove the pan from the heat and let the mixture cool slightly.

3. In a large bowl, combine onion mixture, beef, bread crumbs, parsley, and egg; mix thoroughly with dampened hands.

4. Form beef mixture into 1" balls; arrange on the prepared baking sheet. Bake for 18 to 20 minutes, or until nicely browned. Transfer to a paper towel–lined plate to drain.

NUTRIENTS PER SERVING

Calories	78
Carbohydrate	2 g
Fiber	0 g
Protein	7 g
Fat, total	4 g
Fat, saturated	2 g
Sodium	125 mg
Cholesterol	28 mg

EXCHANGES PER SERVING

1	Medium-fat Meat

Spanakopita

Makes 12 servings

TIPS

● It's best to stick to 1 serving of this delicious but relatively high-fat appetizer. The fat is mainly from olive oil, a source of desirable mono-unsaturated fat, but even "good" fats should be consumed in moderation. When appetizers are higher in fat, keep an eye on your intake, and make lower-fat choices for the remainder of the meal.

● While you're working with 1 phyllo sheet at a time, cover the remainder with plastic wrap, and place a damp towel on top to prevent it from drying out.

NUTRIENTS PER SERVING

Calories	157
Carbohydrate	13 g
Fiber	2 g
Protein	6 g
Fat, total	10 g
Fat, saturated	3 g
Sodium	285 mg
Cholesterol	35 mg

EXCHANGES PER SERVING

½	Starch
½	Vegetable
½	Lean Meat
1½	Fat

Spinach and feta pie, a classic Greek comfort food, can be served warm or at room temperature as an appetizer or part of a buffet.

2 bags (10 ounces) fresh spinach	1 cup (5 ounces) finely crumbled light feta cheese
5 tablespoons olive oil (approximately)	¼ cup chopped fresh dill
1 cup sliced scallions	Freshly ground black pepper
2 large eggs	9 sheets phyllo pastry dough (see Tips, left)

1. Preheat the oven to 375°F. Coat a 13" × 9" baking pan with cooking spray.

2. Rinse spinach in cold water; remove tough ends. Place spinach in large saucepan with just the water clinging to leaves; cook over medium-high heat, stirring, until just wilted. Drain well and squeeze dry; finely chop.

3. In a large nonstick skillet, heat 1 tablespoon of the oil over medium-high heat; add spinach and scallions and cook, stirring, until spinach is just tender, about 4 minutes. Remove the pan from the heat and let spinach mixture cool.

4. In a large bowl, beat eggs; add spinach mixture, cheese, and dill, and mix thoroughly. Season with pepper to taste.

5. Place 1 sheet of phyllo on a work surface and brush phyllo lightly with oil. Fit into the prepared baking pan with ends hanging over sides. Layer 4 more phyllo sheets in the pan, brushing each with oil before adding the next. Evenly spread with spinach filling and fold ends over filling. Layer remaining 4 phyllo sheets on top, brushing each lightly with oil before adding the next. Carefully fold pastry edges under bottom pastry.

6. Using a sharp knife, cut the top 4 phyllo layers into squares or a diamond pattern. Brush top with oil. Bake for 35 to 40 minutes, or until golden. Let cool for 10 minutes before cutting into 12 pieces.

Party Pâté

Makes 20 servings (2 tablespoons per serving)

TIPS

● You can make the pâté up to 3 days ahead. Cover the surface with plastic wrap and refrigerate, or pack the pâté into containers and freeze for up to 1 month.

● Freshly grated nutmeg tastes so much better than the pre-ground variety. Whole nutmeg can be found in the spice section of your supermarket or in natural foods stores. Look for inexpensive nutmeg graters in kitchenware shops.

Note: *The suggested accompaniment for this recipe is not included in the nutrients or exchanges per serving. Whether you keep track of exchanges or count carbohydrates, remember to account for what these additional foods contribute.*

NUTRIENTS PER SERVING

Calories	76
Carbohydrate	3 g
Fiber	0 g
Protein	4 g
Fat, total	5 g
Fat, saturated	3 g
Sodium	140 mg
Cholesterol	117 mg

EXCHANGES PER SERVING

1	Medium-fat Meat

Here's a modern spin on an old standby: chicken liver spread. Even if you're not a big fan of liver, you'll be instantly won over when you try this lightly sweetened pâté with currants and Port. Serve the pâté with warm toasted baguette slices.

3 tablespoons dried currants	1 cup peeled, chopped apples
3 tablespoons ruby Port	¾ teaspoon salt
1 pound chicken livers	½ teaspoon freshly ground black pepper
½ cup water	
2 tablespoons butter, plus ⅓ cup, cut into small cubes	½ teaspoon dried sage
	¼ teaspoon freshly grated nutmeg (see Tips, left)
1 onion, finely chopped	

1. In a small microwaveable dish, combine currants and Port; microwave on High for 1 minute, or until plump. Set aside.

2. Trim chicken livers and cut into quarters. In a large nonstick skillet, combine livers and water; bring to a boil over medium heat, stirring often, until livers are no longer pink, about 5 minutes. Drain in a strainer; transfer livers to a food processor.

3. Rinse and dry the skillet. Add 2 tablespoons of the butter and melt over medium heat. Add onion, apples, salt, pepper, sage, and nutmeg; cook, stirring often, until softened, about 5 minutes.

4. Add onion-apple mixture to livers in the food processor; purée until very smooth. Let cool slightly in the food processor. Add cubed butter to liver mixture and purée until creamy. Add reserved currants and Port; pulse until just combined.

5. Spoon liver mixture into a serving bowl. Cover the surface with plastic wrap and refrigerate until firm, about 4 hours or overnight. Serve with toasted baguette slices (see box, page 31).

WARMING
SOUPS

Homemade Chicken Stock

Makes 12 servings

TIPS

● The more economical parts of the chicken, such as necks, backs, and wings, make the best stock.

● To freeze stock, transfer it to airtight containers in small, measured portions (2 cups or 4 cups are handy), leaving at least 1" of space for expansion. Refrigerate until chilled, cover, and freeze for up to 3 months. Thaw in the refrigerator or microwave before using.

Homemade chicken stock is very easy to make—you can cook it overnight in the slow cooker, strain it in the morning, and refrigerate it during the day. Both this recipe and the one for Basic Vegetable Stock (opposite) make enough for 2 average soup recipes and can be made ahead and frozen. If your slow cooker is not large enough to make a full batch, you can halve the recipe.

● **Large (minimum 6-quart) slow cooker**

4 pounds bone-in skin-on chicken parts (see Tips, left)	6 sprigs parsley
3 onions, coarsely chopped	3 bay leaves
4 carrots, scrubbed and coarsely chopped	10 black peppercorns
4 stalks celery, coarsely chopped	1 teaspoon dried thyme
	12 cups water

In the slow cooker stoneware, combine chicken, onions, carrots, celery, parsley, bay leaves, peppercorns, thyme, and water. Cover and cook on High for 8 hours. Strain into a large bowl, discarding solids. Refrigerate liquid until fat forms on the surface, about 6 hours. Skim off fat. Cover and refrigerate for up to 5 days.

STOCK AND BROTH

What's the difference between stock and broth? Generally speaking, stock is prepared by simmering meat, fish, or poultry (often just the bones) and/or vegetables, together with seasonings, for several hours. The stock is then strained off. Broth may be the liquid in which meat has been cooked, the clear portion of a soup with other ingredients, or a soup on its own, usually with added seasonings.

In this book, "lower-sodium chicken broth" and "lower-sodium vegetable broth" refer to commercially prepared products in cans or cartons. Look for a product with less than 600 milligrams of sodium per cup. Typically, these will be labeled "reduced-sodium" or "reduced-salt," but others may also qualify. Use the sodium values on the Nutrition Facts panel to help you choose.

When a recipe calls for Homemade Chicken Stock or Basic Vegetable Stock, be sure to make it without salt.

NUTRIENTS PER SERVING

Calories	21
Carbohydrate	0 g
Fiber	0 g
Protein	3 g
Fat, total	1 g
Fat, saturated	0 g
Sodium	21 mg
Cholesterol	20 mg

EXCHANGES PER SERVING

1	Free Food

Basic Vegetable Stock

Makes 12 servings

Enhanced Vegetable Stock: To enhance 8 cups of Basic Vegetable Stock, in a large saucepan over medium heat, combine the stock with 2 large carrots, peeled and coarsely chopped; 1 tablespoon tomato paste; 1 teaspoon celery seeds; 1 teaspoon cracked black peppercorns; ½ teaspoon dried thyme; 4 parsley sprigs; 1 bay leaf; and 1 cup white wine. Bring to a boil. Reduce the heat to low and simmer, covered, for 30 minutes, then strain and discard solids.

This recipe for a wonderful vegetable stock makes enough for 2 average soup recipes and can be made ahead and frozen. For convenience, cook the stock overnight in the slow cooker. If your slow cooker is not large enough to make a full batch, you can halve the recipe.

• **Large (minimum 6-quart) slow cooker**

8 carrots, scrubbed and coarsely chopped	6 sprigs parsley
6 stalks celery, coarsely chopped	3 bay leaves
	10 black peppercorns
3 onions, coarsely chopped	1 teaspoon dried thyme
3 cloves garlic, coarsely chopped	12 cups water

In the slow cooker stoneware, combine carrots, celery, onions, garlic, parsley, bay leaves, peppercorns, thyme, and water. Cover and cook on Low for 8 hours or on High for 4 hours. Strain and discard solids. Cover and refrigerate for up to 5 days or freeze in an airtight container (see Tips, opposite).

MINDFUL MORSELS

Basic Vegetable Stock contains virtually no nutrients, so it counts as a Free Food. The advantage to making your own vegetable broth is to reduce your consumption of sodium. One cup of this broth, with no salt added, contains zero milligrams of sodium. The same quantity of a purchased broth will likely contain 500 to 800 milligrams of sodium.

NUTRIENTS PER SERVING

Calories	10
Carbohydrate	2 g
Fiber	0 g
Protein	0 g
Fat, total	0 g
Fat, saturated	0 g
Sodium	5 mg
Cholesterol	0 mg

EXCHANGES PER SERVING

1	Free Food

Scotch Broth

Makes 10 servings

● To clean leeks: Fill a clean sink with lukewarm water. Split the leeks in half lengthwise and submerge them in the water, swishing them around to remove all traces of dirt. Transfer to a colander and rinse thoroughly under cold water.

Note: *The suggested accompaniments for this recipe are not included in the nutrients or exchanges per serving. Whether you keep track of exchanges or count carbohydrates, remember to account for what these additional foods contribute.*

This hearty meal-in-a-bowl is known as Scotland's pot-au-feu, a traditional boiled dinner. It is usually made with lamb, but an old Scottish recipe that suggests that beef or a "good marrow bone" may be substituted. Serve this as a light dinner, accompanied by a simple green salad and warm, crusty rolls.

● **Large (minimum 6-quart) slow cooker**

1 tablespoon olive oil	8 cups lower-sodium beef broth
1 pound lamb shoulder or stewing beef, trimmed of fat and diced	1 bay leaf
4 carrots, peeled and diced	1 cup whole (hulled) or pot barley, rinsed (see Tip, page 221)
3 leeks, white and light green parts only, cleaned and thinly sliced (see Tip, left)	1 cup green peas, thawed if frozen
2 parsnips, peeled and diced	½ cup finely chopped parsley leaves
4 stalks celery, diced	
2 teaspoons dried thyme	
½ teaspoon cracked black peppercorns	

1. In a large skillet, heat 1½ teaspoons of the oil over medium-high heat for 30 seconds. Add lamb in batches and cook, stirring, adding remaining oil as necessary, until browned, about 1 minute per batch. Using a slotted spoon, transfer to the slow cooker stoneware. Drain off fat.

2. Reduce the heat to medium. Add carrots, leeks, parsnips, and celery; cook, stirring, until vegetables are softened, about 7 minutes. Add thyme and peppercorns; cook, stirring, for 1 minute. Transfer to the slow cooker. Stir in broth and bay leaf. Stir in barley.

3. Cover and cook on Low for 7 hours or on High for 3½ hours, or until vegetables are tender. Stir in peas and cook on High for 20 minutes, or until tender. Discard bay leaf. Serve hot, liberally garnished with parsley.

NUTRIENTS PER SERVING

Calories	210
Carbohydrate	30 g
Fiber	5 g
Protein	13 g
Fat, total	5 g
Fat, saturated	1 g
Sodium	465 mg
Cholesterol	26 mg

EXCHANGES PER SERVING

2	Starch
1	Lean Meat

Black Bean and Corn Soup

Makes 6 servings

● Supermarkets are full of beans these days. With this recipe, why not try chick-peas, Romanos, or white kidney beans?

● Canned products, such as tomatoes and beans, contain hefty quantities of salt, so extra salt is usually not needed in soups containing them. Instead, rely on your pepper mill for a seasoning boost.

Note: *The suggested accompaniment for this recipe is not included in the nutrients or exchanges per serving. Whether you keep track of exchanges or count carbohydrates, remember to account for what these additional foods contribute.*

When you want a no-fuss dinner, serve this easy soup with warm bread. It's especially reassuring to know that when you come home late from work, you can reach into your cupboard and pull out some convenient canned products—and dinner is on the table in no time!

1 tablespoon olive oil	4 cups reduced-sodium chicken broth or vegetable broth
1 onion, chopped	1 can (14.5 ounces) tomatoes, including juice, chopped
1 green bell pepper, diced	
1 large stalk celery, diced	1 can (19 ounces) black beans, drained and rinsed
2 cloves garlic, minced	
1 teaspoon dried oregano	1 cup corn kernels (frozen, canned, or fresh)
1 teaspoon ground cumin	
½ teaspoon dried thyme	¼ cup chopped fresh cilantro or parsley
Pinch of cayenne pepper	

1. In a large saucepan, heat oil over medium-high heat. Add onion, bell pepper, celery, garlic, oregano, cumin, thyme, and cayenne; cook, stirring, until vegetables are softened, about 5 minutes.

2. Add broth and tomatoes and their juice; bring to a boil. Reduce the heat to medium-low and simmer, covered, for 20 minutes.

3. Stir in beans and corn. Cook until vegetables are tender, about 5 minutes. Stir in cilantro and ladle into warm bowls.

NUTRIENTS PER SERVING

Calories	158
Carbohydrate	26 g
Fiber	7 g
Protein	8 g
Fat, total	3 g
Fat, saturated	0 g
Sodium	680 mg
Cholesterol	0 mg

EXCHANGES PER SERVING

1½	Vegetable
1	Other Carbohydrate
1	Lean Meat

Two-Bean Soup with Pistou

Makes 8 servings

In this classic French country soup, the hint of licorice in the fennel and the nip of paprika are nicely balanced by the pleasing blandness of the potatoes and beans.

• If your market is out of fennel, use 6 stalks of diced celery instead.

• Adding the green beans while they are still frozen ensures that they will not be mushy when the soup has finished cooking. If you prefer to use fresh green beans, cut them into 2" lengths and cook them in a pot of boiling water for 4 minutes, or until crisp-tender. Add them to the slow cooker after stirring in the paprika.

• **Large (minimum 6-quart) slow cooker**

1 teaspoon fennel seeds	2 potatoes, peeled and shredded
1 tablespoon olive oil	2 teaspoons paprika, dissolved in 1 tablespoon water
3 onions, finely chopped	
2 carrots, peeled and diced	2 cups frozen sliced green beans (see Tips, left)
1 pound fennel, base and leafy stems discarded, bulb thinly sliced vertically and cut into ½" lengths (see Tips, left)	Freshly ground black pepper

1 teaspoon fennel seeds
1 tablespoon olive oil
3 onions, finely chopped
2 carrots, peeled and diced
1 pound fennel, base and leafy stems discarded, bulb thinly sliced vertically and cut into ½" lengths (see Tips, left)
1 can (28 ounces) diced tomatoes, including juice
6 cups Basic Vegetable Stock or Homemade Chicken Stock (see pages 41 and 40) or lower-sodium broth
2 cans (14 ounces each) white beans, drained and rinsed, or 2 cups dried white beans, soaked, cooked, and drained (see Basic Beans, page 236)

2 potatoes, peeled and shredded
2 teaspoons paprika, dissolved in 1 tablespoon water
2 cups frozen sliced green beans (see Tips, left)
Freshly ground black pepper

PISTOU

1 cup packed fresh basil leaves
½ cup grated Parmesan cheese
4 cloves garlic, minced
¼ cup extra virgin olive oil

1. **Make the soup:** In a large dry skillet over medium heat, toast fennel seeds, stirring, until fragrant, about 3 minutes. Immediately transfer to a mortar or spice grinder and grind. Set aside.

2. In the same skillet, heat oil over medium heat for 30 seconds. Add onions, carrots, and fennel; cook, stirring, until vegetables are softened, about 7 minutes. Add reserved fennel seeds and cook, stirring, for 1 minute. Add tomatoes and their juice; bring to a boil. Transfer to the slow cooker stoneware.

NUTRIENTS PER SERVING

Calories	270
Carbohydrate	35 g
Fiber	10 g
Protein	10 g
Fat, total	11 g
Fat, saturated	2 g
Sodium	549 mg
Cholesterol	5 mg

EXCHANGES PER SERVING

2	Starch
1	Lean Meat
1	Fat

This soup can be partially prepared in advance. Complete Steps 1 and 2. Cover and refrigerate vegetables overnight or for up to 2 days. When you're ready to finish the recipe, continue with Steps 3 and 4.

3. Add stock, beans, and potatoes to the slow cooker. Cover and cook on Low for 8 hours or on High for 4 hours, or until vegetables are tender. Stir in paprika solution and green beans; season to taste with pepper. Cover and cook on High for 20 minutes.

4. **Make the pistou:** In a food processor fitted with a metal blade, combine basil, cheese, and garlic. Process until smooth. Slowly add olive oil down the feeder tube until integrated. Ladle soup into bowls and top each serving with a dollop of pistou.

MINDFUL MORSELS

Canned beans are high in sodium. In this recipe, they contribute about 250 milligrams of sodium per serving. You may want to look for reduced-sodium varieties or those with no salt added, or cook your own beans with no added salt (see Basic Beans, page 236). Rinsing also helps reduce the salt content.

Mediterranean Seafood Soup

Makes 6 servings

TIP

• For a less expensive version of this recipe, replace the scallops and shrimp with an equal quantity of mild fish.

MAKE AHEAD

This soup can be prepared through Step 2, covered, and refrigerated for up to 1 day or frozen for up to 3 months. When ready to finish the recipe, continue with Step 3. When reheating, return to a full boil.

Note: *The suggested accompaniments for this recipe are not included in the nutrients or exchanges per serving. Whether you keep track of exchanges or count carbohydrates, remember to account for what these additional foods contribute.*

NUTRIENTS PER SERVING

Calories	215
Carbohydrate	11 g
Fiber	2 g
Protein	26 g
Fat, total	6 g
Fat, saturated	1 g
Sodium	435 mg
Cholesterol	74 mg

EXCHANGES PER SERVING

2	Vegetable
3	Very Lean Meat
1	Fat

Here's an inviting soup that's fragrant with garlic and brimming with fresh seafood in a rich wine and tomato broth. When you've invited friends over for a relaxed dinner, accompany this soup with crusty bread, followed by a simple salad and a fresh fruit dessert.

2 tablespoons olive oil	4 cups fish stock or reduced-sodium chicken broth (approximately)
1 large Spanish onion, chopped (about 1 pound)	
1 red bell pepper, diced	1 cup dry white wine or vermouth or additional broth
1 green bell pepper, diced	
1 large stalk celery, including leaves, chopped	1 pound halibut or other mild white fish, cubed
3 cloves garlic, minced	8 ounces scallops, halved if large
1 teaspoon paprika	
¼ teaspoon red pepper flakes	8 ounces uncooked medium shrimp, peeled and deveined, tails left on
¼ teaspoon saffron threads, crushed	
1 bay leaf	⅓ cup finely chopped fresh parsley
1 can (14.5 ounces) tomatoes, including juice, chopped	

1. In a Dutch oven or large saucepan, heat oil over medium-high heat. Add onion, bell peppers, celery, garlic, paprika, red pepper flakes, saffron, and bay leaf; cook, stirring often, until vegetables are softened, about 5 minutes.

2. Add tomatoes and their juice, broth, and wine. Bring to a boil, reduce the heat to medium-low, and simmer, covered, for 30 minutes.

3. Stir in halibut, scallops, shrimp, and parsley; cover and simmer for 3 to 5 minutes, or until fish is opaque. Serve immediately in warmed soup bowls.

Luscious Fish Chowder

Makes 10 servings

This recipe makes a nice peppery chowder, but if you're heat-averse, omit the cayenne. Although you can make an acceptable soup using water, clam juice or a good fish stock produces better results.

• **Works in slow cookers from 3½ to 6 quarts**

2 slices bacon, chopped	1 bay leaf
1 tablespoon olive oil	1 potato, cut into ½" cubes
3 leeks, white part only, cleaned and thinly sliced (see Tip, page 42)	¼ teaspoon cayenne pepper, or to taste (see Tip, left)
3 stalks celery, thinly sliced	1 cup 2% milk
2 tablespoons all-purpose flour	2 pounds skinless firm white fish fillets, such as halibut or snapper, cut into 1" cubes
½ teaspoon dried thyme	
5 cups fish stock or water, or 2 cups bottled clam juice diluted with 3 cups water	Finely chopped parsley or chives

1. In a large skillet, cook bacon over medium-high heat until crisp. Using a slotted spoon, remove bacon and drain on a paper towel. Cover and refrigerate until ready to use. Drain fat from the pan.

2. Add oil to the pan. Add leeks and celery; cook over medium heat, stirring, until softened, about 5 minutes. Stir in flour and thyme; cook, stirring, for 1 minute. Add stock and bay leaf. Bring to a boil and cook, stirring, until slightly thickened. Transfer mixture to the slow cooker stoneware.

3. Add potato and stir. Cover and cook on Low for 8 to 10 hours or on High for 4 to 5 hours, or until vegetables are tender.

4. Stir in cayenne. Add milk, fish, and reserved bacon. Cover and cook on High for 30 minutes, or until fish is cooked through. Discard bay leaf. Ladle chowder into individual bowls and garnish liberally with parsley.

NUTRIENTS PER SERVING

Calories	164
Carbohydrate	9 g
Fiber	2 g
Protein	21 g
Fat, total	5 g
Fat, saturated	1 g
Sodium	275 mg
Cholesterol	33 mg

EXCHANGES PER SERVING

1½	Vegetable
3	Very Lean Meat

Old-Fashioned Pea Soup with Smoked Ham

Makes 8 (1½-cup) servings

TIPS

● For a wonderful rich, smoky flavor, traditional recipes add a meaty ham bone to the soup as it simmers. As most hams sold today in supermarkets are boneless, however, this recipe calls for chopped smoked ham and chicken stock. If you have a ham bone, add it (first removing any fat) and use water instead of stock. Smoked pork hock is another flavorful alternative.

● This soup will thicken as it cools; if you're not serving it immediately, thin it with additional stock or water to the desired consistency and reheat.

This warming soup has Dutch roots, and its flavor gets a nice smokiness from the addition of a ham bone (see Tips, left) along with the chopped ham.

1 tablespoon canola oil	1 bay leaf
1 large onion, chopped	6 cups reduced-sodium chicken broth
1 leek, white and light green part only, chopped (see Tip, page 42)	2 cups water
3 carrots, peeled and chopped	2 cups chopped lean smoked ham
1 large stalk celery, including leaves, chopped	1½ cups dried yellow or green split peas, rinsed and picked over
2 large cloves garlic, minced	¼ cup chopped fresh parsley
1½ teaspoons dried marjoram	
¼ teaspoon freshly ground black pepper	

1. In a Dutch oven or stockpot, heat oil over medium heat. Add onion, leek, carrots, celery, garlic, marjoram, pepper, and bay leaf; cook, stirring often, until vegetables are softened, about 8 minutes.

2. Stir in broth, water, ham, and split peas. Bring to a boil; reduce the heat, cover, and simmer, stirring occasionally, until split peas are tender, about 1½ hours.

3. Remove bay leaf, stir in parsley, and serve (see Tips, left).

NUTRIENTS PER SERVING

Calories	208
Carbohydrate	29 g
Fiber	5 g
Protein	16 g
Fat, total	4 g
Fat, saturated	1 g
Sodium	685 mg
Cholesterol	14 mg

EXCHANGES PER SERVING

1	Starch
1	Vegetable
2	Very Lean Meat

Greek-Style Split Pea Soup

Makes 8 servings

This is a soup version of the Greek appetizer fava, a purée of yellow split peas often topped with capers or stewed tomatoes. It uses a persillade (a mixture of parsley and garlic) made with red wine vinegar as a flavor enhancer, but you can also finish the soup with a dollop of warm tomato sauce. For a smoother result, purée the soup after it has finished cooking.

TIPS

● Traditional wisdom suggests that yellow split peas do not need to be soaked before cooking. However, I have found that without a good presoaking, they are a bit tough.

● Persillade counts as 1 Free Food.

MAKE AHEAD

This soup can be partially prepared in advance. Complete Steps 1 and 2. Cover and refrigerate the split peas and vegetables overnight or for up to 2 days. When you're ready to finish the recipe, continue with Steps 3 and 4.

NUTRIENTS PER SERVING

Calories	230
Carbohydrate	40 g
Fiber	6 g
Protein	13 g
Fat, total	2 g
Fat, saturated	0 g
Sodium	47 mg
Cholesterol	0 mg

EXCHANGES PER SERVING

2	Starch
1	Vegetable
1	Very Lean Meat

● **Large (minimum 5-quart) slow cooker**

2 cups	yellow split peas (see Tips, left)
8 cups	cold water
1 tablespoon	olive oil
2	onions, finely chopped
4	carrots, peeled and diced
4	stalks celery, diced
4	cloves garlic, minced
1 teaspoon	dried oregano
½ teaspoon	cracked black peppercorns
6 cups	Enhanced Vegetable Stock (see Variation, page 41) or lower-sodium vegetable broth

PERSILLADE (OPTIONAL)

1 cup	packed parsley leaves, finely chopped
4	cloves garlic, minced
4 teaspoons	red wine vinegar

1. **Make the soup:** In a large stockpot or saucepan, bring split peas and water to a boil over medium-high heat and boil rapidly for 3 minutes. Remove from the heat set aside to soak for 1 hour. Drain and rinse thoroughly. Set aside.

2. In a large skillet, heat oil over medium heat for 30 seconds. Add onions, carrots, and celery; cook, stirring, until carrots are softened, about 7 minutes. Add garlic, oregano, and peppercorns; cook, stirring, for 1 minute. Transfer to the slow cooker stoneware. Add reserved split peas and stock and stir well.

3. Cover and cook on Low for 8 to 10 hours or on High for 4 to 5 hours, or until split peas are tender.

4. **Make the persillade:** In a small bowl, combine parsley, garlic, and vinegar. (You can also make this in a mini-chopper.) Set aside at room temperature for 30 minutes to allow the flavors to develop. To serve, ladle soup into individual bowls and garnish with persillade, if using.

Ribollita

Makes 8 servings

● If you can't find Swiss chard, use an equal quantity of spinach. Be sure to wash Swiss chard thoroughly, as with spinach (see Tip, page 113).

● When handling hot peppers, wear rubber gloves to avoid skin irritation.

Originally intended as a method for using up leftover minestrone—hence the name "ribollita," which means "twice cooked"—this hearty Italian soup has acquired an illustrious reputation of its own. The distinguishing ingredient is country-style bread, which is added to the soup and cooked in the broth. Drizzled with olive oil and sprinkled with grated Parmesan cheese, this makes a satisfying light meal.

● **Works best in a large (minimum 5-quart) slow cooker**

2 cups cooked dried white kidney beans (see Basic Beans, page 236) or canned white kidney beans, drained and rinsed	¼ teaspoon salt
	½ teaspoon cracked black peppercorns
5 cups lower-sodium vegetable or chicken broth	2 potatoes, peeled and grated
3 tablespoons olive oil	4 cups (about 1 bunch) packed torn Swiss chard leaves (see Tips, left)
2 onions, finely chopped	
2 carrots, peeled and diced	1 long red chile pepper, minced, optional (see Tips, left)
2 stalks celery, diced	
4 cloves garlic, minced	3 thick slices day-old country-style bread
¼ cup finely chopped parsley	
1 tablespoon grated lemon zest	½ cup freshly grated Parmesan cheese
1 tablespoon finely chopped fresh rosemary or 1 teaspoon dried	

1. In a food processor, combine beans with 1 cup of the broth and purée until smooth. Set aside.

2. In a large skillet, heat 1 tablespoon of the oil over medium heat. Add onions, carrots, and celery; cook, stirring, until vegetables are softened, about 7 minutes. Add garlic, parsley, zest, rosemary, salt, and peppercorns; cook, stirring, for 1 minute. Add reserved bean mixture and bring to a boil. Transfer mixture to the slow cooker stoneware.

NUTRIENTS PER SERVING

Calories	228
Carbohydrate	32 g
Fiber	7 g
Protein	9 g
Fat, total	8 g
Fat, saturated	2 g
Sodium	585 mg
Cholesterol	4 mg

EXCHANGES PER SERVING

2	Starch
½	High-fat Meat

Cook this soup overnight or the day before you intend to serve it. Refrigerate it until you are ready to serve, then reheat it in the oven. Ladle the soup into oven-proof bowls, drizzle with the olive oil, and sprinkle with the Parmesan. Bake in a preheated 350°F oven for about 30 minutes, or until the top is lightly browned.

3. Stir in potatoes and remaining 4 cups broth. Cover and cook on Low for 8 to 10 hours or on High for 4 to 5 hours, or until vegetables are tender. Stir in Swiss chard, chile pepper (if using), and bread. Cover and cook on High for 30 minutes, or until chard is tender.

4. When ready to serve, ladle into bowls, breaking bread into pieces. Drizzle with remaining 2 tablespoons oil and sprinkle with cheese.

MINDFUL MORSELS

Swiss chard, a relative of the beet family (the red stems of some chard varieties remind us of this relationship), is an excellent source of beta carotene and also contains vitamin E, both of which act as antioxidants. Together with other components of diets containing generous amounts of vegetables, antioxidants are believed to work to reduce the risk of some types of cancer.

Chunky Minestrone

Makes 12 servings

> **TIP**

● For fresher flavor and less sodium, replace the canned tomatoes with 4 large ripe tomatoes, peeled and chopped.

● Count 2 tablespoons of grated Parmesan as ½ Medium-fat Meat Exchange.

This nourishing soup is chock-full of vegetables and excels at chasing away the winter chills. It's soothing to both body and soul.

1 tablespoon olive oil	1 can (14.5 ounces) tomatoes, including juice, chopped
2 onions, chopped	2 cups small cauliflower florets
3 carrots, peeled and diced	1½ cups fresh green beans, trimmed and cut into 1" lengths
2 stalks celery, including leaves, chopped	
4 cloves garlic, minced	¾ cup small shaped pasta, such as tubetti or shells
1½ teaspoons dried basil	
1 teaspoon dried oregano or marjoram	1 can (19 ounces) chickpeas or small white beans, drained and rinsed
½ teaspoon freshly ground black pepper	⅓ cup chopped fresh parsley
8 cups reduced-sodium chicken broth	Freshly grated Parmesan cheese (optional)
2 cups water	

1. In a Dutch oven or large stockpot, heat oil over medium heat. Add onions, carrots, celery, garlic, basil, oregano, and pepper; cook, stirring, until vegetables are softened, about 5 minutes.

2. Stir in broth, water, tomatoes and their juice, cauliflower, and green beans. Bring to a boil, reduce the heat to medium-low, and simmer, covered, until vegetables are tender, about 20 minutes.

3. Stir in pasta, cover, and simmer for 10 minutes, stirring occasionally, or until pasta is just tender.

4. Add chickpeas and parsley; cook for 5 minutes longer, or until heated through. Ladle into warmed bowls and sprinkle with cheese, if using.

NUTRIENTS PER SERVING

Calories	132
Carbohydrate	21 g
Fiber	4 g
Protein	6 g
Fat, total	3 g
Fat, saturated	0 g
Sodium	505 mg
Cholesterol	0 mg

EXCHANGES PER SERVING

1	Starch
1½	Vegetable
½	Fat

Perfect Potato and Leek Soup

Makes 6 servings

MAKE AHEAD

You can make this soup a day ahead and reheat it until it's piping hot. It's also delicious served cold.

Watercress adds vibrant color and an unmistakable peppery flavor to the classic combo of creamed potato and leek soup.

1 tablespoon butter	4 cups reduced-sodium chicken broth
2 leeks, white and light green part only, chopped (see Tip, page 42)	1 bunch watercress, tough stems removed, chopped
2 cups diced peeled potatoes	1 cup low-fat milk
1 teaspoon dried tarragon or fines herbes	Freshly ground black pepper
2 tablespoons all-purpose flour	Watercress sprigs

1. In a large saucepan, melt butter over medium heat. Add leeks, potatoes, and tarragon; cook, stirring, until leeks are softened but not browned, about 5 minutes. Blend in flour, then stir in broth. Bring to a boil, reduce the heat, cover, and simmer, stirring occasionally, until potatoes are very tender, about 20 minutes.

2. Add watercress and simmer for 1 minute, or until watercress is limp and bright green in color.

3. In a food processor or blender, purée soup in batches until smooth. Return to the saucepan. Stir in milk and season with pepper to taste. Heat until piping hot; do not let boil. Ladle into bowls and garnish with watercress sprigs.

NUTRIENTS PER SERVING

Calories	114
Carbohydrate	18 g
Fiber	3 g
Protein	5 g
Fat, total	3 g
Fat, saturated	1 g
Sodium	390 mg
Cholesterol	2 mg

EXCHANGES PER SERVING

½	Starch
2	Vegetable
½	Fat

New World Leek and Sweet Potato Soup

Makes 8 servings

This soup is called New World because it's a variation on the classic French leek and potato soup, using sweet potatoes and peppers, 2 ingredients that Christopher Columbus introduced to Europe during his explorations of the Americas.

• **Large (minimum 5-quart) slow cooker**

1 tablespoon cumin seeds	2 pounds sweet potatoes, peeled and cut into 1" cubes (about 3 potatoes)
1 tablespoon olive oil	2 green bell peppers, diced (see Tips, left)
4 large leeks, white part with just a bit of green, cleaned and thinly sliced (see Tips, page 42)	1 long red chile pepper, minced, optional (see Tips, left)
4 cloves garlic, minced	½ cup heavy cream or soy milk
½ teaspoon cracked black peppercorns	Roasted red pepper strips (optional)
6 cups Basic Vegetable Stock or Homemade Chicken Stock (see pages 41 and 40) or lower-sodium broth	Finely snipped chives

1. In a large dry skillet over medium heat, toast cumin seeds, stirring, until fragrant and just beginning to brown, about 3 minutes. Immediately transfer to a mortar or spice grinder and grind. Set aside.

2. In the same skillet, heat oil over medium heat for 30 seconds. Add leeks and cook, stirring, until softened, about 5 minutes. Add garlic, peppercorns, and reserved cumin; cook, stirring, for 1 minute. Transfer to the slow cooker stoneware.

NUTRIENTS PER SERVING

Calories	222
Carbohydrate	34 g
Fiber	4 g
Protein	5 g
Fat, total	8 g
Fat, saturated	4 g
Sodium	44 mg
Cholesterol	34 mg

EXCHANGES PER SERVING

1½	Starch
2	Vegetable
1½	Fat

MAKE AHEAD

This dish can be partially prepared in advance. Complete Steps 1 and 2. Cover and refrigerate the vegetables overnight or for up to 2 days. When you're ready to finish the recipe, continue with Steps 3 to 5.

3. Add stock and sweet potatoes to the slow cooker and stir to combine. Cover and cook on Low for 7 to 8 hours or on High for 3 to 4 hours, or until potatoes are tender.

4. Once potatoes are tender, add bell peppers and chile pepper, if using. Cover and cook on High for 20 to 30 minutes, or until peppers are tender.

5. Working in batches, purée soup in a food processor or blender. (You can also do this right in the slow cooker using an immersion blender.) To serve, ladle soup into bowls, drizzle with cream, and garnish each serving with 2 thin roasted red pepper strips, if using, and chives.

MINDFUL MORSELS

One serving of this soup is an excellent source of vitamin A, which mainly comes from the sweet potatoes. Sweet potatoes are one of the best sources of beta carotene, which our bodies convert to vitamin A. The more colorful a fruit or vegetable, the higher it is in vitamins. Remember that most vegetables are also low in calories and carbohydrate—½ cup of a cooked vegetable (or 1 cup of salad greens) usually counts as a Free Food. Aim for at least 7 servings per day, and be sure to include at least 1 serving of an orange vegetable (such as the sweet potatoes in this recipe) and a dark green one such as broccoli, romaine lettuce, or spinach.

Santa Fe Sweet Potato Soup

Makes 10 servings

TIPS

● To roast peppers: Preheat the oven to 400°F. Place the peppers on a baking sheet and roast, turning 2 or 3 times, until the skin on all sides is blackened. (This will take about 25 minutes.) Transfer the peppers to a heatproof bowl. Cover with a plate and let stand until cool. Remove the peppers and, using a sharp knife, lift off the skins. Discard the skins, then stem, core, seed, and slice the peppers according to the recipe instructions.

● When handling hot peppers, wear rubber gloves to avoid skin irritation.

Here's a flavorful soup with lots of pizzazz and universal appeal. New Mexico chiles add an enticing, slightly smoky flavor, but ancho or guajillo chiles also work well. The lime, roasted red pepper, and cilantro finish provides a nice balance to the sweet potatoes. If you are a heat seeker, add the jalapeño pepper.

● **Works best in a large (minimum 5 quart) slow cooker**

1 tablespoon olive oil	1 jalapeño pepper, finely chopped, optional (see Tips, left)
2 onions, finely chopped	
4 cloves garlic, minced	2 cups corn kernels, thawed if frozen
1 teaspoon dried oregano	
1 teaspoon salt	2 tablespoons fresh lime juice
6 cups lower-sodium vegetable or chicken broth	1 teaspoon grated lime zest
4 cups cubed peeled sweet potatoes (½" cubes)	2 roasted red peppers, cut into thin strips, for garnish (see Tips, left)
2 dried New Mexico, ancho, or guajillo chile peppers	Finely chopped cilantro, for garnish
2 cups boiling water	

1. In a large skillet, heat oil over medium heat for 30 seconds. Add onions and cook, stirring, until softened, about 3 minutes. Add garlic, oregano, and salt; cook, stirring, for 1 minute. Transfer to the slow cooker stoneware.

2. Add broth and stir to combine. Add sweet potatoes and stir to combine. Cover and cook on Low for 8 to 10 hours or on High for 4 to 6 hours, or until potatoes are tender.

NUTRIENTS PER SERVING

Calories	157
Carbohydrate	32 g
Fiber	4 g
Protein	4 g
Fat, total	2 g
Fat, saturated	0 g
Sodium	525 mg
Cholesterol	0 mg

EXCHANGES PER SERVING

2	Starch

This soup can be partially prepared in advance. Complete Step 1. Cover and refrigerate the onion mixture for up to 2 days. When you're ready to finish the recipe, continue through Step 4.

3. Half an hour before soup has finished cooking, in a heatproof bowl, soak dried chile peppers in boiling water for 30 minutes, weighing them down with a cup to ensure they remain submerged. Drain, discarding soaking liquid and stems. Pat dry, chop coarsely, and add to the slow cooker, along with jalapeño, if using.

4. Working in batches, purée soup in a food processor or blender and return to the slow cooker. (You can also do this in the slow cooker using an immersion blender.) Add corn, lime juice, and zest. Cover and cook on High for 30 minutes, or until corn is tender. When ready to serve, ladle soup into individual bowls and garnish with red pepper strips and cilantro.

MINDFUL MORSELS

From mild and fruity to smoky and just plain fiery, chiles add depth as well as heat to any dish. Capsaicin is the substance that gives chiles their burn. Well known for causing a runny nose, chile peppers have long been used as a natural remedy for congestion from the common cold. Capsaicin has also been found useful for treating certain types of pain; research into other uses, including disease prevention, is ongoing.

Creamy Mushroom Soup

Makes 6 servings

TIP

● The stems of shiitake mushrooms are flavorful but very tough. Save them in the freezer and use to flavor soups and stocks.

Use shiitake mushrooms along with less expensive brown mushrooms to create this intensely flavored soup. It makes a great starter for a special dinner.

1 tablespoon butter	½ teaspoon salt
1 large onion, finely chopped	¼ teaspoon freshly ground black pepper
2 cloves garlic, minced	
8 ounces assorted mushrooms, such as shiitake and cremini, sliced (see Tip, left)	1 cup half-and-half
	¼ cup medium-dry sherry (optional)
1½ teaspoons chopped fresh thyme or ½ teaspoon dried	2 tablespoons chopped fresh chives or parsley
2 tablespoons all-purpose flour	
4 cups reduced-sodium chicken broth	

1. In a Dutch oven or large saucepan, heat butter over medium-high heat. Add onion and garlic; cook, stirring, until onion is softened, about 2 minutes. Stir in mushrooms and thyme; cook, stirring often, until mushrooms are tender, about 5 minutes. Sprinkle with flour, then stir in broth, salt, and pepper. Bring to a boil over high heat. Reduce the heat to medium-low, cover, and simmer for 25 minutes. Remove from the heat and let cool slightly.

2. In a food processor or blender, purée soup in batches. Return to the saucepan. Place over medium heat and stir in half-and-half and sherry, if using. Season with pepper to taste. Heat until piping hot. Ladle into warmed bowls and sprinkle with chives.

NUTRIENTS PER SERVING

Calories	113
Carbohydrate	11 g
Fiber	2 g
Protein	4 g
Fat, total	6 g
Fat, saturated	3 g
Sodium	570 mg
Cholesterol	13 mg

EXCHANGES PER SERVING

1½	Vegetable
½	Medium-fat Meat
1	Fat

Corn and Red Pepper Chowder

Makes 6 servings

Sweet young corn, combined with tender leeks and bell pepper, makes a delicately flavored fall soup. If you have fresh corn, cut the kernels from 3 cooked cobs (see Tip, left).

1 tablespoon oil	1 large red bell pepper, diced
2 medium leeks, white and light green parts only, finely chopped (see Tip, page 42)	3 tablespoons all-purpose flour
	2 cups low-fat milk
½ teaspoon dried thyme	Freshly ground black pepper
2½ cups reduced-sodium chicken broth	2 tablespoons chopped fresh parsley or chives
1½ cups frozen corn kernels	

1. In a large saucepan, heat oil over medium heat. Add leeks and thyme; cook, stirring often, until leeks are softened, about 4 minutes. Do not brown. Stir in broth and corn; bring to a boil. Reduce the heat, cover, and simmer for 10 minutes. Add bell pepper, cover, and simmer for 5 minutes longer, or until vegetables are tender.

2. In a medium bowl, blend flour with ⅓ cup of the milk to make a smooth paste, then stir remaining milk into paste. Add to the saucepan and bring to a boil over medium heat, stirring, until thickened. Season with black pepper to taste. Ladle into soup bowls and sprinkle with parsley before serving.

NUTRIENTS PER SERVING

Calories	124
Carbohydrate	19 g
Fiber	2 g
Protein	6 g
Fat, total	4 g
Fat, saturated	1 g
Sodium	250 mg
Cholesterol	3 mg

EXCHANGES PER SERVING

½	Milk, Fat-free/Low-fat
1	Other Carbohydrate
½	Fat

Southwestern Corn and Roasted Red Pepper Soup

Makes 8 servings

NUTRIENTS PER SERVING

Calories	180
Carbohydrate	26 g
Fiber	4 g
Protein	4 g
Fat, total	8 g
Fat, saturated	4 g
Sodium	505 mg
Cholesterol	19 mg

EXCHANGES PER SERVING

1½	Starch
1	Vegetable
1½	Fat

Although the roots of this soup lie deep in the heart of Tex-Mex cuisine, it is elegant enough for even the most gracious occasion. Hot sourdough bread makes a perfect accompaniment.

● **Works best in a large (minimum 5-quart) slow cooker**

1 tablespoon cumin seeds	1 cup boiling water
1 tablespoon olive oil	1 jalapeño pepper, seeded and coarsely chopped, optional (see Tips, left)
1 large onion, finely chopped	
6 cloves garlic, minced	4 cups corn kernels, thawed if frozen
1 tablespoon finely chopped fresh rosemary or 1 teaspoon dried	2 red bell peppers, roasted and cut into ½" pieces (see Tips, left)
½ teaspoon salt	
½ teaspoon cracked black peppercorns	½ cup heavy cream
1 bay leaf	Finely chopped parsley or cilantro
6 cups lower-sodium vegetable or chicken broth	
1 dried New Mexico, ancho, or guajillo chile pepper	

1. In a large dry skillet over medium heat, toast cumin seeds, stirring, until fragrant and just beginning to brown, about 3 minutes. Immediately transfer to a mortar or spice grinder and grind. Set aside.

2. In the same skillet, heat oil over medium heat for 30 seconds. Add onion and cook, stirring, until softened, about 3 minutes. Add garlic, reserved cumin, rosemary, salt, peppercorns, and bay leaf; cook, stirring, for 1 minute. Transfer to the slow cooker stoneware. Add broth and stir well.

Note: *The suggested accompaniment for this recipe is not
included in the nutrients or
exchanges per serving. Whether
you keep track of exchanges or
count carbohydrates, remember
to account for what these
additional foods contribute.*

MAKE AHEAD

This soup can be partially
prepared in advance.
Complete Steps 1 and 2.
Cover and refrigerate the
onion mixture for up to 2
days. When you're ready to
finish the recipe, continue
with Steps 3 and 4.

3. Cover and cook on Low for 6 to 8 hours or on High for 3 to 4 hours,
   or until flavors meld.

4. Half an hour before soup has finished cooking, in a heatproof
   bowl, soak dried chile pepper in boiling water for 30 minutes,
   weighing it down with a cup to ensure it remains submerged.
   Drain, discarding soaking liquid and stem, pat dry, and chop
   coarsely. Transfer to a blender. Add 1 cup of broth from soup and
   the jalapeño, if using, and purée. Add to the slow cooker and stir
   well. Add corn, roasted peppers, and cream. Cover and cook on
   High for 30 minutes, or until corn is tender. Discard bay leaf. Spoon
   soup into individual bowls and garnish with parsley.

MINDFUL MORSELS

The rich color of red bell peppers (also known as sweet red peppers)
lets us know that this tasty, versatile vegetable is high in important
nutrients. A medium red pepper contains only about 30 calories and
is an excellent source of both vitamin A (mostly as beta carotene) and
vitamin C. In fact, ounce for ounce, red peppers contain more
vitamin C than oranges do. Both beta carotene and vitamin C act as
antioxidants; consumed as part of a healthy diet, they may help to
prevent some age-related ailments.

Creamy Carrot Orange Soup

Makes 6 servings

Looking for a great opener for a meal? Here it is. The sweetness of carrots and orange is balanced by the tang of yogurt in this low-calorie soup.

1 tablespoon vegetable oil	1 cup orange juice
1 onion, chopped	1 cup low-fat plain yogurt
1 large clove garlic, minced	1 tablespoon cornstarch
2 teaspoons mild curry paste or powder	Freshly ground black pepper
4 cups sliced carrots	2 tablespoons chopped fresh parsley or chives
4 cups reduced-sodium chicken broth	Grated orange zest

1. In a large saucepan, heat oil over medium heat. Add onion, garlic, and curry paste; cook, stirring, until onion is softened, about 2 minutes. Add carrots, broth, and orange juice. Bring to a boil, cover, and simmer until carrots are very tender, about 45 minutes. Remove the pan from the heat and let cool for 10 minutes.

2. Working in batches, purée soup in a food processor or blender; return to the saucepan.

3. In a small bowl, combine yogurt and cornstarch. Stir into soup. Cook over medium heat, stirring, for 5 minutes, or until heated through. Season with pepper to taste. Ladle into bowls and sprinkle with parsley and zest.

NUTRIENTS PER SERVING

Calories	132
Carbohydrate	20 g
Fiber	3 g
Protein	5 g
Fat, total	4 g
Fat, saturated	1 g
Sodium	470 mg
Cholesterol	2 mg

EXCHANGES PER SERVING

2	Vegetable
2	Other Carbohydrate
½	Fat

Soup à la Crécy

Makes 8 servings

TIP

● Store brown rice in the refrigerator, or use it within a month of purchase.

MAKE AHEAD

This dish can be partially prepared in advance. Complete Step 1. Cover and refrigerate the carrot mixture for up to 2 days. When you're ready to finish the recipe, continue with Steps 2 and 3.

Note: *The suggested accompaniments for this recipe are not included in the nutrients or exchanges per serving. Whether you keep track of exchanges or count carbohydrates, remember to account for what these additional foods contribute.*

In French cooking, crécy *is a term for certain dishes containing carrots. This classic soup, which may be thickened with potatoes or rice, is one of the tastiest. It makes either a nice centerpiece for a light soup-and-salad dinner accompanied with dark rye bread or an elegant first course for a more sophisticated meal.*

● **Works best in a large (minimum-5 quart) slow cooker**

1 tablespoon olive oil	1 teaspoon cracked black peppercorns
4 cups thinly sliced carrots (about 1 pound)	2 bay leaves
2 leeks, white part with just a bit of green, cleaned and thinly sliced (see Tip, page 42)	6 cups lower-sodium vegetable or chicken broth
	½ cup brown rice (see Tip, left)
2 teaspoons dried thyme, crumbled	½ cup finely chopped parsley or snipped chives

1. In a large skillet, heat oil over medium heat for 30 seconds. Add carrots and leeks; cook, stirring, until carrots are softened, about 7 minutes. Add thyme, peppercorns, and bay leaves; cook, stirring, for 1 minute. Transfer to the slow cooker stoneware. Add broth and stir well.

2. Stir in rice. Cover and cook on Low for 8 hours or on High for 4 hours, or until carrots are tender. Discard bay leaves.

3. Working in batches, purée soup in a food processor or blender. (You can also do this in the slow cooker using an immersion blender.) Ladle into individual serving bowls, garnish with parsley, and serve hot.

NUTRIENTS PER SERVING

Calories	123
Carbohydrate	23 g
Fiber	4 g
Protein	3 g
Fat, total	3 g
Fat, saturated	0 g
Sodium	393 mg
Cholesterol	0 mg

EXCHANGES PER SERVING

2	Vegetable
1	Starch

Super Suppertime Lentil Soup

Makes 6 servings

TIP

• To save time, chop the mushrooms, onion, carrots, and celery in batches in the food processor.

VARIATION

Add ½ cup finely chopped baked ham to the soup along with the broth.

Note: *The suggested accompaniments for this recipe are not included in the nutrients or exchanges per serving. Whether you keep track of exchanges or count carbohydrates, remember to account for what these additional foods contribute.*

Of all dried legumes, lentils are one of the most popular. They're fast and easy to cook—and healthy, too! With this soup, toss vegetables into the broth, bring it to a boil, relax, and savor the aroma. In 40 minutes, you'll be ladling out bowlfuls of wholesome soup.

6 cups reduced-sodium chicken broth

2 cups water

1 cup green lentils, rinsed and sorted

8 ounces mushrooms, chopped

1 large onion, finely chopped

2 carrots, finely chopped

2 stalks celery, including leaves, chopped

2 cloves garlic, minced

1 teaspoon dried thyme or marjoram

¼ cup chopped fresh dill or parsley

Freshly ground black pepper

In a large Dutch oven or stockpot, combine broth, water, lentils, mushrooms, onion, carrots, celery, garlic, and thyme. Bring to a boil. Reduce the heat, cover, and simmer until lentils are tender, 35 to 40 minutes. Stir in dill and pepper to taste.

NUTRIENTS PER SERVING

Calories	155
Carbohydrate	26 g
Fiber	7 g
Protein	12 g
Fat, total	1 g
Fat, saturated	0 g
Sodium	520 mg
Cholesterol	0 mg

EXCHANGES PER SERVING

3	Vegetable
1	Other Carbohydrate
1	Very Lean Meat

Mediterranean Lentil Soup with Spinach

Makes 8 servings

This delicious soup, delicately flavored with lemon and cumin, is reminiscent of hot, languid days under the Mediterranean sun. Serve it as a starter course, or add a green salad and warm country-style bread for a refreshing and nutritious light meal.

TIP

• To defrost spinach, remove packaging and place the spinach in a 4-cup casserole dish. Cover and microwave on High, stirring once, for 6 to 8 minutes, or until defrosted. Place in a strainer to press out excess moisture.

Note: *The suggested accompaniments for this recipe are not included in the nutrients or exchanges per serving. Whether you keep track of exchanges or count carbohydrates, remember to account for what these additional foods contribute.*

MAKE AHEAD

This soup can be partially prepared in advance. Complete Step 1. Cover and refrigerate the vegetable mixture for up to 2 days. When you're ready to finish the recipe, continue with Step 2.

NUTRIENTS PER SERVING

Calories	157
Carbohydrate	26 g
Fiber	6 g
Protein	9 g
Fat, total	3 g
Fat, saturated	0 g
Sodium	396 mg
Cholesterol	0 mg

EXCHANGES PER SERVING

1½	Starch
1	Vegetable
1	Lean Meat

• **Works best in a large (minimum 5-quart) slow cooker**

1 teaspoon cumin seeds, toasted and ground	1 cup green or brown lentils, rinsed
1 tablespoon olive oil	1 potato, peeled and grated
2 onions, chopped	2 tablespoons fresh lemon juice
2 large carrots, peeled and chopped	1 pound fresh spinach, stems removed, or 1 package (10 ounces) spinach leaves, thawed if frozen (see Tip, left)
2 stalks celery, chopped	
1 clove garlic, minced	
1 teaspoon grated lemon zest	
6 cups lower-sodium vegetable or chicken broth	

1. In a large dry skillet over medium heat, toast cumin seeds, stirring, until fragrant and just beginning to brown, about 3 minutes. Immediately transfer to a mortar or spice grinder and grind. Set aside.

2. In the same skillet, heat oil over medium heat for 30 seconds. Add onions, carrots, and celery; cook, stirring, until carrots are softened, about 7 minutes. Add garlic, reserved cumin, and zest; cook, stirring, for 1 minute. Transfer to the slow cooker stoneware.

3. Add broth to the slow cooker. Stir in lentils and potato. Cover and cook on Low for 8 to 10 hours or on High for 4 to 6 hours, or until vegetables are tender. Add lemon juice and stir. Add spinach. Cover and cook on High for 20 minutes, or until spinach is cooked and soup is hot and bubbly.

Hearty Beef and Barley Soup

Makes 8 servings

TIPS

● Balance the relatively high sodium content of this soup with lower-sodium choices for the rest of your meal.

● If you're going to the trouble of making homemade soup, be sure to make a big pot so there are plenty of leftovers for the freezer. Ladle the soup into containers and freeze for up to 3 months.

Note: *The suggested accompaniment for this recipe is not included in the nutrients or exchanges per serving. Whether you keep track of exchanges or count carbohydrates, remember to account for what these additional foods contribute.*

There's no better combination than thick slices of warm bread from the oven and steaming bowls of soup when you come in from the cold. This tried-and-true soup has a hearty beefy-mushroom taste and lots of old-fashioned appeal.

1 tablespoon vegetable oil	1 teaspoon dried thyme
1½ pounds meaty beef shanks, trimmed of fat (about 2 or 3)	¼ teaspoon freshly ground black pepper
1 pound mushrooms, chopped	12 cups water
2 large onions, chopped	4 carrots, chopped
4 cloves garlic, minced	¾ cup pearl or pot barley, rinsed
2 bay leaves	2 large stalks celery, including leaves, chopped
1½ teaspoons salt	

1. In a Dutch oven or stockpot, heat oil over medium-high heat. Add beef and cook until nicely browned on both sides, about 5 minutes per side. Transfer to a plate.

2. Reduce the heat to medium. Add mushrooms, onions, garlic, bay leaves, salt, thyme, and pepper; cook, stirring often, until onions are softened, about 5 minutes. Return beef to the pan. Pour in water and bring to a boil. Reduce the heat to medium-low and simmer, covered, stirring occasionally, for 1 hour. Skim any fat from surface.

3. Add carrots, barley, and celery. Cover and simmer, stirring occasionally, for 1 hour longer, or until beef is tender.

4. Remove beef with a slotted spoon. Discard bones and finely chop the meat. Return meat to soup. Discard bay leaves and season with pepper to taste.

NUTRIENTS PER SERVING

Calories	180
Carbohydrate	24 g
Fiber	4 g
Protein	13 g
Fat, total	4 g
Fat, saturated	1 g
Sodium	495 mg
Cholesterol	22 mg

EXCHANGES PER SERVING

1	Starch
2	Vegetable
1	Lean Meat

Cabbage Borscht

Makes 8 servings

TIP

● If you prefer a smoother soup, do not purée the vegetables in Step 2. Instead, wait until they have finished cooking, then purée the soup in the slow cooker using an immersion blender before adding the cabbage and vinegar. Allow the soup time to reheat (cook on High for 10 or 15 minutes) before adding the cabbage to ensure that it cooks.

Note: *The suggested accompaniment for this recipe is not included in the nutrients or exchanges per serving. Whether you keep track of exchanges or count carbohydrates, remember to account for what these additional foods contribute.*

This hearty soup goes well with dark rye bread. The flavor is best when it's made with a combination of beef and lower-sodium vegetable broth, but for a vegetarian meal, using only vegetable broth works well, too.

● **Large (minimum 6-quart) slow cooker**

1 tablespoon olive oil	1 potato, peeled and diced
2 onions, finely chopped	1 tablespoon brown sugar
2 carrots, diced	4 cups Basic Vegetable Stock (see page 41) or 2 cups each lower-sodium vegetable and beef broth
4 stalks celery, diced	
4 cloves garlic, minced	
1 teaspoon caraway seeds	4 cups finely shredded cabbage
1 teaspoon salt	1 tablespoon red wine vinegar
½ teaspoon cracked black peppercorns	½ cup light sour cream (optional)
1 can (28 ounces) diced tomatoes, including juice	Finely chopped dill, for garnish
3 medium beets, peeled and diced	

1. In a large skillet, heat oil over medium heat for 30 seconds. Add onions, carrots, and celery; cook, stirring, until carrots are softened, about 7 minutes. Add garlic, caraway seeds, salt, and peppercorns; cook, stirring, for 1 minute.

2. Transfer vegetable mixture to a food processor fitted with a metal blade (see Tip, left). Add half of the tomatoes and their juice; process until smooth. Transfer to the slow cooker stoneware. Add beets, potato, brown sugar, and remaining tomatoes and their juice to food processor and process until smooth. Transfer to the slow cooker. Add stock.

3. Cover and cook on Low for 6 hours or on High for 3 hours, or until vegetables are tender. Add cabbage and vinegar; stir well. Cover and cook on High for 20 to 30 minutes, or until cabbage is tender. To serve, ladle into bowls; add 1 tablespoon of sour cream, if using, to each; and garnish with dill.

NUTRIENTS PER SERVING

Calories	98
Carbohydrate	19 g
Fiber	3 g
Protein	3 g
Fat, total	2 g
Fat, saturated	0 g
Sodium	487 mg
Cholesterol	0 mg

EXCHANGES PER SERVING

1	Starch
1	Vegetable

Gingery Squash Soup

Makes 4 servings

TIP

• To make squash purée, cut 1 small butternut or large acorn squash (about 2 pounds) into quarters; remove the seeds. Place the squash in a large casserole dish with ½ cup water. Cover and microwave on High for 15 to 20 minutes, or until the squash is tender when pierced with a fork. (Cooking time varies with size and type of squash.) Let stand for 15 minutes or until cool enough to handle. Scoop out the pulp, place it in a food processor, and purée. Makes about 2 cups.

Serve cupfuls of this colorful soup as an elegant starter to a fall menu. It's perfect for the time when fresh-picked squash are plentiful in the market. Make extra purée to freeze in containers so, in the future, you can make the soup in no time at all. The finished soup also freezes well.

1 tablespoon vegetable oil	½ cup light cream
1 large onion, chopped	1 teaspoon grated orange zest
2 cloves garlic, minced	Freshly ground black pepper
4 teaspoons minced fresh ginger	Freshly grated nutmeg
2 tablespoons all-purpose flour	2 tablespoons chopped fresh chives or parsley
2 cups reduced-sodium chicken broth	
2 cups cooked squash purée, such as butternut or acorn (see Tip, left)	

1. In a large saucepan, heat oil over medium-low heat. Add onion, garlic, and ginger; cook, stirring often, until onion is softened, about 5 minutes. Blend in flour, then stir in broth and squash. Bring to a boil and cook, stirring, until thickened. Reduce the heat, cover, and simmer for 10 minutes.

2. Working in batches, purée vegetables in a food processor or blender until smooth. Return to the saucepan. Add cream and zest; season with pepper and nutmeg to taste. Heat just until piping hot; do not boil or soup will curdle. Ladle soup into bowls and sprinkle with chives.

NUTRIENTS PER SERVING

Calories	151
Carbohydrate	22 g
Fiber	4 g
Protein	6 g
Fat, total	6 g
Fat, saturated	2 g
Sodium	390 mg
Cholesterol	6 mg

EXCHANGES PER SERVING

1½	Starch
½	Vegetable
½	Fat

Butternut Apple Soup with Swiss Cheese

Makes 8 servings

MAKE AHEAD

This soup can be partially prepared in advance. Complete Step 1. Cover and refrigerate the onion mixture for up to 2 days. When you're ready to finish the recipe, continue with Steps 2 and 3.

Topped with melted cheese, this creamy and delicious soup is the ideal antidote to a blustery day.

● **Works best in a large (minimum 5-quart) slow cooker**

1 tablespoon olive oil	1 butternut squash, peeled, seeded, and cut into 1" cubes (about 2½ pounds)
2 onions, chopped	
4 cloves garlic, minced	2 tart apples, such as Granny Smith, cored, peeled, and coarsely chopped
1 tablespoon chopped fresh rosemary or 2 teaspoons dried	
	1 cup shredded light Swiss cheese
½ teaspoon cracked black peppercorns	½ cup finely chopped walnuts (optional)
5 cups lower-sodium vegetable or chicken broth	

1. In a large skillet, heat oil over medium heat for 30 seconds. Add onions and cook, stirring, until softened, about 3 minutes. Add garlic, rosemary, and peppercorns; cook, stirring, for 1 minute. Transfer to the slow cooker stoneware.

2. Add broth, then stir in squash and apples. Cover and cook on Low for 8 hours or on High for 4 hours, or until squash is tender.

3. Preheat the broiler. Working in batches, purée soup in a food processor or blender. (You can also do this in the slow cooker using an immersion blender.) Ladle soup into ovenproof bowls. Sprinkle with cheese and broil until cheese melts, about 2 minutes. (You can also do this in a microwave oven, in batches, on High, about 1 minute per batch.) Sprinkle with walnuts, if using.

NUTRIENTS PER SERVING

Calories	158
Carbohydrate	26 g
Fiber	4 g
Protein	6 g
Fat, total	5 g
Fat, saturated	2 g
Sodium	329 mg
Cholesterol	9 mg

EXCHANGES PER SERVING

1	Starch
2	Vegetable
1	Fat

Curried Parsnip Soup with Green Peas

Makes 8 servings

MAKE AHEAD

This dish can be partially prepared in advance. Complete Steps 1 and 2. Cover and refrigerate the onion mixture overnight or for up to 2 days. When you're ready to finish the recipe, continue with Steps 3 and 4.

NUTRIENTS PER SERVING

Calories	146
Carbohydrate	22 g
Fiber	4 g
Protein	3 g
Fat, total	6 g
Fat, saturated	3 g
Sodium	40 mg
Cholesterol	13 mg

EXCHANGES PER SERVING

1	Starch
1	Vegetable
1	Fat

Flavorful and elegant, this soup makes a great introduction to a meal.

• **Large (minimum 5-quart) slow cooker**

2 teaspoons cumin seeds	4 cups (about 1 pound) sliced peeled parsnips (see Tip, left)
1 teaspoon coriander seeds	
1 tablespoon olive oil or extra virgin coconut oil	2 teaspoons curry powder dissolved in 4 teaspoons fresh lemon juice
2 onions, finely chopped	2 cups sweet green peas, thawed if frozen
4 cloves garlic, minced	⅓ cup heavy cream
½ teaspoon cracked black peppercorns	
1 (1") piece cinnamon stick	
1 bay leaf	
6 cups Basic Vegetable Stock or Homemade Chicken Stock (see pages 41 and 40) or lower-sodium broth	

1. In a large dry skillet over medium heat, toast cumin and coriander seeds, stirring, until fragrant and just beginning to brown, about 3 minutes. Immediately transfer to a mortar or spice grinder and grind. Set aside.

2. In the same skillet, heat oil over medium heat for 30 seconds. Add onions and cook, stirring, until softened, about 3 minutes. Add garlic, peppercorns, cinnamon stick, bay leaf, and reserved cumin and coriander; cook, stirring, for 1 minute. Transfer to the slow cooker stoneware. Add stock and parsnips; stir well.

3. Cover and cook on Low for 6 hours or on High for 3 hours, or until parsnips are tender. Discard cinnamon stick and bay leaf.

4. Working in batches, purée the soup in a food processor or blender. (You can also do this in the slow cooker using an immersion blender.) Return to the slow cooker. Add curry powder solution, peas, and cream. Cover and cook on High for 20 minutes, or until peas are tender and cream is heated through.

Vegetable Gumbo

Makes 6 servings

> **TIP**

• Choose young okra pods 2" to 4" long that don't feel sticky to the touch, which indicates that they're too ripe. Gently scrub the pods; cut off the top and tail; and cut, crosswise, into ¼"-wide slices.

Note: *The suggested accompaniment for this recipe is not included in the nutrients or exchanges per serving. Whether you keep track of exchanges or count carbohydrates, remember to account for what these additional foods contribute.*

This tasty vegetable soup might remind you of a canned soup you enjoyed as a kid. Served with whole grain bread, this delicious version makes an excellent lunch. This quantity of rice, combined with the okra, produces a dense soup, which condenses even more when refrigerated overnight. If you prefer a soupier consistency, add an additional cup of broth.

• **Large (minimum 5-quart) slow cooker**

1 tablespoon olive oil	4 cups Basic Vegetable Stock or Homemade Chicken Stock (see pages 41 and 40) or lower-sodium broth
2 onions, finely chopped	
6 stalks celery, diced	
4 cloves garlic, minced	½ cup brown rice
2 teaspoons dried thyme	2 teaspoons paprika dissolved in 4 teaspoons lemon juice
½ teaspoon cracked black peppercorns	2 cups sliced okra (see Tip, left)
1 bay leaf	1 green bell pepper, diced
1 can (28 ounces) diced tomatoes, including juice	

1. In a large skillet, heat oil over medium heat for 30 seconds. Add onions and celery; cook, stirring, until celery is softened, about 5 minutes. Add garlic, thyme, peppercorns, and bay leaf; cook, stirring, for 1 minute. Add tomatoes with their juice and bring to a boil. Transfer to the slow cooker stoneware.

2. Add stock and rice. Cover and cook on Low for 6 hours or on High for 3 hours, or until rice is tender. Discard bay leaf. Add paprika solution and stir well. Stir in okra and bell pepper. Cover and cook on High for 20 minutes, or until pepper is tender.

NUTRIENTS PER SERVING

Calories	148
Carbohydrate	28 g
Fiber	5 g
Protein	5 g
Fat, total	3 g
Fat, saturated	1 g
Sodium	238 mg
Cholesterol	0 mg

EXCHANGES PER SERVING

1	Starch
2	Vegetable
½	Fat

MINDFUL MORSELS

The brown rice in this recipe replaces the roux (flour cooked in oil) traditionally used to thicken gumbo. This reduces the quantity of fat and replaces refined flour with a healthy whole grain, adding fiber and other nutrients to the soup.

Curried Cream of Root Vegetable Soup

Makes 6 servings

TIP

• The carrots, sweet potato, and rutabaga, cut into ½" dice, should total 4 cups.

Here's a seductive soup with a Caribbean accent to serve for a special dinner. The surprising combination of earthy root vegetables, married with spices like ginger and curry, lends a delicious island flair. Your friends will want to take the recipe home.

1 tablespoon vegetable oil	Pinch of cayenne pepper
1½ cups peeled, diced apples	4 cups reduced-sodium chicken broth
1 onion, chopped	
2 cloves garlic, minced	2 carrots, diced
1 tablespoon minced fresh ginger	1 sweet potato (about 7 ounces), peeled and diced
1½ teaspoons mild curry paste or powder	1 cup diced rutabaga
½ teaspoon ground coriander	1 cup half-and-half
½ teaspoon ground cumin	¼ cup chopped fresh cilantro or parsley
¼ teaspoon dried thyme	

1. In a large saucepan, heat oil over medium heat. Add apples, onion, garlic, ginger, curry paste, coriander, cumin, thyme, and cayenne; cook, stirring, until onion and apple are softened, about 5 minutes.

2. Add broth, carrots, sweet potato, and rutabaga. Bring to a boil, reduce the heat to medium-low, and simmer, covered, until vegetables are very tender, about 30 minutes. Remove from the heat and let cool slightly.

3. Working in batches, in a food processor or blender, purée soup until smooth. Return to the saucepan; stir in half-and-half and heat through. Do not allow the soup to boil or it may curdle. Ladle into bowls and sprinkle with cilantro.

NUTRIENTS PER SERVING

Calories	126
Carbohydrate	19 g
Fiber	3 g
Protein	3 g
Fat, total	4 g
Fat, saturated	1 g
Sodium	395 mg
Cholesterol	3 mg

EXCHANGES PER SERVING

½	Starch
1	Vegetable
1	Fat

Cheese-Smothered Onion Soup

Makes 6 servings

This savory soup will warm you up on cold, blustery days. The assertive flavor of onions mellows and sweetens when cooked until golden. This classic makes an easy transition from an everyday dish to an entertainment standout.

2 tablespoons butter	3 cups reduced-sodium beef broth
8 cups thinly sliced Spanish onions (2 to 3)	3 cups water
¼ teaspoon freshly ground black pepper	6 slices French bread, about ¾" thick
¼ teaspoon dried thyme	1½ cups shredded light Swiss cheese
2 tablespoons all-purpose flour	

1. In a Dutch oven or large heavy saucepan, melt butter over medium heat. Add onions, pepper, and thyme; cook, stirring often, until onions are tender and a rich golden color, about 15 minutes. Blend in flour, then stir in broth and water. Bring to a boil, stirring until thickened. Reduce the heat to medium-low, cover, and simmer for 15 minutes.

2. Meanwhile, position an oven rack or broiler pan 6" from the broiler; preheat the broiler.

3. Arrange bread slices on a baking sheet, place under the broiler, and toast on both sides.

4. Place toasts in deep ovenproof soup bowls. Sprinkle with half of the cheese. Arrange the bowls in a large shallow baking pan. Ladle hot soup into bowls. Sprinkle with remaining cheese. Place under the broiler for 3 minutes, or until cheese melts and is lightly browned. Serve immediately.

NUTRIENTS PER SERVING

Calories	256
Carbohydrate	30 g
Fiber	3 g
Protein	13 g
Fat, total	9 g
Fat, saturated	4 g
Sodium	595 mg
Cholesterol	17 mg

EXCHANGES PER SERVING

1	Starch
2½	Vegetable
1	Medium-fat Meat
½	Fat

Creamy Onion Soup with Kale

Makes 6 servings

● If you are making this soup for vegetarians, omit the bacon, and heat the 1 tablespoon olive oil in a skillet over medium heat for 30 seconds. Add the onions and continue with the recipe.

● You can use any kind of paprika in this recipe: regular, hot (for a nicely peppery taste), or smoked (which adds a delicious note of smokiness). If you have regular paprika and would like a bit a heat, dissolve ¼ teaspoon of cayenne pepper in the lemon juice along with the paprika.

There is no cream in this delicious soup—unless you decide to drizzle a bit over individual servings. The creaminess is achieved with the addition of potatoes, which are puréed into the soup and provide a velvety texture.

● **Works best in a large (minimum 5-quart) slow cooker**

4 slices bacon (see Tips, left)	4 cups lower-sodium vegetable or chicken broth
1 tablespoon olive oil	3 medium potatoes, peeled and diced
4 onions, thinly sliced	4 cups chopped kale
2 cloves garlic, minced	1 teaspoon paprika dissolved in 2 tablespoons fresh lemon juice (see Tips, left)
1 teaspoon grated lemon zest	
½ teaspoon cracked black peppercorns	
1 bay leaf	
4 whole allspice	

1. In a large skillet, cook bacon over medium-high heat until crisp. Drain on a paper towel and crumble. Cover and refrigerate until ready to use. Drain fat from the pan.

2. Reduce the heat to medium, add olive oil, and heat for 30 seconds. Add onions and cook, stirring, until softened, about 5 minutes. Add garlic, zest, peppercorns, bay leaf, and allspice; cook, stirring, for 1 minute. Transfer to the slow cooker stoneware.

3. Add broth and stir well. Stir in potatoes. Cover and cook on Low for 8 hours or on High for 4 hours, or until potatoes are tender. Discard bay leaf and allspice. Stir in kale, paprika solution, and reserved bacon. Cover and cook on High for 20 minutes, or until kale is tender. Working in batches, purée soup in a food processor or blender. (You can also do this in the stoneware using an immersion blender.) Serve immediately.

NUTRIENTS PER SERVING

Calories	155
Carbohydrate	24 g
Fiber	3 g
Protein	5 g
Fat, total	5 g
Fat, saturated	1 g
Sodium	404 mg
Cholesterol	4 mg

EXCHANGES PER SERVING

2	Vegetable
1	Starch
1	Fat

MEATY
ENTRÉES

Shepherd's Pie

Makes 6 servings

TIP

● To speed preparation, the lean ground beef in this recipe is not drained after browning. If drained, the fat per serving would be reduced by 3 grams. If you plan not to drain fat from ground beef, look for a package that is 85% or more lean.

Mushrooms add a depth of flavor to this dish and help cut down on the amount of meat used. If you're serving children, who may not like the sight of mushrooms in their supper, finely chop the mushrooms in a food processor. The kids will never know the difference.

MASHED POTATO TOPPING

6 potatoes, peeled and cubed (about 2 pounds)

¾ cup low-fat milk or buttermilk

Freshly ground black pepper

MEAT LAYER

1 pound lean ground beef or veal (see Tip, left)

8 ounces mushrooms, sliced or chopped

1 onion, finely chopped

2 cloves garlic, minced

½ teaspoon dried marjoram

½ teaspoon dried thyme

3 tablespoons all-purpose flour

1½ cups reduced-sodium beef broth

2 tablespoons tomato paste (see Tip, opposite)

2 teaspoons Worcestershire sauce

Freshly ground black pepper

1 can (12 ounces) corn kernels, drained

BREAD CRUMB TOPPING

2 tablespoons dried bread crumbs (see Tip, page 81)

2 tablespoons freshly grated Parmesan cheese

¼ teaspoon paprika

1. Preheat the oven to 375°F.

2. **Make the mashed potato topping:** In a large saucepan of boiling water, cook potatoes until tender. Drain and mash using a potato masher or an electric mixer; beat in milk until smooth. Season with pepper to taste.

NUTRIENTS PER SERVING

Calories	320
Carbohydrate	40 g
Fiber	4 g
Protein	22 g
Fat, total	9 g
Fat, saturated	4 g
Sodium	425 mg
Cholesterol	41 mg

EXCHANGES PER SERVING

2½	Starch
1	Vegetable
1½	Lean Meat

● Unless you're using expensive tomato paste from a tube, you can freeze leftover tomato paste. Put tablespoons of leftover canned tomato paste on a waxed paper–lined plate or in ice cube trays; freeze until firm. Transfer to a small freezer bag and have handy to add to recipes.

MAKE AHEAD

This recipe can be prepared through Step 4 up to 1 day ahead. Cover and refrigerate. Increase the baking time to 40 minutes.

3. **Make the meat layer:** In a large nonstick skillet, cook beef over medium-high heat, breaking up with a wooden spoon, until no longer pink, about 5 minutes. Reduce the heat to medium. Add mushrooms, onion, garlic, marjoram, and thyme; cook, stirring often, until softened, about 5 minutes. Sprinkle with flour, then stir in broth, tomato paste, and Worcestershire sauce. Bring to a boil, reduce the heat, and simmer, covered, for 8 minutes. Season with pepper to taste and remove the pan from the heat.

4. Spread meat mixture in a shallow 12" × 8" baking dish, layering the meat with the corn and ending with a layer of meat. Place small spoonfuls of mashed potatoes on top and spread evenly.

5. **Make the bread crumb topping:** In a small bowl, combine bread crumbs, cheese, and paprika; sprinkle over top of shepherd's pie.

6. Bake for 25 to 30 minutes, or until filling is bubbly.

Southwest Meat Loaf

Makes 6 servings

TIPS

● Driven by the popularity of Tex-Mex foods, salsa sales now rival those of ketchup. Salsa usually contains little or no salt and is much lower in sodium than ketchup. As always, check labels for sodium content.

● When handling hot peppers, wear rubber gloves to avoid skin irritation.

VARIATION

Instead of using all beef, try ¾ pound each of ground pork and ground beef.

Instead of ketchup, serve salsa with this oregano-and-cumin-flavored meat loaf (see Tips, left).

2 teaspoons olive oil	1 teaspoon salt
1 onion, finely chopped	¼ teaspoon freshly ground black pepper
1 small green bell pepper, finely chopped	1 large egg
2 jalapeño peppers, minced, optional (see Tips, left)	2 teaspoons Dijon mustard
2 cloves garlic, minced	1 cup soft bread crumbs (see Tips, page 253)
1 teaspoon ground cumin	1½ pounds lean ground beef or veal
1 teaspoon dried oregano	

1. Preheat the oven to 350°F.

2. In a large nonstick skillet, heat oil over medium heat. Add onion, bell pepper, jalapeños (if using), garlic, cumin, oregano, salt, and black pepper; cook, stirring often, until softened, about 5 minutes. Remove the pan from the heat and let mixture cool slightly.

3. In a large bowl, beat egg and mustard. Stir in vegetable mixture, bread crumbs, and beef. Using a wooden spoon, gently mix until evenly combined.

4. Press mixture lightly into a 9" × 5" loaf pan. Bake for 1 hour, or until a meat thermometer registers 170°F. Remove from the oven and let stand for 5 minutes. Drain pan juices; turn meat loaf out onto a plate and cut into 6 thick slices.

NUTRIENTS PER SERVING

Calories	247
Carbohydrate	7 g
Fiber	1 g
Protein	23 g
Fat, total	13 g
Fat, saturated	5 g
Sodium	545 mg
Cholesterol	89 mg

EXCHANGES PER SERVING

1	Vegetable
3	Medium-fat Meat

Mama's Italian Cheeseburgers

Makes 4 burgers

TIP

● For an easy vegetable topping, cut green or red bell peppers and a large red onion into rounds, brush lightly with olive oil, and grill alongside the burgers.

If your burgers are becoming mundane, inject some excitement into those patties. Instead of a slice of cheese on top of the burger, put shredded cheese right in the ground meat mixture for moist burgers with a twist. Mama would be pleased.

¼ cup grated or minced onion

¼ cup tomato pasta sauce

1 clove garlic, minced

¼ teaspoon dried basil or oregano

¼ teaspoon salt

¼ teaspoon freshly ground black pepper

½ cup shredded part-skim mozzarella cheese

⅓ cup seasoned dried bread crumbs (see Tip, page 81)

1 pound lean ground beef

4 hamburger buns, split and lightly toasted

1. Coat a grill with cooking spray and preheat to medium-high.

2. In a large bowl, combine onion, pasta sauce, garlic, basil, salt, and pepper. Stir in cheese and bread crumbs; mix in beef. Shape into four ¾"-thick patties.

3. Grill burgers, turning once, for 6 to 7 minutes per side, or until no longer pink in center. Serve in buns.

NUTRIENTS PER SERVING

Calories	307
Carbohydrate	15 g
Fiber	1 g
Protein	27 g
Fat, total	15 g
Fat, saturated	6 g
Sodium	505 mg
Cholesterol	69 mg

EXCHANGES PER SERVING

1	Starch
3½	Lean Meat
½	Fat

Basic Meatballs

Makes 48 meatballs (6 meatballs per serving)

TIP

• To freeze meatballs, place them in a single layer on a baking sheet until frozen, then transfer to a covered container or freezer bag. To quickly reheat, place the frozen meatballs in a microwaveable casserole dish, cover, and microwave on Medium until defrosted.

We often think of meatballs with spaghetti and tomato sauce, but they're equally delicious in a variety of sauces, such as pesto (see pages 191 to 192).

1 large egg	1 clove garlic, minced
2 tablespoons water	¾ teaspoon salt
⅓ cup fine dried bread crumbs (see Tip, page 81)	½ teaspoon freshly ground black pepper
⅓ cup minced scallions	1½ pounds lean ground beef

1. Preheat the oven to 400°F.

2. In a large bowl, beat egg with water; stir in bread crumbs, scallions, garlic, salt, and pepper. Mix in beef.

3. Form by tablespoonfuls into 48 balls; arrange on baking sheets. Bake for 15 minutes, or until browned and no longer pink inside. Drain on paper towels.

NUTRIENTS PER SERVING

Calories	168
Carbohydrate	4 g
Fiber	0 g
Protein	17 g
Fat, total	9 g
Fat, saturated	3 g
Sodium	305 mg
Cholesterol	68 mg

EXCHANGES PER SERVING

2½	Lean Meat
½	Fat

Salisbury Steak

• It's easy to make your own bread crumbs in a food processor. Lightly toast some fresh bread slices, or use day-old bread. Tear the bread into pieces, place them in the machine, and pulse to the desired texture. Freeze the bread crumbs in zip-top bags for future use. To season the bread crumbs, simply add dried herbs of your choice, plus salt and pepper to taste.

Note: *The suggested accompaniment for this recipe is not included in the nutrients or exchanges per serving. Whether you keep track of exchanges or count carbohydrates, remember to account for what these additional foods contribute.*

Here's a satisfying meat loaf–like dish with a tasty gravy that's wonderful accompanied by creamy mashed potatoes. Peel the potatoes and start them cooking on the stovetop before you begin preparing the patties so both will be ready at about the same time.

1 large egg	2 teaspoons vegetable oil
2 tablespoons fine dried bread crumbs (see Tip, left)	1½ cups chopped mushrooms
1 small onion, minced	1 clove garlic, minced
1 tablespoon Worcestershire sauce	¼ teaspoon dried thyme or marjoram
½ teaspoon salt	1 tablespoon all-purpose flour
¼ teaspoon freshly ground black pepper	1 cup reduced-sodium beef broth
1 pound lean ground beef	1 tablespoon tomato paste (see Tip, page 77)

1. In a large bowl, beat egg; stir in bread crumbs, half of the onion, 1½ teaspoons of the Worcestershire sauce, the salt, and pepper. Mix in beef. Form into 4 patties, each 4" in diameter.

2. In a large nonstick skillet, heat oil over medium-high heat. Add patties and cook for 2 minutes on each side. Transfer to a plate and drain fat from the pan. Add mushrooms, garlic, thyme, and remaining onion to the pan; cook, stirring, until softened, about 2 minutes. Sprinkle with flour; stir in broth, tomato paste, and remaining 1½ teaspoons Worcestershire sauce. Cook, stirring, for 1 minute, or until thickened. Return patties to the skillet; reduce the heat, cover, and simmer, turning once, for 10 minutes, or until patties are no longer pink in the center.

NUTRIENTS PER SERVING

Calories	270
Carbohydrate	9 g
Fiber	1 g
Protein	25 g
Fat, total	15 g
Fat, saturated	5 g
Sodium	595 mg
Cholesterol	106 mg

EXCHANGES PER SERVING

½	Starch
1	Vegetable
3	Lean Meat
1	Fat

Saucy Swiss Steak

Makes 10 servings

TIP

● While round steak is traditionally used for this dish, an equally successful version can be made with "simmering steak." This is cut from the blade or cross rib and is available at many supermarkets.

Note: *The suggested accompaniments for this recipe are not included in the nutrients or exchanges per serving. Whether you keep track of exchanges or count carbohydrates, remember to account for what these additional foods contribute.*

Here's a dish that many people will remember from the 1950s. Back then it required a fair bit of muscle to pound the steak with a mallet. Today, you can avoid all that dreary work by using the slow cooker. Serve Swiss steak with garlic mashed potatoes and a plain green vegetable.

● **Large (minimum 5-quart) slow cooker**

1 tablespoon olive oil	¼ teaspoon cracked black peppercorns
2 pounds round steak or "simmering" steak (see Tip, left), trimmed of fat	2 tablespoons all-purpose flour
2 onions, finely chopped	1 can (28 ounces) diced tomatoes, drained, ½ cup juice reserved
1 carrot, peeled and thinly sliced	1 tablespoon Worcestershire sauce
1 stalk celery, thinly sliced	1 bay leaf
½ teaspoon salt	

1. In a large skillet, heat oil over medium-high heat for 30 seconds. Add steak, in pieces if necessary, and brown on both sides, about 2 minutes per side. Transfer to the slow cooker stoneware.

2. Reduce the heat under the skillet to medium-low. Add onions, carrot, celery, salt, and peppercorns. Cover and cook until carrots are softened, about 7 minutes. Sprinkle flour over vegetables and cook, stirring, for 1 minute. Add tomatoes, reserved juice, and Worcestershire sauce. Bring to a boil, stirring until slightly thickened. Add bay leaf.

3. Pour tomato mixture over steak. Cover and cook on Low for 8 hours or on for High for 4 hours, or until meat is tender. Discard bay leaf.

NUTRIENTS PER SERVING

Calories	142
Carbohydrate	7 g
Fiber	1 g
Protein	20 g
Fat, total	4 g
Fat, saturated	1 g
Sodium	280 mg
Cholesterol	39 mg

EXCHANGES PER SERVING

1	Vegetable
2½	Very Lean Meat

Ranch House Chicken Fried Steak

Makes 8 servings

TIP

● Wear rubber gloves when handling jalapeños to avoid skin irritation.

MAKE AHEAD

This dish can be partially prepared in advance. Complete Step 2, heating 1 tablespoon of oil in the pan before softening the onions. Cover and refrigerate the mixture for up to 2 days. When you're ready to finish the recipe, brown the steak (Step 1), or omit this step and place the meat directly in the slow cooker. Continue with the recipe.

There's no chicken in it, so where did this classic cowboy dish get its name? Frankly, who cares? Making it in the slow cooker eliminates the traditional tasks of pounding the meat and watching the frying pan. It also produces melt-in-your-mouth results. The rich, spicy pan gravy served over mashed potatoes is a marriage made in heaven. To turn up the heat, increase the quantity of jalapeño pepper.

● **Large (minimum-5 quart) slow cooker**

1 tablespoon olive oil	¾ cup lower-sodium chicken broth
2 pounds round steak or "simmering" steak (see Tip, page 82), trimmed of fat	1 teaspoon paprika
2 onions, thinly sliced	¼ teaspoon cayenne pepper
3 cloves garlic, minced	¼ cup heavy cream
1 teaspoon salt	1 to 2 jalapeño peppers, finely chopped (see Tip, left)
1 teaspoon cracked black peppercorns	Hot fluffy mashed potatoes
¼ cup all-purpose flour	

1. In a large skillet, heat oil over medium-high heat for 30 seconds. Add steak, in pieces if necessary, and brown on both sides, about 2 minutes per side. Transfer to the slow cooker stoneware.

2. Reduce the heat under the skillet to medium. Add onions and cook, stirring, until softened, about 3 minutes. Add garlic, salt, and peppercorns; cook, stirring, for 1 minute. Sprinkle flour over mixture and cook, stirring, for 1 minute. Add broth and cook, stirring, until thickened (sauce will be very thick).

3. Spoon sauce over meat in the slow cooker, cover, and cook on Low for 8 hours or on High for 4 hours, or until meat is tender.

4. In a small bowl, combine paprika and cayenne. Gradually add cream, mixing until blended. Add to the slow cooker along with jalapeño. Cover and cook on High for 15 minutes, or until flavors meld. Serve with mashed potatoes.

NUTRIENTS PER SERVING

Calories	193
Carbohydrate	6 g
Fiber	1 g
Protein	24 g
Fat, total	7 g
Fat, saturated	3 g
Sodium	381 mg
Cholesterol	59 mg

EXCHANGES PER SERVING

½	Other Carbohydrate
3	Lean Meat

Quick Bistro-Style Steak

Makes 4 servings

● Serve with Classic Scalloped Potatoes (see page 294).

● Herbes de Provence is a blend of French herbs that often includes thyme, rosemary, basil, and sage. If you can't find this blend in your supermarket, substitute a generous pinch of each of these herbs.

Dressed up with wine, garlic, and herbs, this steak recipe becomes a special dish when you're entertaining friends.

2 boneless strip loin steaks (8 ounces each), well trimmed	⅓ cup red wine or additional beef broth
½ teaspoon coarsely ground black pepper	½ cup reduced-sodium beef broth
2 teaspoons butter	1 tablespoon Dijon mustard
2 teaspoons olive oil	2 tablespoons chopped fresh parsley
¼ cup finely chopped shallots	Salt
1 large clove garlic, minced	
¼ teaspoon dried herbes de Provence (see Tips, left)	

1. Season steaks with pepper.

2. Heat a large heavy nonstick skillet over medium heat until hot. Add butter and oil and increase heat to high. Add steaks and brown about 1 minute on each side. Reduce the heat to medium and cook to desired degree of doneness, about 5 minutes per side for medium-rare. Transfer to a heated serving platter; keep warm.

3. Add shallots, garlic, and herbes de Provence to skillet; cook, stirring, for 1 minute. Stir in wine; cook, scraping up any brown bits from the bottom of the pan, until liquid has almost evaporated.

4. Stir in broth, mustard, and parsley; season with salt and pepper to taste. Cook, stirring, until slightly reduced. Spoon sauce over steaks. Serve immediately.

NUTRIENTS PER SERVING

Calories	207
Carbohydrate	5 g
Fiber	1 g
Protein	21 g
Fat, total	11 g
Fat, saturated	4 g
Sodium	255 mg
Cholesterol	46 mg

EXCHANGES PER SERVING

1	Vegetable
2	Lean Meat

Stuffed Cabbage Rolls

Makes 12 rolls (2 rolls per serving)

Satisfying casseroles like this one are always a welcome choice when planning make-ahead meals for the freezer.

1 head green cabbage, cored (about 3 pounds)	1 teaspoon salt
4 teaspoons vegetable oil	½ teaspoon freshly ground black pepper
1 large onion, finely chopped	1 can (28 ounces) plum tomatoes, including juice
2 large cloves garlic, minced	2 teaspoons packed brown sugar
1 teaspoon paprika	
1½ cups cooked rice	
1 pound lean ground beef	

1. Preheat the oven to 350°F.

2. In a large pot of boiling water, cook cabbage until leaves are softened, 5 to 6 minutes. Drain and rinse under cold water, carefully separating 12 leaves. Using a knife, trim coarse veins from leaves.

3. In a large saucepan, heat oil over medium heat. Add onion, garlic, and paprika; cook, stirring, until onion is softened, about 5 minutes.

4. In a large bowl, combine half of the onion mixture, rice, beef, salt, and pepper; mix well.

5. In a food processor, purée tomatoes, including juice. Add puréed tomatoes and brown sugar to onion mixture remaining in saucepan; bring to a boil. Cover and reduce the heat; simmer for 15 minutes, stirring occasionally. Season with pepper to taste.

6. Spoon ¼ cup rice mixture onto each cabbage leaf just above the stem. Fold ends and sides over filling; roll up. Spoon 1 cup of the tomato sauce into the bottom of a Dutch oven or a 12-cup casserole dish. Layer with half of the cabbage rolls, and pour 1 cup of the tomato sauce over the rolls. Top with remaining cabbage rolls and pour remaining sauce on top. Cover and bake for 1 to 1¼ hours, or until rolls are tender.

NUTRIENTS PER SERVING

Calories	284
Carbohydrate	22 g
Fiber	2 g
Protein	18 g
Fat, total	14 g
Fat, saturated	4 g
Sodium	350 mg
Cholesterol	45 mg

EXCHANGES PER SERVING

½	Starch
2	Vegetable
2	Medium-fat Meat
1	Fat

Stuffed Onions

Makes 6 servings

TIP

• Use an apple corer to make the cavities for stuffing.

MAKE AHEAD

This dish can be assembled in advance. Complete Steps 1 through 4, cooling the filling thoroughly before stuffing the onions. Cover and refrigerate overnight or for up to 2 days. When you're ready to finish the recipe, continue with Step 5.

Note: *The suggested accompaniments for this recipe are not included in the nutrients or exchanges per serving. Whether you keep track of exchanges or count carbohydrates, remember to account for what these additional foods contribute.*

NUTRIENTS PER SERVING

Calories	294
Carbohydrate	34 g
Fiber	4 g
Protein	20 g
Fat, total	10 g
Fat, saturated	4 g
Sodium	508 mg
Cholesterol	38 mg

EXCHANGES PER SERVING

1	Starch
1½	Carbohydrate
2	Medium-fat Meat

Here's a tasty solution to the midweek dining blues: onions filled with ground beef and bulgur, topped with Parmesan and dill. Use any sweet onion— Vidalia, Spanish, or red onions all work well. Just make sure they are as crisp and fresh as possible and that all will fit into the slow cooker. Serve the stuffed onions with a tossed green salad sprinkled with shredded carrots to add a sparkle of color along with nutrients and flavor.

• **Large (minimum 6-quart) oval slow cooker**

½ cup bulgur	½ teaspoon cracked black peppercorns
½ cup boiling water	
6 large sweet onions	½ cup dry white wine or lower-sodium chicken broth
1 tablespoon olive oil	
12 ounces extra-lean ground beef	1 can (14.5 ounces) diced tomatoes, including juice
6 cloves garlic, minced	½ cup grated Parmesan cheese
1 teaspoon dried oregano	½ cup finely chopped dill or parsley
½ teaspoon salt	

1. Bring a large pot of water to a boil.

2. In a large bowl, combine bulgur and boiling water. Set aside for 20 minutes.

3. Cut off tops and bottoms of onions and peel. Hollow out the centers (see Tip, left) and discard. Lower onions into boiling water and blanch for 5 minutes. Drain and rinse under cold running water; set aside.

4. In a large skillet, heat oil over medium heat for 30 seconds. Add beef, garlic, oregano, salt, and peppercorns; cook, stirring and breaking up beef with a spoon, until meat is no longer pink, about 5 minutes. Add wine and tomatoes and their juice; bring to a boil. Stir in reserved bulgur and remove the pan from the heat. Fill centers of onions with some of the beef mixture, packing the filling in as tightly as possible.

5. Place onions in the slow cooker stoneware with the hollows facing up. Pour remaining beef mixture over onions.

6. Cover and cook on Low for 8 hours or on High for 4 hours, or until onions are tender and mixture is hot and bubbly. To serve, place an onion on each plate. Sprinkle with cheese and garnish with dill.

Classic Beef Stew

Makes 8 servings

This stew can be partially prepared in advance. Skip Step 1 and begin with Step 2, heating 1 tablespoon of the oil in the skillet before softening the vegetables. Cover and refrigerate the vegetables for up to 2 days. When you're ready to finish the recipe, brown the meat (Step 1), or, if you're pressed for time, omit this step and place the meat directly into the slow cooker. Continue with the recipe.

Here's an old-fashioned stew that is simply delicious. Invite friends over for dinner soon.

● **Large (minimum 5-quart) slow cooker**

1 tablespoon olive oil	1 teaspoon salt
2 pounds trimmed stewing beef, cut into 1" cubes	½ teaspoon cracked black peppercorns
2 large onions, finely chopped	¼ cup all-purpose flour
4 stalks celery, diced	1 cup lower-sodium beef broth
2 large carrots, peeled and diced	½ cup dry red wine or broth
2 cloves garlic, minced	2 bay leaves
1 teaspoon dried thyme	Finely chopped fresh parsley, for garnish

1. In a large skillet, heat 1½ teaspoons of the oil over medium-high heat for 30 seconds. Add beef in batches and cook, stirring, adding remaining oil as necessary, until lightly browned, about 4 minutes per batch. Using a slotted spoon, transfer beef to the slow cooker stoneware.

2. Reduce the heat to medium. Add onions, celery, and carrots; cook, stirring, until vegetables are softened, about 7 minutes. Add garlic, thyme, salt, and peppercorns; cook, stirring, for 1 minute. Add flour and cook, stirring, for 1 minute longer. Add broth and wine and cook, stirring, until thickened. Add bay leaves.

3. Transfer mixture to the slow cooker and stir thoroughly to combine ingredients. Cover and cook on Low for 8 to 10 hours or on High for 4 to 5 hours, or until beef is very tender. Discard bay leaves. Just before serving, garnish liberally with parsley.

NUTRIENTS PER SERVING

Calories	212
Carbohydrate	9 g
Fiber	1 g
Protein	23 g
Fat, total	9 g
Fat, saturated	3 g
Sodium	516 mg
Cholesterol	47 mg

EXCHANGES PER SERVING

2	Vegetable
3	Lean Meat

Old-Fashioned Beef Stew

Makes 6 servings

TIPS

● You can use 1 cup of additional beef broth instead of red wine, if you prefer.

● A word about parsley: Use either the curly leaf variety or the more strongly flavored flat-leaf type. Wash it well in plenty of water to remove any dirt, then dry parsley in a salad spinner or wrap in a clean towel. The drier the parsley, the longer it lasts in your refrigerator. Wrap it in paper towels, then in a plastic bag, and refrigerate until ready to use.

NUTRIENTS PER SERVING

Calories	362
Carbohydrate	35 g
Fiber	5 g
Protein	27 g
Fat, total	12 g
Fat, saturated	3 g
Sodium	815 mg
Cholesterol	47 mg

EXCHANGES PER SERVING

1½	Starch
3	Vegetable
2½	Very Lean Meat
1½	Fat

What's more comforting than a satisfying stew? You start feeling good the minute you set this one-pot dish to simmer on the stovetop. As the herb-infused aroma wafts through your kitchen, the contentment grows. The first forkful confirms that this stew is comfort food at its best. What's more, it can comfort you all over again the next day with easy-to-reheat leftovers. It's delicious served with crusty bread to mop up the flavorful sauce.

¼ cup all-purpose flour	1 cup red wine (see Tips, left)
1 teaspoon salt	3 tablespoons tomato paste
½ teaspoon freshly ground black pepper	3 cups reduced-sodium beef broth (approximately)
1½ pounds lean stewing beef, cut into 1½" cubes	5 large carrots, halved lengthwise
2 tablespoons vegetable oil (approximately), divided	2 stalks celery
2 onions, chopped	4 to 5 potatoes (about 1½ pounds)
3 cloves garlic, minced	12 ounces fresh green beans
1 teaspoon dried marjoram	¼ cup chopped fresh parsley (see Tips, left and opposite)
1 teaspoon dried thyme	
1 bay leaf	

1. In a large zip-top plastic bag, combine flour, salt, and pepper. Add beef in batches to flour mixture and toss to coat. Transfer to a plate. Reserve remaining flour mixture.

2. In a Dutch oven or large saucepan, heat 1 tablespoon of the oil over medium-high heat. Add beef in batches and cook, adding more oil as needed, until browned all over, about 4 minutes per batch. Transfer to a plate.

3. Reduce the heat to medium-low. Add onions, garlic, marjoram, thyme, bay leaf, and reserved flour mixture to the pan; cook, stirring, until onions are softened, about 4 minutes. Add wine and tomato paste; cook, stirring, scraping up any brown bits. Return beef and any accumulated juices to the pan; pour in broth. Bring to a boil, stirring, until slightly thickened. Reduce the heat to medium-low, cover, and simmer, stirring occasionally, for 1 hour.

● To save time, every few weeks, finely chop a few bunches of parsley, pack into a container, and freeze. Though not suitable for fresh salads, frozen parsley is perfect to add to soups, stews, meat loaves, and casseroles.

Note: *The suggested accompaniments for this recipe are not included in the nutrients or exchanges per serving. Whether you keep track of exchanges or count carbohydrates, remember to account for what these additional foods contribute.*

4. Meanwhile, cut carrots and celery into 1½" pieces. Peel potatoes and quarter. After stew has cooked for 1 hour, add vegetables to the pan. Cover and simmer for 30 minutes longer.

5. Meanwhile, trim ends of beans and cut into 2" lengths. After stew has simmered for 30 minutes, add beans and more broth, if necessary, until vegetables are just covered. Cover and simmer for 30 minutes longer, or until vegetables are tender. Remove bay leaf and stir in parsley. Season with pepper to taste.

FREEZING AND REHEATING SOUPS, STEWS, AND CASSEROLES

Label and date containers and casseroles before refrigerating or freezing.

Meat-based (and chicken-based) soups, stews, and casseroles can be kept safely for up to 3 days in the refrigerator. Vegetable-based dishes can be refrigerated for 5 days.

To reheat, place in a saucepan over medium heat, stirring occasionally, until piping hot; or place in a covered casserole and bake in a 350°F oven for 30 to 45 minutes, or until piping hot. You can also microwave it, covered with a lid or microwave-safe plastic wrap, on Medium-high for 9 to 15 minutes, stirring occasionally, or until heated through to the center. For single servings, microwave, covered, on Medium-high for 3 to 5 minutes.

Stews, soups, and casseroles can be frozen for up to 3 months. Defrost in the refrigerator overnight and reheat as directed above.

Pot Roast with Beer and Caramelized Onions

Makes 8 servings (2½ ounces meat per serving, with sauce and vegetables)

TIP

● Use a light-colored beer or an amber one, such as pale ale. For a robust-flavored stew, try a dark beer, such as porter or stout.

There's nothing more enticing than the smell of a roast slowly braising in the oven. This recipe features a richly colored sauce from caramelized onions and a subtle sweet-sour taste from the beer and brown sugar. It's delicious served with creamy mashed potatoes or egg noodles.

1 beef pot roast, such as cross-rib, rump, or brisket (about 3 pounds)	½ teaspoon ground cinnamon
¼ cup all-purpose flour	½ teaspoon ground ginger
2 tablespoons vegetable oil (approximately)	½ teaspoon freshly ground black pepper
4 onions, halved lengthwise and thinly sliced (about 1¼ pounds)	3 large cloves garlic, minced
2 tablespoons packed brown sugar	2 tablespoons balsamic vinegar
2 bay leaves	1 bottle (12 ounces) beer (see Tip, left)
1 teaspoon salt	1 can (8 ounces) tomato sauce
	1½ pounds carrots (about 8)
	1 small rutabaga (about 1 pound)

1. Preheat the oven to 325°F.

2. On a large plate, roll meat in flour to coat. Shake off excess. Set any remaining flour aside.

3. In a Dutch oven or large ovenproof saucepan, heat 1 tablespoon of the oil over medium-high heat. Brown meat on all sides, about 6 minutes. Transfer to a plate.

4. Reduce the heat to medium. Add remaining 1 tablespoon oil, onions, brown sugar, bay leaves, salt, cinnamon, ginger, and pepper; cook, stirring often, until onions are softened and nicely colored, 12 to 15 minutes. (Add more oil, if needed, to prevent onions from burning.)

NUTRIENTS PER SERVING

Calories	339
Carbohydrate	27 g
Fiber	4 g
Protein	30 g
Fat, total	12 g
Fat, saturated	3 g
Sodium	570 mg
Cholesterol	63 mg

EXCHANGES PER SERVING

3½	Vegetable
½	Other Carbohydrate
3½	Lean Meat
½	Fat

Note: *The suggested accompaniments for this recipe are not included in the nutrients or exchanges per serving. Whether you keep track of exchanges or count carbohydrates, remember to account for what these additional foods contribute.*

5. Add reserved flour and garlic; cook, stirring, for 30 seconds. Add vinegar; cook until evaporated. Pour in beer and tomato sauce; bring to a boil, stirring, until thickened. Return meat and accumulated juices to the pan. Cover and bake for 2 hours.

6. Meanwhile, cut carrots and rutabaga into 2" × ½" strips. When beef has cooked for 2 hours, add to the pan. Cover and cook 1 to 1½ hours longer, or until meat is tender.

7. Transfer pot roast to a cutting board and cut into thin slices. Arrange on a serving platter and surround with vegetables. Skim any fat from sauce, remove bay leaves, and spoon some sauce over meat. Pour the remaining sauce into a warmed sauceboat to serve on the side.

Osso Buco with Lemon Gremolata

Makes 8 servings

● Prepackaged veal shanks are usually too big for a single serving of this recipe. Ask the butcher to cut them into 1" slices.

This is an all-time favorite veal dish. The wine-flavored sauce and succulent meat are enhanced with just a soupçon of gremolata, pungent with fresh garlic and lemon zest. Pass coffee spoons to ensure that every mouthwatering morsel of the marrow is extracted from the bones.

● **Large (minimum 5-quart) slow cooker**

OSSO BUCO

| 1 package (½ ounce) dried porcini mushrooms |
| 1 cup boiling water |
| ¼ cup all-purpose flour |
| 1 teaspoon salt |
| ½ teaspoon freshly ground black pepper |
| 8 sliced veal shanks, each about 6 ounces (see Tip, left) |
| 1 tablespoon butter |
| 1 tablespoon olive oil |
| 3 leeks, white part only, cleaned and thinly sliced (see Tip, page 42) |

2 carrots, peeled and finely chopped
2 stalks celery, finely chopped
2 cloves garlic, minced
1 teaspoon dried thyme or 2 sprigs fresh
½ cup dry white wine

LEMON GREMOLATA

1 cup finely chopped parsley
2 cloves garlic, minced
1 tablespoon extra virgin olive oil
Grated zest of 1 lemon

1. **Make the osso buco:** In a small heatproof bowl, combine mushrooms and boiling water. Let stand for 30 minutes. Drain through a fine strainer, reserving liquid. Pat mushrooms dry with paper towel and finely chop. Set aside.

2. In a large bowl, mix together flour, salt, and pepper. Lightly coat veal shanks with mixture, shaking off the excess. Set any flour mixture remaining aside.

3. In a large skillet, heat butter and oil over medium heat. Add veal and cook until lightly browned on both sides, about 4 minutes. Transfer to the slow cooker stoneware.

NUTRIENTS PER SERVING

Calories	205
Carbohydrate	12 g
Fiber	3 g
Protein	24 g
Fat, total	7 g
Fat, saturated	2 g
Sodium	390 mg
Cholesterol	101 mg

EXCHANGES PER SERVING

1½	Vegetable
3	Lean Meat

This dish can be partially prepared in advance. Complete Steps 1 and 4, heating 1 tablespoon olive oil in the pan before softening leeks, carrots, and celery. Cover the sauce and refrigerate for up to 2 days. When you're ready to complete the dish, continue with the recipe. Alternatively, osso buco can be cooked overnight in the slow cooker, covered, and refrigerated for up to 2 days. When ready to complete the dish, spoon off any congealed fat and transfer stew to a Dutch oven. Bring to a boil and simmer for 10 minutes, or until the meat is heated through and the sauce is bubbly.

4. Add leeks, carrots, and celery to the skillet; stir well. Reduce the heat to low, cover, and cook until vegetables are softened, about 10 minutes. Increase the heat to medium. Add garlic, thyme, and reserved mushrooms (without their liquid); cook, stirring, for 1 minute. Add reserved flour mixture and cook, stirring, for 1 minute longer. Add wine and reserved mushroom liquid and bring to a boil.

5. Pour mixture over veal in the slow cooker, cover, and cook on Low for 12 hours, or until veal is very tender.

6. **Make the gremolata:** Just before serving, in a small serving bowl, combine parsley, garlic, oil, and zest. Pass around the table, allowing guests to individually garnish the osso buco.

MINDFUL MORSELS

The dried porcini mushrooms in this recipe add deep, delicious flavor to the luscious sauce. Not only are mushrooms very low in calories (less than 20 calories per cup of raw sliced), they're also a source of potassium (which helps control blood pressure) and zinc (which boosts immune-system function).

Mediterranean Beef Ragout

Makes 10 servings

Succulent peppers, sweet or hot, are so much a part of Mediterranean cooking that it's interesting to recall that they are indigenous to North America and didn't cross the Atlantic until Columbus brought them to Spain. Here they combine with cumin, olives, and tomatoes to transform humble stewing beef into an epicurean delight.

● **Works in slow cookers from 3½ to 6 quarts**

1 tablespoon cumin seeds, toasted and ground	4 cloves garlic, minced
¼ cup all-purpose flour	1 can (14.5 ounces) diced tomatoes, including juice
1 teaspoon dried thyme	1 cup lower-sodium beef broth
1 teaspoon grated lemon zest (optional)	½ cup dry red wine
½ teaspoon salt	2 bay leaves
½ teaspoon cracked black peppercorns	2 roasted red bell peppers, thinly sliced, then cut into 1" pieces (see Tips, left and page 56)
2 pounds trimmed stewing beef, cut into 1" cubes	½ cup sliced pitted green olives
2 tablespoons olive oil	½ cup finely chopped parsley
2 large onions, chopped	

1. In a large dry skillet over medium heat, toast cumin seeds, stirring, until fragrant and just beginning to brown, about 3 minutes. Immediately transfer to a mortar or spice grinder and grind. Set aside.

2. In a large zip-top plastic bag, combine flour, thyme, zest (if using), salt, and peppercorns. Add beef in batches, and toss until evenly coated. Set aside, shaking any excess flour from beef and reserving.

3. In the same skillet, heat 1 tablespoon of the oil over medium-high heat for 30 seconds. Add beef in batches and cook, stirring, adding more oil as necessary, until browned, about 4 minutes per batch. Transfer to the slow cooker stoneware.

NUTRIENTS PER SERVING

Calories	216
Carbohydrate	8 g
Fiber	1 g
Protein	22 g
Fat, total	10 g
Fat, saturated	3 g
Sodium	542 mg
Cholesterol	44 mg

EXCHANGES PER SERVING

1½	Vegetable
2½	Lean Meat
½	Fat

This dish can be partially prepared in advance. Start with Step 4 and prepare the vegetables. Refrigerate overnight or for up to 2 days. When you are ready to finish the recipe, complete Steps 1 to 3 and 5.

4. Reduce the heat to medium. Add onions and garlic to the pan; cook, stirring, until onions are softened, about 3 minutes. Sprinkle with reserved cumin and flour mixture; cook, stirring, for 1 minute. Add tomatoes and their juice, broth, wine, and bay leaves; bring to a boil. Cook, stirring, until slightly thickened, about 2 minutes. Add to the slow cooker and stir well.

5. Cover and cook on Low for 8 hours or on High for 4 hours, or until mixture is bubbly and beef is tender. Stir in roasted peppers, olives, and parsley. Cover and cook on High for 15 minutes, or until peppers are heated through. Discard bay leaves.

MINDFUL MORSELS

Like all animal foods, the meat in this recipe is a source of dietary cholesterol. The relationship between the cholesterol you consume in food and the cholesterol in your blood is not clear, although research shows that some people react more than others do to the cholesterol in foods. Nevertheless, the American Heart Association recommends that healthy adults take in less than 300 milligrams of dietary cholesterol a day.

Country Stew with Fennel

Makes 6 servings

• If you don't have a mortar or spice grinder, place the toasted fennel seeds on a cutting board and use the bottom of a wine bottle or measuring cup to grind them.

• Large cans of tomatoes come in 28-ounce and 35-ounce sizes. For convenience, we've called for the 28-ounce size here. If you're using the 35-ounce size, drain off 1 cup of juice before adding to the recipe.

Full of character, this robust beef stew, which is rooted in French country cooking, is the perfect antidote to a bone-chilling night. Don't worry if you're not a fan of anchovies—they add depth to the sauce, but their taste is negligible in the finished dish. The stew is delicious served over quinoa or whole wheat couscous, but mashed potatoes work well, too.

• **Large (minimum 5-quart) slow cooker**

½ teaspoon fennel seeds	¼ teaspoon salt
1 tablespoon olive oil	½ teaspoon cracked black peppercorns
1½ pounds trimmed stewing beef, cut into 1" cubes	1 tablespoon all-purpose flour
2 large onions, finely chopped	1 can (28 ounces) diced tomatoes, including juice (see Tips, left)
4 stalks celery, thinly sliced	2 bay leaves
1 bulb fennel, trimmed, cored, and thinly sliced vertically	½ cup chopped pitted black olives
4 cloves garlic, minced	
4 anchovy fillets, minced	
1 teaspoon dried thyme	

1. In a large dry skillet over medium heat, toast fennel seeds, stirring, until fragrant, about 3 minutes. Immediately transfer to a mortar or spice grinder and grind. Set aside.

2. In the same skillet, heat 1½ teaspoons of the oil over medium-high heat for 30 seconds. Add beef in batches and cook, stirring, adding remaining oil as necessary, until lightly browned, about 4 minutes per batch. Using a slotted spoon, transfer to the slow cooker stoneware.

NUTRIENTS PER SERVING

Calories	257
Carbohydrate	16 g
Fiber	4 g
Protein	25 g
Fat, total	11 g
Fat, saturated	3 g
Sodium	624 mg
Cholesterol	49 mg

EXCHANGES PER SERVING

3	Vegetable
3	Lean Meat

This dish can be partially prepared in advance. Complete Step 1 and skip Step 2. Complete Step 3, heating 1 tablespoon of the oil in the pan before softening the onions. Cover and refrigerate for up to 2 days. When you're ready to finish the recipe, either brown the beef as outlined in Step 2 or add it to the slow cooker without browning. Stir well and continue with Step 4.

Note: *The suggested accompaniments for this recipe are not included in the nutrients or exchanges per serving. Whether you keep track of exchanges or count carbohydrates, remember to account for what these additional foods contribute.*

3. Reduce the heat to medium. Add onions, celery, and fennel to the pan; cook, stirring, until celery is softened, about 5 minutes. Add garlic, anchovies, thyme, salt, peppercorns, and reserved fennel seeds; cook, stirring, for 1 minute. Add flour and cook, stirring, for 1 minute longer. Add tomatoes and their juice; bring to a boil. Cook, stirring, just until mixture begins to thicken, about 2 minutes. Add bay leaves and stir well.

4. Transfer to the slow cooker. Cover and cook on Low for 8 hours or on High for 4 hours, or until beef is tender. Discard bay leaves. Stir in olives and serve.

MINDFUL MORSELS

When cooking beef, trim as much of the visible fat as possible from the meat to reduce the calories and the amount of saturated fat you consume. About half of the calories in untrimmed beef comes from the fat.

Tex-Mex Cobbler
with Cheddar Cornbread Crust

Makes 6 servings

Looking for an inviting dinner-in-a-dish everyone in the family will enjoy? This hearty chili-flavored beef casserole topped with a tasty cornbread crust fills the bill. We've kept the seasonings tame so the cobbler will appeal to the sensitive taste buds of young diners, but you can boost the seasonings, if desired.

TIPS

• Although canned vegetables contain significant amounts of sodium, many frozen vegetables are quite low in sodium. In this recipe, the frozen corn contributes 2 milligrams of sodium, compared with about 140 milligrams for the same amount of canned corn.

• Add 1 teaspoon additional chili powder and ¼ teaspoon red pepper flakes, or to taste, to the ground beef mixture for a more assertive chili flavor.

COBBLER

- 1 pound lean ground beef
- 1 onion, chopped
- 2 cloves garlic, minced
- 1 large green bell pepper, chopped
- 2 teaspoons chili powder
- 1 teaspoon dried oregano
- ½ teaspoon ground cumin
- 2 tablespoons all-purpose flour
- 1½ cups reduced-sodium beef broth
- 1 can (8 ounces) tomato sauce
- 1½ cups frozen corn kernels

CHEDDAR CORNBREAD CRUST

- ⅔ cup whole wheat flour
- ½ cup cornmeal
- 1½ teaspoons baking powder
- 1½ teaspoons sugar
- ½ cup shredded light Cheddar cheese
- 1 large egg
- ⅔ cup low-fat milk

1. Preheat the oven to 400°F.

2. **Make the cobbler:** In a large nonstick skillet over medium-high heat, cook beef, breaking up with a wooden spoon, until no longer pink, about 5 minutes.

3. Stir in onion, garlic, bell pepper, chili powder, oregano, and cumin; cook, stirring, until onion is softened, about 4 minutes.

NUTRIENTS PER SERVING

Calories	379
Carbohydrate	39 g
Fiber	5 g
Protein	25 g
Fat, total	15 g
Fat, saturated	6 g
Sodium	605 mg
Cholesterol	84 mg

EXCHANGES PER SERVING

2	Starch
1	Vegetable
2½	Lean Meat
1	Fat

4. Stir in flour, then stir in broth and tomato sauce. Bring to a boil, stirring, until thickened. Reduce the heat, cover, and simmer for 5 minutes. Stir in corn; cook for 2 minutes, or until piping hot. Spoon into a 10-cup casserole dish.

5. **Make the crust:** In a large bowl, combine flour, cornmeal, baking powder, and sugar; mix in cheese.

6. In a medium bowl, beat together egg and milk. Stir into dry ingredients to make a smooth batter.

7. Spoon batter over beef mixture in an even layer. Bake for 20 to 25 minutes, or until top is light golden and filling is bubbly.

Moroccan-Spiced Beef

Makes 8 servings

MAKE AHEAD

This dish can be partially prepared in advance. Follow Step 1 and skip Step 2. In Step 3, heat 1 tablespoon of the oil in the pan before softening the vegetables. Cover and refrigerate the mixture overnight. The next morning, brown the beef (Step 2), or, if you're pressed for time, omit this step and add the meat directly to the slow cooker. Continue cooking as directed in Step 4. Alternatively, cook the stew overnight, but do not add the parsley. Cover and refrigerate for the day. When you're ready to finish the recipe, bring to a boil in a Dutch oven and simmer for 10 minutes, or until the meat is heated through and the sauce is bubbly.

NUTRIENTS PER SERVING

Calories	277
Carbohydrate	24 g
Fiber	4 g
Protein	25 g
Fat, total	10 g
Fat, saturated	3 g
Sodium	344 mg
Cholesterol	47 mg

EXCHANGES PER SERVING

2	Vegetable
1	Other Carbohydrate
3	Lean Meat

Here's a stew that is every bit as delicious as it is unusual. The parsnips provide a hint of sweetness, and the cumin, coriander, cinnamon, peppercorns, and cayenne combine to richly flavor the broth. Accompanied by a bowl of steaming couscous, this makes a perfect meal for any occasion.

- **Large (minimum 5-quart) slow cooker**

2 tablespoons cumin seeds	1 (6") cinnamon stick
2 teaspoons coriander seeds	2 tablespoons all-purpose flour
1 tablespoon olive oil	1 can (28 ounces) diced tomatoes, drained
2 pounds trimmed stewing beef, cut into 1" cubes	1 cup lower-sodium beef broth
2 onions, chopped	½ cup dry red wine
4 large carrots, peeled and chopped (about 1 pound)	1 tablespoon tomato paste
4 large parsnips, peeled and chopped (about 1 pound)	1 tablespoon fresh lemon juice
4 cloves garlic, minced	½ teaspoon cayenne pepper
1 teaspoon cracked black peppercorns	Finely chopped parsley, for garnish
	Couscous (optional)

1. In a large dry skillet over medium heat, toast cumin and coriander seeds, stirring, until fragrant and just beginning to brown, about 3 minutes. Immediately transfer to a mortar or spice grinder and grind. Set aside.

2. In the same skillet, heat 1½ teaspoons of the oil over medium-high heat for 30 seconds. Add beef in batches and cook, stirring, adding remaining oil as necessary, until lightly browned, about 4 minutes per batch. Using a slotted spoon, transfer to the slow cooker stoneware.

Note: *The suggested accompaniment for this recipe is not included in the nutrients or exchanges per serving. Whether you keep track of exchanges or count carbohydrates, remember to account for what these additional foods contribute.*

3. Reduce the skillet heat to medium. Add onions, carrots, and parsnips to the pan and cook, stirring, until carrots are softened, about 7 minutes. Add garlic, peppercorns, cinnamon stick, and reserved cumin and coriander; cook, stirring, for 1 minute. Add flour and cook, stirring, for 1 minute longer. Add tomatoes, broth, red wine, and tomato paste; bring to a boil, stirring.

4. Transfer vegetable mixture to the slow cooker. Cover and cook on Low for 8 hours or on High for 4 hours, or until vegetables are tender.

5. In a small bowl, combine lemon juice and cayenne; add to the slow cooker and stir to combine. Garnish liberally with parsley before serving. Serve with couscous, if desired.

MINDFUL MORSELS

When one thinks about vegetables, parsnips are usually a bit of an afterthought, which is unfortunate. They belong to the same plant family as parsley, coriander, carrots, and celery. Half a cup of cooked parsnips is high in folate and potassium and is a source of several other nutrients as well, including fiber, vitamin C, and magnesium.

Herbed Wiener Schnitzel

Makes 4 servings (2 cutlets per serving)

TIP

● Make sure the cutlets are thin; if necessary, pound the meat between sheets of plastic wrap, using a meat mallet or rolling pin.

Note: *The suggested accompaniments for this recipe are not included in the nutrients or exchanges per serving. Whether you keep track of exchanges or count carbohydrates, remember to account for what these additional foods contribute.*

Tender milk-fed veal is preferred over grain-fed in this classic pan-fried recipe with flavorful herbs. This schnitzel goes well with a salad of vibrant mesclun mix or watercress greens.

1 pound thin veal or turkey cutlets (8 cutlets)	⅓ cup all-purpose flour
½ teaspoon salt	2 large eggs, beaten
½ teaspoon freshly ground black pepper	2 tablespoons butter
1 cup dried bread crumbs (see Tip, page 81)	2 tablespoons vegetable oil (approximately)
⅓ cup lightly packed fresh parsley	Lemon wedges
¾ teaspoon dried herbes de Provence (see Tip, page 84) or thyme	

1. Preheat oven to warm.

2. Blot veal dry with paper towels. Season with the salt and pepper.

3. In a food processor, process bread crumbs, parsley, and herbes de Provence until well combined.

4. Place flour, eggs, and bread crumb mixture in 3 separate shallow bowls. Just before cooking, dredge veal in flour, shaking off excess; dip in egg and then coat both sides well in bread crumb mixture.

5. In a large nonstick skillet, heat 1½ teaspoons each of the butter and the oil over medium-high heat. Cook veal in batches, 2 cutlets at a time, for 1½ minutes per side, or until golden. Wipe skillet clean with paper towels before repeating for next batch. Transfer veal to a baking sheet; place in a warm oven while cooking remaining schnitzel. Serve accompanied with lemon wedges.

NUTRIENTS PER SERVING

Calories	300
Carbohydrate	19 g
Fiber	1 g
Protein	29 g
Fat, total	11 g
Fat, saturated	3 g
Sodium	570 mg
Cholesterol	158 mg

EXCHANGES PER SERVING

1	Starch
3½	Lean Meat

Wine-Braised Veal with Rosemary

Makes 10 servings

TIP

• If you are using fresh rosemary and prefer a more pronounced flavor, bury a whole sprig in the meat before adding the sauce.

MAKE AHEAD

This dish can be partially prepared in advance. Complete Steps 1 and 3, skipping Step 2; refrigerate for up to 2 days. When you're ready to finish the recipe, place the veal in the slow cooker (don't bother with browning) and continue with Step 4.

Note: *The suggested accompaniments for this recipe are not included in the nutrients or exchanges per serving. Whether you keep track of exchanges or count carbohydrates, remember to account for what these additional foods contribute.*

This delicious, Italian-inspired stew is both simple and elegant. Serve it over hot Basic Polenta (see page 257) and accompany with steamed broccoli or broccoli rabe.

• **Large (minimum 5-quart) slow cooker**

3 slices bacon, cut crosswise into thin strips	1½ tablespoons chopped fresh rosemary or 1½ teaspoons dried (see Tip, left)
1 tablespoon olive oil	1 teaspoon salt
2 pounds trimmed stewing veal, cut into 1" cubes	½ teaspoon cracked black peppercorns
3 large carrots, peeled and diced	2 tablespoons all-purpose flour
3 leeks, white part only, cleaned and coarsely chopped (see Tip, page 42)	½ cup lower-sodium chicken broth
2 stalks celery, diced	½ cup dry red wine
2 cloves garlic, minced	Fresh rosemary sprigs, optional

1. Heat a large skillet over medium heat for 30 seconds. Add bacon and cook, stirring, until crisp, 6 to 8 minutes. Drain off fat.

2. Add 1½ teaspoons of the oil. Add veal in batches and cook, stirring, adding remaining oil as necessary, just until meat begins to brown, about 4 minutes. Using a slotted spoon, transfer to the slow cooker stoneware.

3. Add carrots, leeks, and celery to the pan; cook, stirring, until softened, about 7 minutes. Add garlic, rosemary, salt, peppercorns, and reserved bacon; cook, stirring, for 1 minute. Sprinkle flour over mixture and cook, stirring, for 1 minute longer. Add broth and wine; cook, stirring, until mixture thickens.

4. Pour mixture over meat and stir to combine. Cover and cook on Low for 8 to 10 hours or on High for 4 to 6 hours, or until meat is tender. Garnish with rosemary sprigs, if using, and serve.

NUTRIENTS PER SERVING

Calories	158
Carbohydrate	8 g
Fiber	2 g
Protein	20 g
Fat, total	5 g
Fat, saturated	1 g
Sodium	388 mg
Cholesterol	78 mg

EXCHANGES PER SERVING

1½	Vegetable
2½	Lean Meat

Veal Goulash

Makes 8 servings

TIPS

● There is a hint of caraway flavor in this version. If you prefer a stronger flavor, increase the quantity of caraway seeds to as much as 2 teaspoons.

● Small whole cremini mushrooms work well in this stew, but if you can't find them, use white mushrooms or larger cremini mushrooms, quartered or sliced, depending on their size.

This version of goulash, a luscious Hungarian stew seasoned with paprika, is lighter than the traditional version made with beef. It is usually served over hot noodles, but fluffy mashed potatoes also make a fine accompaniment. The red bell peppers not only enhance the flavor but also add valuable nutrients to the dish.

● **Works in slow cookers from 3½ to 6 quarts**

2 tablespoons olive oil	1 can (14.5 ounces) diced tomatoes, including juice
2 pounds trimmed stewing veal, cut into 1" cubes	1 cup lower-sodium chicken broth
2 onions, finely chopped	1 tablespoon sweet Hungarian paprika, dissolved in 2 tablespoons water or lower-sodium chicken broth
4 cloves garlic, minced	
1 teaspoon caraway seeds (see Tips, left)	
½ teaspoon cracked black peppercorns	2 red bell peppers, diced
1 pound mushrooms (see Tips, left)	½ cup finely chopped dill
2 tablespoons all-purpose flour	Sour cream (optional)

1. In a large skillet, heat 1 tablespoon of the oil over medium-high heat for 30 seconds. Add veal in batches and cook, stirring, adding more oil as necessary, until browned, about 5 minutes per batch. Using a slotted spoon, transfer to the slow cooker stoneware.

2. Reduce the heat to medium. Add onions to the pan and cook, stirring, until softened, about 3 minutes. Add garlic, caraway seeds, and peppercorns; cook, stirring, for 1 minute. Add mushrooms and toss to coat. Add flour and cook, stirring, for 1 minute. Add tomatoes and their juice and broth; bring to a boil. Transfer to the slow cooker. Stir well. Cover and cook on Low for 8 hours or on High for 4 hours, or until veal is tender.

NUTRIENTS PER SERVING

Calories	207
Carbohydrate	11 g
Fiber	2 g
Protein	26 g
Fat, total	7 g
Fat, saturated	1 g
Sodium	221 mg
Cholesterol	95 mg

EXCHANGES PER SERVING

2	Vegetable
3	Lean Meat

This dish can be partially prepared in advance. Begin with Step 2, using 1 tablespoon of the oil. Cover and refrigerate the mushroom mixture overnight or for up to 1 day. When you're ready to finish the recipe, either brown the veal as outlined in Step 1 or add it to the slow cooker without browning. Stir well and continue with Steps 3 and 4.

Note: *The suggested accompaniments for this recipe are not included in the nutrients or exchanges per serving. Whether you keep track of exchanges or count carbohydrates, remember to account for what these additional foods contribute.*

3. Add paprika solution to the slow cooker and stir well. Add bell peppers and stir well. Cover and cook on High for 30 minutes, or until peppers are tender.

4. To serve, ladle goulash into bowls and top each serving with 1 tablespoon of the dill and a dollop of sour cream, if using.

MINDFUL MORSELS

Earthy and pungent, caraway is an ancient herb that has served medicinal and culinary purposes throughout history. It was taken for centuries as a digestive aid and is often used to add balance to robust spice blends, such as the fiery Tunisian harissa or the slightly sweet Indian garam masala. According to spice guru Ian Hemphill, Holland is the world's largest producer of caraway, and Dutch caraway seed is the world's best.

Dilled Veal Stew

Makes 10 servings

This dish can be partially prepared in advance. Start with Step 3; cover the vegetable mixture and refrigerate for up to 2 days. When you're ready to finish the recipe, begin with Step 1, skipping Step 3, and moving on to Step 4.

Note: *The suggested accompaniments for this recipe are not included in the nutrients or exchanges per serving. Whether you keep track of exchanges or count carbohydrates, remember to account for what these additional foods contribute.*

This is a streamlined and lower-fat version of a veal blanquette. It's a great choice for Sunday dinner and makes enough for 10 guests. Serve it over hot whole wheat fettuccine or brown rice noodles.

- **Large (minimum-5 quart) slow cooker**

2 tablespoons all-purpose flour	4 stalks celery, thinly sliced
1 tablespoon paprika	1 cup lower-sodium chicken broth
¼ teaspoon ground nutmeg	½ cup dry vermouth or white wine
1 teaspoon salt	
½ teaspoon freshly ground black pepper	½ cup heavy cream
1 tablespoon butter	½ cup finely chopped dill
2 tablespoons olive oil	Hot buttered noodles (optional)
2 pounds trimmed stewing veal, cut into 1" cubes	
2 onions, thinly sliced	
2 large carrots, peeled, cut into quarters lengthwise, and very thinly sliced	

1. In a small bowl, combine flour, paprika, nutmeg, salt, and pepper. Set aside.

2. In a large skillet, melt butter and 1 tablespoon of the oil over medium heat. Add veal and cook, stirring, for 3 to 4 minutes without browning. Sprinkle flour mixture over meat, turn to coat, and, using a slotted spoon, transfer to slow cooker stoneware.

3. Add remaining 1 tablespoon oil to the pan. Add onions, carrots, and celery; cook, stirring, until vegetables are softened, about 7 minutes. Add broth and vermouth; bring to a boil.

4. Pour mixture over veal, cover, and cook on Low for 8 to 10 hours or on High for 4 to 5 hours, or until stew is hot and bubbly. Stir in cream and dill and serve over noodles, if desired.

NUTRIENTS PER SERVING

Calories	204
Carbohydrate	6 g
Fiber	1 g
Protein	20 g
Fat, total	11 g
Fat, saturated	4 g
Sodium	385 mg
Cholesterol	92 mg

EXCHANGES PER SERVING

1	Vegetable
2½	Medium-fat Meat

Pork Chops with Honey and Thyme

Makes 6 servings (1 chop with sauce per serving)

Note: *The suggested accompaniments for this recipe are not included in the nutrients or exchanges per serving. Whether you keep track of exchanges or count carbohydrates, remember to account for what these additional foods contribute.*

Simple and tasty—these pork chops cook up fast. Serve them with Rice and Bulgur Pilaf (page 233) and steamed broccoli.

½ cup reduced-sodium chicken broth
1 tablespoon honey
1 tablespoon cider vinegar
1 teaspoon cornstarch
1 pound thin boneless loin pork chops, trimmed (about 6)

2 teaspoons vegetable oil
Freshly ground black pepper
3 scallions, sliced
½ teaspoon dried thyme

1. In a small bowl, combine broth, honey, vinegar, and cornstarch. Set aside.

2. Blot pork chops dry with paper towels. In a large nonstick skillet, heat oil over high heat. Add pork chops and cook for 1 to 2 minutes per side, or until lightly browned. Season with pepper. Transfer to a plate.

3. Reduce the heat to medium. Stir in scallions and thyme; cook, stirring, for 30 seconds. Stir reserved chicken broth mixture and add to skillet. Cook, stirring, for 1 minute, or until sauce boils and thickens. Return pork and any juices to skillet; cover and cook for 2 minutes, or until pork is no longer pink in the center. Season sauce, if necessary, with additional pepper to taste. Serve hot.

NUTRIENTS PER SERVING

Calories	135
Carbohydrate	4 g
Fiber	0 g
Protein	15 g
Fat, total	6 g
Fat, saturated	2 g
Sodium	110 mg
Cholesterol	41 mg

EXCHANGES PER SERVING

½	Other Carbohydrate
2	Lean Meat

Company Pork Roast with Fruit Stuffing

Makes 8 servings (4 ounces meat per serving, with fruit and sauce)

TIP

● It may appear that you have too much stuffing when you first tie the pork. But once all the strings are in place, it's easy to enclose the fruit mixture completely.

The sweetness of dried fruit accents the delicate taste of the pork in this recipe. And when you stuff the loin with a fruit-and-spice mixture, you ensure that the meat will be extra moist and flavorful.

STUFFING

- 1 tablespoon butter
- ⅓ cup chopped scallions
- 1 teaspoon ground cumin
- 1 teaspoon mild curry paste or powder
- 1 large egg
- 1 cup chopped mixed dried fruits, such as apricots, prunes, apples, and cranberries
- ½ cup soft bread crumbs (see Tips, page 253)
- 1 teaspoon finely grated orange zest
- ¼ teaspoon salt
- ¼ teaspoon freshly ground black pepper

PORK ROAST

- 3 pounds boneless pork loin roast
  Freshly ground black pepper
- 2 teaspoons vegetable oil
- 1 large clove garlic, minced
- 1 teaspoon dried sage
- ½ teaspoon dried thyme

GRAVY

- 1 tablespoon all-purpose flour
- ½ cup white wine or reduced-sodium chicken broth
- ¾ cup reduced-sodium chicken broth
  Freshly ground black pepper

1. Preheat the oven to 350°F. Coat a roasting pan and rack with cooking spray.

2. **Make the stuffing:** In a small nonstick skillet, melt butter over medium heat. Add scallions, cumin, and curry paste; cook, stirring, until scallions are softened, about 2 minutes.

3. In a large bowl, beat egg. Add scallion mixture, dried fruits, bread crumbs, and zest. Add salt and pepper.

4. **Make the roast:** Remove strings from pork roast; unfold roast and trim excess fat. Place roast, trimmed side down, on a work surface. Cover with plastic wrap and pound, using a meat mallet, to flatten slightly. Season with pepper. Spread stuffing down center of meat. Roll roast around stuffing and tie securely at 6 intervals with kitchen string. Place roast on a rack in the roasting pan.

NUTRIENTS PER SERVING

Calories	345
Carbohydrate	19 g
Fiber	2 g
Protein	35 g
Fat, total	14 g
Fat, saturated	5 g
Sodium	290 mg
Cholesterol	120 mg

EXCHANGES PER SERVING

1	Fruit
4½	Lean Meat
½	Fat

● Pork today is much leaner than it used to be. All trimmed cuts except ribs contain less than 10 grams of fat per 3 ounces cooked meat, and several contain less than 7 grams.

5. In a small bowl, combine oil, garlic, sage, and thyme; spread over pork roast and season with pepper.

6. Bake for 1½ to 1¾ hours, or until a meat thermometer registers 160°F.

7. Transfer roast to a cutting board; tent with foil and let stand for 10 minutes before carving.

8. **Make the gravy:** While roast is resting, make the gravy. Skim fat from the pan and discard. Place the roasting pan over medium heat; sprinkle with flour. Cook, stirring, for 1 minute, or until flour is lightly colored. Add wine and cook until partially reduced. Add broth and bring to a boil, scraping any brown bits from the bottom of the pan. Season with pepper to taste. Strain gravy through a fine strainer into a warm sauceboat.

9. Cut pork into thick slices and serve accompanied with gravy.

Not Your Granny's Pork and Beans

Makes 12 servings

This dish requires a bit of advance planning because the pork is marinated overnight in a salt-and-garlic rub, which imbues it with deep flavor. Otherwise it is simple, straightforward, and loaded with flavor. To complement the Mediterranean ingredients, accompany it with a platter of marinated roasted peppers. Add warm crusty bread, such as ciabatta, and—if you're feeling festive—a robust Rioja for a perfect meal. It makes a large quantity but reheats well.

● **Works best in a large (minimum 5-quart) slow cooker**

1 tablespoon puréed garlic (see Tip, left)	1 teaspoon white wine vinegar
½ teaspoon cracked black peppercorns	1 can (14.5 ounces) diced tomatoes, including juice
2 pounds trimmed boneless pork shoulder, cut into bite-size pieces	2 cans (each 19 ounces) white kidney or navy beans, drained and rinsed
2 tablespoons olive oil	1 cup chopped pitted kalamata olives (about 48 olives)
3 onions, thinly sliced vertically	1 cup finely chopped parsley
6 anchovy fillets, finely chopped	1 teaspoon paprika, preferably smoked, dissolved in 1 tablespoon white wine or water
2 teaspoons dried thyme	
1 cup dry white wine	

1. In a bowl large enough to accommodate the pork, combine garlic and peppercorns. Add pork and toss until well coated with mixture. Cover and refrigerate overnight.

2. In a large skillet, heat 1 tablespoon of the oil over medium-high heat for 30 seconds. Pat pork dry with a paper towel. Add pork to the pan in batches and cook, stirring, adding more oil as necessary, until browned, about 5 minutes per batch. Using a slotted spoon, transfer to the slow cooker stoneware.

NUTRIENTS PER SERVING

Calories	268
Carbohydrate	21 g
Fiber	8 g
Protein	22 g
Fat, total	11 g
Fat, saturated	3 g
Sodium	549 mg
Cholesterol	55 mg

EXCHANGES PER SERVING

1	Vegetable
1	Starch
3	Lean Meat

This dish can be partially prepared in advance. Complete Step 1 and skip Step 2. Heat 1 tablespoon of the oil and complete Step 3. Cover and refrigerate the meat and onion mixtures separately for up to 2 days. When you're ready to finish the recipe, either brown the pork as outlined in Step 2 or add it to the slow cooker without browning. Stir well and continue with Step 4.

Note: *The suggested accompaniments for this recipe are not included in the nutrients or exchanges per serving. Whether you keep track of exchanges or count carbohydrates, remember to account for what these additional foods contribute.*

3. Reduce the heat to medium. Add onions and anchovies to the pan; cook, stirring, until onions are softened, about 3 minutes. Add thyme and cook, stirring, for 1 minute. Add wine and vinegar; cook for 2 minutes longer, stirring and scraping up any brown bits on the bottom of the pan. Add tomatoes and their juice and bring to a boil. Transfer to the slow cooker. Add beans to the slow cooker and stir well.

4. Cover and cook on Low for 8 to 10 hours or on High for 4 to 5 hours, or until pork is very tender (it should be falling apart). Stir in olives, parsley, and paprika solution. Cover and cook on High for 15 minutes, or until heated through.

MINDFUL MORSELS

Contemporary farming has changed the way we think about pork. Once dismissed by health-conscious consumers as extremely fatty, pork has become almost 50 percent leaner than it was just a decade ago. This makes pork, eaten in moderation, a nutritious food choice.

Zesty Barbecued Spareribs

Makes 6 servings

● While today's pork, including ribs, is much leaner than in the past, it's still important to eat spareribs in moderation, as much of the fat is saturated.

● Ribs are great on the barbecue, too. Partially cook the ribs in the oven for 30 minutes, as directed in the recipe. Complete the cooking on the grill over medium-low heat, basting often with the sauce.

Your kids will ask for these succulent spareribs over and over again. Since the only way to eat ribs is with your fingers, be sure to have plenty of napkins handy.

3 pounds pork back ribs Freshly ground black pepper	2 tablespoons Worcestershire sauce
1 cup prepared chili sauce or ketchup	1 tablespoon Dijon mustard
⅓ cup honey	1 teaspoon hot pepper sauce, or to taste
1 small onion, finely chopped	1 lemon, cut into wedges
2 cloves garlic, minced	
2 tablespoons freshly squeezed lemon juice	

1. Preheat the oven to 375°F.

2. Place ribs on a rack in a roasting pan; season with pepper and cover with foil. Bake for 30 minutes.

3. In a small saucepan, combine chili sauce, honey, onion, garlic, lemon juice, Worcestershire sauce, mustard, and hot pepper sauce. Bring to a boil, reduce the heat, and simmer, stirring occasionally, for 10 to 15 minutes, or until slightly thickened.

4. Remove the foil and brush ribs generously on both sides with sauce. Continue to bake, uncovered, for 25 to 30 minutes, brushing generously every 10 minutes with sauce, or until spareribs are nicely glazed and tender.

5. Cut into serving portions. Serve with lemon wedges.

NUTRIENTS PER SERVING

Calories	325
Carbohydrate	20 g
Fiber	1 g
Protein	29 g
Fat, total	15 g
Fat, saturated	5 g
Sodium	410 mg
Cholesterol	66 mg

EXCHANGES PER SERVING

1½	Other Carbohydrate
4	Lean Meat
½	Fat

Lamb with Lentils and Chard

Makes 12 servings

Rich with the flavors of the French countryside, this hearty stew is perfect for guests or a family meal. All it needs is a simple green salad finished with a scattering of shredded carrots.

TIPS

● If you can't find Swiss chard, use 2 packages (each 10 ounces) of fresh or frozen spinach. If using fresh spinach, remove the stems and chop leaves before using. If the spinach has not been prewashed, rinse it thoroughly in a basin of luke-warm water. If using frozen spinach, thaw it first.

● Although this makes a large quantity, you'll enjoy the leftovers. It reheats very well and may even be better the day after it is made.

Note: *The suggested accompaniments for this recipe are not included in the nutrients or exchanges per serving. Whether you keep track of exchanges or count carbohydrates, remember to account for what these additional foods contribute.*

● Large (minimum 5-quart) slow cooker

2 tablespoons olive oil (approximately)	1 can (28 ounces) diced tomatoes, including juice
2 pounds trimmed stewing lamb, cut into 1" cubes	1 cup lower-sodium vegetable or chicken broth
2 onions, finely chopped	2 bay leaves
8 carrots, peeled and sliced	2 cups green or brown lentils, rinsed
4 stalks celery, sliced	8 cups (about 2 bunches) chopped stemmed Swiss chard (see Tips, left)
4 cloves garlic, minced	
2 teaspoons herbes de Provence (see Tips, page 84)	
1 teaspoon salt	
½ teaspoon cracked black peppercorns	

NUTRIENTS PER SERVING

Calories	277
Carbohydrate	30 g
Fiber	7 g
Protein	25 g
Fat, total	7 g
Fat, saturated	2 g
Sodium	462 mg
Cholesterol	0 mg

EXCHANGES PER SERVING

2	Starch
3	Very Lean Meat
1	Fat

1. In a large skillet, heat 1 tablespoon of the oil over medium-high heat for 30 seconds. Add lamb in batches and cook, stirring, adding more oil as necessary, until browned, about 4 minutes per batch. Transfer to the slow cooker stoneware.

2. Reduce the heat to medium. Drain all but 1 tablespoon of the fat from the pan. Add onions, carrots, and celery to the pan and cook, stirring, until carrots are softened, about 7 minutes. Add garlic, herbes de Provence, salt, and peppercorns; cook, stirring, for 1 minute. Add tomatoes and their juice, broth, and bay leaves; bring to a boil. Transfer to the slow cooker. Stir in the lentils.

3. Cover and cook on Low for 8 hours or on High for 4 hours, or until mixture is bubbly and lamb and lentils are tender. Add chard in batches, stirring each batch into the stew until wilted. Cover and cook on High for 20 to 30 minutes, or until chard is tender. Discard bay leaves.

Spicy Lamb Stew

Makes 6 servings

> **TIP**

● Buy a 3-pound leg of lamb or shoulder roast to get 1½ pounds of boneless lamb.

> **VARIATION**

Spicy Beef Stew Substitute an equal amount of lean stewing beef for the lamb; increase cooking time to 1½ hours, or until the meat is tender.

Note: The suggested accompaniment for this recipe is not included in the nutrients or exchanges per serving. Whether you keep track of exchanges or count carbohydrates, remember to account for what these additional foods contribute.

NUTRIENTS PER SERVING

Calories	316
Carbohydrate	7 g
Fiber	1 g
Protein	30 g
Fat, total	18 g
Fat, saturated	6 g
Sodium	340 mg
Cholesterol	107 mg

EXCHANGES PER SERVING

½	Other Carbohydrate
4	Lean Meat
1	Fat

Sometimes you crave a dish that explodes with spicy flavors. The ginger and red pepper flakes used here will satisfy that craving—and soothe your soul, too. Serve this spice-infused stew with basmati rice.

2 tablespoons vegetable oil (approximately)	½ teaspoon salt
1½ pounds lean boneless lamb (cut into 1" cubes)	¼ teaspoon red pepper flakes, or to taste
1 large onion, chopped	Pinch ground cloves
2 cloves garlic, minced	1 tablespoon all-purpose flour
1 tablespoon minced fresh ginger	½ cup low-fat plain yogurt
1 teaspoon ground coriander	1 large tomato, chopped
1 teaspoon ground cumin	½ cup reduced-sodium chicken broth or lamb stock
½ teaspoon ground cinnamon	¼ cup chopped fresh cilantro or parsley

1. In a large saucepan, heat 1 tablespoon of the oil over medium-high heat. Add lamb in batches and cook, stirring, adding more oil as necessary, until browned, about 4 minutes per batch. Using a slotted spoon, transfer lamb to a plate and set aside.

2. Reduce the heat to medium. Add onion, garlic, ginger, coriander, cumin, cinnamon, salt, red pepper flakes, and cloves to the pan; cook, stirring, until onion is softened, about 2 minutes.

3. Sprinkle onion mixture with flour and stir in yogurt. Cook for 1 minute, or until thickened. Add reserved lamb with any accumulated juices, tomato, and broth; bring to a boil. Reduce the heat and simmer, covered, for 45 minutes, or until lamb is tender. Sprinkle with cilantro before serving.

Irish Stew

Makes 8 servings

This recipe can be partially prepared in advance. Skip Steps 1 and 2 and complete Step 3, heating 1 tablespoon of the oil in the pan before softening the vegetables. Cover and refrigerate the vegetables for up to 2 days. When you're ready to finish the recipe, brown the lamb (Steps 1 and 2), then complete Step 4.

Note: *The suggested accompaniments for this recipe are not included in the nutrients or exchanges per serving. Whether you keep track of exchanges or count carbohydrates, remember to account for what these additional foods contribute.*

This hearty and delicious stew is an old favorite that really can't be improved upon. All it needs is a green vegetable such as string beans or broccoli, a crusty roll, and a glass of Guinness or a robust red wine.

● **Works best in a large (minimum 5-quart) slow cooker**

¼ cup all-purpose flour	1 teaspoon dried thyme
1 teaspoon salt	1 cup lower-sodium beef broth
½ teaspoon cracked black peppercorns	2 tablespoons tomato paste
2 pounds trimmed stewing lamb, cut into 1" cubes	1 tablespoon Worcestershire sauce
2 tablespoons olive oil	4 medium potatoes, peeled and cut into ½" cubes
3 onions, finely chopped	1½ cups frozen green peas
2 large carrots, peeled and diced	

1. On a large plate, combine flour, salt, and peppercorns. Lightly coat lamb with mixture, shaking off the excess. Set any remaining flour mixture aside.

2. In a large skillet, heat 1 tablespoon of the oil over medium-high heat for 30 seconds. Add lamb in batches and cook, stirring, adding more oil as necessary, until browned, about 4 minutes per batch. Using a slotted spoon, transfer to the slow cooker stoneware. Drain all but 1 tablespoon fat from the pan.

3. Reduce the heat to medium. Add onions and carrots to the pan and cook, stirring, until carrots are softened, about 7 minutes. Add thyme and reserved flour mixture; cook, stirring, for 1 minute. Stir in broth, tomato paste, and Worcestershire sauce; bring to a boil.

4. Place potatoes in the slow cooker. Add onion mixture and stir to combine. Cover and cook on Low for 8 to 10 hours or on High for 4 to 5 hours, or until mixture is bubbly and potatoes are tender. Stir in peas. Cover and cook on High for 15 to 20 minutes, or until peas are heated through.

NUTRIENTS PER SERVING

Calories	286
Carbohydrate	22 g
Fiber	3 g
Protein	27 g
Fat, total	10 g
Fat, saturated	3 g
Sodium	567 mg
Cholesterol	73 mg

EXCHANGES PER SERVING

1	Starch
1	Vegetable
3	Lean Meat

Rosemary Roast Lamb with New Potatoes

Makes 8 servings (4 ounces meat per serving, with 3 tablespoons sauce and 1 cup potatoes)

Lamb is a great choice when planning a special dinner—it's always a crowd pleaser. The heavenly aroma of garlic and rosemary will fill the house and make an especially warm welcome for friends as they come through the door.

8 cloves garlic	½ teaspoon freshly ground black pepper
1 leg of lamb (about 5 to 6 pounds)	12 whole new potatoes, scrubbed (about 3 pounds)
Grated zest and juice of 1 lemon	1 tablespoon all-purpose flour
2 tablespoons olive oil	½ cup white wine
2 tablespoons chopped fresh rosemary or 1 tablespoon dried	1 cup reduced-sodium chicken broth
½ teaspoon salt	

1. Preheat the oven to 350°F. Coat a large shallow roasting pan with cooking spray.

2. Cut 6 cloves of the garlic into 8 to 10 slivers each. Using the tip of a sharp knife, cut shallow slits all over lamb and insert a garlic sliver into each. Finely chop remaining 2 garlic cloves.

3. In a small bowl, combine chopped garlic, lemon zest and juice, oil, rosemary, salt, and pepper. Place lamb in the prepared pan and surround with potatoes. Brush lamb and potatoes generously with lemon-garlic mixture. Insert a meat thermometer into the thickest part of the leg.

4. Roast for about 1½ hours, turning potatoes over halfway through cooking, or until meat thermometer registers 135°F for medium-rare. (For medium, remove the potatoes and continue to roast lamb for 15 to 20 minutes more, or to your liking.)

NUTRIENTS PER SERVING

Calories	374
Carbohydrate	31 g
Fiber	3 g
Protein	35 g
Fat, total	12 g
Fat, saturated	4 g
Sodium	325 mg
Cholesterol	113 mg

EXCHANGES PER SERVING

2	Starch
4½	Very Lean Meat
1	Fat

• In the past it was customary to cook lamb to well-done, but this does it a disservice. For the best flavor and juiciness, be sure at least a hint of pink remains. Trimmed lean lamb, whether domestic or imported, is lower in fat than many people think—about 6 grams per 3 ounces of lean roast leg of lamb.

5. Remove lamb to a platter, tent with foil, and let rest 10 minutes before carving. Transfer potatoes to a serving dish; keep warm.

6. Skim fat in roasting pan and place pan over medium heat. Stir in flour and cook, stirring, until flour is lightly colored. Pour in wine and cook, scraping up any brown bits from the pan, until wine is reduced by half. Stir in broth and bring to a boil; continue stirring until thickened. Strain through a fine strainer into a warm sauceboat.

7. Carve lamb. Arrange slices on a serving platter and moisten with some of the sauce; surround with roasted potatoes. Serve with remaining sauce.

Lamb Shanks with Luscious Legumes

Makes 12 servings (1½ ounces meat, plus beans, per serving)

● A whole lamb shank is too big for a single serving of this recipe. Ask your butcher to cut each shank into 2 equal pieces.

Note: *The suggested accompaniments for this recipe are not included in the nutrients or exchanges per serving. Whether you keep track of exchanges or count carbohydrates, remember to account for what these additional foods contribute.*

Lamb cooked with legumes in a flavorful wine-based sauce is a French tradition. No wonder—it's a mouthwatering combination. If you prefer more assertive flavors, bury a whole branch of fresh rosemary, stem and all, in the lamb before adding the sauce. Serve this with crusty bread, a green salad, or garden-fresh tomatoes in vinaigrette and a robust red wine for a memorable meal.

● **Works best in a large (minimum 5-quart) slow cooker**

2 cups dried white navy beans or flageolets, soaked, rinsed, and drained	4 stalks celery, diced
	6 cloves garlic, minced
¼ cup all-purpose flour	1 tablespoon finely chopped rosemary
1 teaspoon salt	
½ teaspoon cracked black peppercorns	Grated zest and juice of 1 orange
6 lamb shanks, sliced in half	1 cup lower-sodium beef broth
2 tablespoons olive oil	½ cup dry red wine
2 onions, finely chopped	Finely chopped fresh parsley
2 carrots, peeled and diced	

1. Place soaked beans in the slow cooker stoneware.

2. On a large plate, combine flour, salt, and peppercorns. Lightly coat lamb shanks with mixture, shaking off the excess. Set any remaining flour mixture aside.

3. In a large skillet, heat 1 tablespoon of the oil over medium-high heat. Add lamb in batches and cook, turning, adding more oil as necessary, until lightly browned on all sides. Using tongs, transfer to the slow cooker. Drain all but 1 tablespoon oil from the pan.

NUTRIENTS PER SERVING

Calories	253
Carbohydrate	28 g
Fiber	6 g
Protein	21 g
Fat, total	7 g
Fat, saturated	2 g
Sodium	326 mg
Cholesterol	44 mg

EXCHANGES PER SERVING

2	Starch
2½	Very Lean Meat

This dish can be partially prepared in advance. Soak the beans and begin with Step 4. Complete Step 4, heating 1 tablespoon of the oil in the pan before softening the vegetables and sprinkling 1 tablespoon of the flour over the vegetables. Cover and refrigerate the beans and vegetables for up to 2 days. When you're ready to finish the recipe, start with Step 1.

4. Reduce the heat to medium. Add onions, carrots, and celery to the pan and cook, stirring, until carrots are softened, about 7 minutes. Add garlic, rosemary, and zest; cook, stirring, for 1 minute. Sprinkle reserved flour mixture over vegetables and cook, stirring, for 1 minute longer. Add orange juice, broth, and wine; bring to a boil.

5. Pour vegetable mixture over lamb. Cover and cook on Low for 10 to 12 hours or on High for 5 to 6 hours, or until lamb is falling off the bone and beans are tender. Discard bones and transfer lamb and beans to a deep platter or serving dish; keep warm. Transfer cooking liquid to a small saucepan and cook over medium-high heat until reduced by one-third. Pour over lamb and garnish liberally with parsley.

MINDFUL MORSELS

The navy beans in this recipe make it very high in fiber—you'll get more than 6 grams per serving.

POULTRY ENTRÉES

1-Hour Roast Chicken with Sage and Garlic

Makes 4 servings (4 ounces meat, no skin, per serving)

Who has time to wait around for a chicken to roast when you're in a hurry? You can easily slash an hour off the roasting time: Simply cut the bird open along the backbone, place it flat on a broiler pan, and then boost the oven temperature to 400°F. The result—a golden, succulent bird in about half the time.

1 chicken (about 3½ pounds)
1 tablespoon butter, softened
2 cloves garlic, minced
1 tablespoon minced fresh sage or 1 teaspoon dried
1½ teaspoons grated lemon zest

½ teaspoon salt
½ teaspoon freshly ground black pepper
2 teaspoons olive oil
¼ teaspoon paprika

1. Preheat the oven to 400°F. Coat a broiler pan rack with cooking spray.

2. Remove giblets and neck from chicken. Rinse and pat chicken dry inside and out with paper towels. Using heavy-duty kitchen scissors, cut chicken open along backbone; press down on breastbone to flatten slightly and arrange skin side up on the broiler pan rack.

3. In a small bowl, blend butter with garlic, sage, zest, salt, and pepper. Gently lift breast skin; using your fingers, spread butter mixture under skin to coat breasts and part of legs. Press down on outside of skin to smooth and spread butter mixture.

4. In another small bowl, whisk together olive oil and paprika; brush over chicken.

5. Roast chicken for 1 hour, or until juices run clear and a meat thermometer inserted in the thickest part of the thigh registers 185°F. Transfer chicken to a platter. Tent with foil and let rest 5 minutes before carving.

NUTRIENTS PER SERVING

Calories	256
Carbohydrate	1 g
Fiber	0 g
Protein	36 g
Fat, total	11 g
Fat, saturated	3 g
Sodium	415 mg
Cholesterol	116 mg

EXCHANGES PER SERVING

5	Very Lean Meat
1	Fat

Thyme-Roasted Chicken with Garlic Gravy

Makes 4 servings (4 ounces, no skin, per serving, with ¼ cup gravy)

It's always a special occasion when there's a roast chicken in the oven. It conjures up a homey smell and feel and is perhaps one of the most satisfying dishes on earth. Here herbs and seasonings are placed under the bird's skin to produce a succulent, flavorful chicken. Slow roasting with lots of garlic creates a wonderful aroma—yet, surprisingly, imparts only a subtle flavor to the gravy.

1 teaspoon dried thyme
¼ teaspoon salt
¼ teaspoon freshly ground black pepper
10 cloves garlic, peeled
1 chicken (about 3½ pounds)

1⅓ cups reduced-sodium chicken broth (approximately)
½ cup white wine or additional chicken broth
1 tablespoon all-purpose flour

1. Preheat the oven to 325°F.

2. In a small bowl, combine thyme, salt, and pepper.

3. Remove giblets and neck from chicken. Rinse and pat chicken dry inside and out. Place 2 cloves of the garlic inside cavity. Starting at cavity opening, gently lift skin and, using your fingers, push thyme mixture under skin and over breasts and legs. Tie legs together with string; tuck wings under back.

4. Place ⅔ cup of the chicken broth, wine, and remaining 8 cloves garlic in a roasting pan. Place chicken, breast side up, on a rack in the pan.

5. Roast chicken, basting every 30 minutes and adding additional broth if pan juices evaporate, for 1¾ to 2 hours, or until pan juices run clear when chicken is pierced and a meat thermometer inserted in thickest part of thigh registers 185°F.

6. Transfer chicken to a platter, tent with foil, and let stand for 10 minutes before carving.

7. Meanwhile, strain pan juices into a cup measure, pressing down firmly to mash garlic into juices; skim off fat. Add enough of the remaining broth to make ¾ cup.

8. In a small saucepan, stir together flour and 2 tablespoons of the pan juices. Cook, stirring, over medium heat, for 1 minute. Gradually whisk in remaining pan juices. Cook, stirring, until boiling and thickened. Serve gravy with chicken.

NUTRIENTS PER SERVING

Calories	264
Carbohydrate	4 g
Fiber	1 g
Protein	38 g
Fat, total	9 g
Fat, saturated	3 g
Sodium	420 mg
Cholesterol	112 mg

EXCHANGES PER SERVING

5	Very Lean Meat
1	Fat

Yummy Parmesan Chicken Fingers

What a relief to know that when you come home frazzled after a day at work, you can count on these tasty chicken fingers stashed away in your freezer. Round out the meal with rice and a steamed vegetable, such as broccoli, for a dinner that's on the table in 30 minutes.

½ cup finely crushed soda cracker crumbs (about 16 crackers)	½ teaspoon salt
⅓ cup freshly grated Parmesan cheese	¼ teaspoon freshly ground black pepper
½ teaspoon dried basil	4 boneless, skinless chicken breasts
½ teaspoon dried marjoram	1 large egg
½ teaspoon paprika	1 clove garlic, minced

1. Preheat the oven to 400°F. Coat a rack and place it on a baking sheet.

2. In a food processor, combine cracker crumbs, Parmesan, basil, marjoram, paprika, salt, and pepper. Process to make fine crumbs. Transfer to a shallow bowl.

3. Cut chicken breasts into 4 strips each. In a large bowl, beat egg with garlic. Using a fork, coat chicken strips with egg mixture, then dip strips in crumb mixture until evenly coated. Arrange on rack.

4. Bake for 14 to 18 minutes, or until no longer pink in center. (If frozen, bake for up to 25 minutes.)

Terrific Chicken Burgers

Makes 4 servings

Note: *The suggested accompaniments for this recipe are not included in the nutrients or exchanges per serving. Whether you keep track of exchanges or count carbohydrates, remember to account for what these additional foods contribute.*

Accompany these patties with stir-fried rice and steamed vegetables.

1 large egg	½ teaspoon salt
½ cup fine dried bread crumbs (see Tip, page 81)	¼ teaspoon freshly ground black pepper
⅓ cup finely chopped scallions	1 pound ground chicken or turkey
1 teaspoon ground coriander	1 tablespoon vegetable oil
1 teaspoon grated lemon zest	

1. In a large bowl, beat egg; stir in bread crumbs, scallions, coriander, zest, salt, and pepper. Mix in chicken. With wet hands, shape mixture into 4 patties, each 4" in diameter.

2. In a large nonstick skillet, heat oil over medium heat. Add patties and cook for 5 to 6 minutes on each side, or until golden brown on the outside and no longer pink in the center.

NUTRIENTS PER SERVING

Calories	291
Carbohydrate	11 g
Fiber	1 g
Protein	23 g
Fat, total	17 g
Fat, saturated	1 g
Sodium	490 mg
Cholesterol	47 mg

EXCHANGES PER SERVING

½	Starch
3	Medium-fat Meat
½	Fat

Streamlined Chicken and Vegetable Stew

Makes 4 servings

TIP

• Use 5 cups fresh vegetables instead of frozen, if you wish. Cut them into bite-size pieces. For slower-cooking vegetables, such as carrots and celery, add along with the chicken. For faster-cooking ones, such as broccoli and zucchini, add for the last 10 minutes of cooking.

Note: *The suggested accompaniment for this recipe is not included in the nutrients or exchanges per serving. Whether you keep track of exchanges or count carbohydrates, remember to account for what these additional foods contribute.*

Even if you don't have a lot of time to spend in the kitchen, you can rustle up a great-tasting stew using boneless chicken thighs and convenient frozen vegetables. This satisfying dish does away with browning the chicken. You'll save time but not lose any flavor. Serve over noodles.

2 teaspoons vegetable oil	3 tablespoons all-purpose flour
1 large onion, chopped	2 cups reduced-sodium chicken broth
2 cloves garlic, minced	1 package (1 pound) frozen mixed vegetables
1 teaspoon dried Italian herbs or fines herbes (see Tips, page 128)	Freshly ground black pepper
1 pound boneless, skinless chicken thighs (about 8), cut into 1" cubes	

1. In a Dutch oven or large saucepan, heat oil over medium heat. Add onion, garlic, and herbs; cook, stirring, until onion is lightly colored, about 4 minutes.

2. In a medium bowl, toss chicken with flour until well coated. Add to the pan along with any remaining flour. Stir in broth and bring to a boil. Cook, stirring, until sauce thickens. Reduce the heat, cover, and simmer, stirring occasionally, for 20 minutes.

3. Add frozen vegetables and return to a boil. Season with pepper to taste. Reduce the heat, cover, and simmer for 10 minutes, or until chicken and vegetables are tender.

NUTRIENTS PER SERVING

Calories	275
Carbohydrate	25 g
Fiber	5 g
Protein	26 g
Fat, total	8 g
Fat, saturated	2 g
Sodium	360 mg
Cholesterol	75 mg

EXCHANGES PER SERVING

2	Vegetable
1	Other Carbohydrate
3	Lean Meat

Classic Chicken Stew

Makes 12 servings (1 piece of chicken with vegetables per serving)

This creamy stew is reminiscent of chicken pot pie without the crust. You can create a crust effect, however, by serving the stew over crostini (page 31) placed in the bottom of a soup plate. Add a tossed green salad for a complete and delicious meal.

TIP

• Because the chicken cooks for only 6 hours on Low, the potatoes will be a bit firm unless they are blanched (see Step 1) before they're added to the stew.

MAKE AHEAD

This dish can be partially prepared in advance. Complete Steps 1 and 2. Cover and refrigerate the vegetable mixture overnight. The next morning, continue with Step 3.

Note: The suggested accompaniment for this recipe is not included in the nutrients or exchanges per serving. Whether you keep track of exchanges or count carbohydrates, remember to account for what these additional foods contribute.

• Works best in a large (minimum 5-quart) slow cooker

1 potato, peeled and diced	½ cup dry white wine or lower-sodium chicken broth
1 tablespoon olive oil	Freshly ground black pepper
2 onions, finely chopped	
2 carrots, diced	3 pounds skinless bone-in chicken thighs (about 12 thighs)
4 stalks celery, diced	
¼ cup all-purpose flour	1 cup green peas, thawed if frozen
½ teaspoon dried thyme or 3 whole sprigs fresh	
1 bay leaf	
1½ cups lower-sodium chicken broth	

1. In a medium saucepan, combine potato and cold water to cover. Bring to a boil and cook for 2 minutes. Remove from the heat, cover, and set aside.

2. In a large skillet, heat oil over medium heat for 30 seconds. Add onions, carrots, and celery; cook, stirring, until carrots are softened, about 7 minutes. Add flour, thyme, and bay leaf; cook, stirring, for 1 minute. Add broth and wine; cook, stirring, until mixture comes to a boil and thickens, about 4 minutes. Drain reserved potato and add to mixture. Season to taste with pepper.

3. Arrange chicken over bottom of the slow cooker stoneware and cover with vegetable mixture. Cover and cook on Low for 6 hours or on High for 3 hours, or until juices run clear when chicken is pierced with a fork. Add peas and stir well. Cover and cook on High for 20 minutes, or until peas are tender and mixture is hot and bubbly.

NUTRIENTS PER SERVING

Calories	145
Carbohydrate	8 g
Fiber	2 g
Protein	16 g
Fat, total	5 g
Fat, saturated	1 g
Sodium	139 mg
Cholesterol	53 mg

EXCHANGES PER SERVING

1½	Vegetable
2	Lean Meat

Chicken-Vegetable Cobbler with Cheddar Biscuit Crust

Makes 6 servings

TIPS

● If you'd like, omit the topping altogether and serve the chicken and vegetables over rice or noodles.

● Fines herbes, available in the spice section of your grocery store, contains dried parsley, chives, tarragon, and chervil. You can also use an Italian herb mix of basil, oregano, and marjoram.

● The chicken-vegetable mixture without the crust freezes well for up to 2 months.

NUTRIENTS PER SERVING

Calories	353
Carbohydrate	30 g
Fiber	4 g
Protein	25 g
Fat, total	15 g
Fat, saturated	7 g
Sodium	730 mg
Cholesterol	85 mg

EXCHANGES PER SERVING

1½	Starch
1	Vegetable
2½	Medium-fat Meat

Some dishes never lose their appeal—like this old-fashioned favorite, which is perfect to make on a lazy Sunday afternoon. It requires some time to prepare, but once the creamy chicken mixture and its golden biscuit crust are bubbling away in the oven, you'll be glad you made the effort. And so will your family.

CHICKEN AND VEGETABLES

2 pounds chicken legs, with skin and excess fat removed

3½ cups water

1 teaspoon salt

Freshly ground black pepper

1 bay leaf

2 teaspoons butter

2 cups quartered mushrooms

1 onion, chopped

1 large clove garlic, minced

2 teaspoons dried fines herbes (see Tips, left) or dried basil

⅓ cup all-purpose flour

3 carrots, peeled and sliced

2 stalks celery, chopped

1 cup frozen peas

½ cup half-and-half

¼ cup chopped fresh parsley

CHEDDAR BISCUIT CRUST

¾ cup all-purpose flour

⅓ cup shredded Cheddar cheese

1 teaspoon baking powder

¼ teaspoon baking soda

½ cup low-fat plain yogurt

2 tablespoons butter, melted

1. **Make the chicken and vegetables:** In a large saucepan, combine chicken, water, salt, pepper to taste, and bay leaf. Bring to a boil; reduce the heat to medium-low, cover, and simmer for 1 hour. Remove the pan from the heat and let chicken stand in liquid until cool enough to handle. Pull chicken meat from bones and cut into bite-size pieces. Strain stock and skim off any fat; there should be 2½ cups of stock. Add water, if necessary to make that amount. Discard bay leaf. Set stock aside.

2. In the same large saucepan, melt butter over medium heat. Add mushrooms, onion, garlic, and fines herbes. Cook, stirring often, until vegetables are softened, about 5 minutes.

You can make the chicken and vegetable mixture ahead and cover and refrigerate it for up to 1 day. When ready to finish the recipe, microwave on Medium-high or reheat the mixture in a saucepan until piping hot before topping it with the crust.

Note: *The suggested accompaniments for this recipe are not included in the nutrients or exchanges per serving. Whether you keep track of exchanges or count carbohydrates, remember to account for what these additional foods contribute.*

3. Meanwhile, in a medium bowl, blend flour with a small amount of stock until smooth; stir in remaining stock. Add stock to mushroom mixture and stir well. Bring to a boil, stirring, until thickened and smooth. Preheat the oven to 400°F.

4. Add carrots and celery to mushroom mixture. Cover and simmer over low heat, stirring occasionally, for 15 minutes, or until vegetables are just tender.

5. Add chicken, peas, half-and-half, and parsley; season with additional pepper to taste. Cook just to heat through. Spoon hot chicken mixture into a deep 12-cup casserole dish.

6. **Make the crust:** In a large bowl, combine flour, cheese, baking powder, and baking soda.

7. In a small bowl, combine yogurt and butter. Add to flour mixture and stir just until combined.

8. Spoon dough on top of hot chicken mixture. Bake for 25 to 30 minutes, or until crust is golden and filling is bubbly.

Chicken Cassoulet

Makes 8 servings (1 piece of chicken with beans per serving)

This hearty one-dish meal is always a hit. The dill finish adds an intriguing hint of flavor. Serve cassoulet with whole grain bread to soak up the luscious sauce. A salad of shredded carrots makes a nice accompaniment.

TIP

• If you're using small cremini mushrooms (ideal for this recipe), just remove the stems and use them whole. Cut larger creminis in half or quarter them, depending on the size. If using portobello mushrooms, remove the stems and gills and cut each cap into 6 equal wedges.

Note: *The suggested accompaniments for this recipe are not included in the nutrients or exchanges per serving. Whether you keep track of exchanges or count carbohydrates, remember to account for what these additional foods contribute.*

• **Large (minimum 6-quart) slow cooker**

1 tablespoon olive oil	1 can (28 ounces) diced tomatoes, including juice
8 carrots, peeled and sliced	1 cup lower-sodium chicken or vegetable broth
2 onions, finely chopped	
4 stalks celery, sliced	2 bay leaves
4 cloves garlic, minced	2 pounds skinless bone-in chicken thighs (about 8 thighs)
2 teaspoons herbes de Provence	
½ teaspoon salt	1 pound cremini or portobello mushrooms (see Tip, left)
1 teaspoon cracked black peppercorns	½ cup finely chopped dill
2 cans (14 ounces each) white beans, rinsed and drained, or 2 cups dried white beans, soaked, cooked and drained (see Basic Beans, page 236)	

1. In a large skillet, heat oil over medium heat for 30 seconds. Add carrots, onions, and celery; cook, stirring, until carrots are softened, about 7 minutes. Add garlic, herbes de Provence, salt, and peppercorns. Cook, stirring, for 1 minute. Add beans, tomatoes and their juice, broth, and bay leaves; bring to a boil. Remove the pan from the heat.

2. Spoon half of the bean mixture into the slow cooker stoneware. Place chicken evenly on top. Arrange mushrooms evenly over chicken. Spoon remainder of bean mixture over mushrooms.

3. Cover and cook on Low for 6 hours or on High for 3 hours, or until juices run clear when chicken is pierced with a fork. Stir in dill, cover, and cook on High for 15 minutes, or until flavors meld.

NUTRIENTS PER SERVING

Calories	281
Carbohydrate	32.7 g
Fiber	10.3 g
Protein	24.4 g
Fat, total	6.8 g
Fat, saturated	1.4 g
Sodium	762 mg
Cholesterol	69 mg

EXCHANGES PER SERVING

2	Starch
2½	Extra-lean Meat
½	Fat

French Basil Chicken

Makes 12 servings (1 piece of chicken with vegetables per serving)

This recipe is named French Basil Chicken to distinguish it from the well-known dish Thai Basil Chicken. Here the chicken pairs with the complementary flavors of tomato, artichoke, and sweet red bell pepper. A healthy quantity of finely chopped fresh basil leaves is stirred in at the end.

• **Works in slow cookers from 3½ to 6 quarts**

1 tablespoon olive oil	1 cup lower-sodium chicken broth
2 onions, finely chopped	
4 cloves garlic, minced	1 can (14 ounces) artichoke hearts, drained, rinsed, and quartered
1 teaspoon herbes de Provence (see Tips, page 84)	
½ teaspoon salt	3 pounds skinless bone-in chicken thighs (about 12 thighs)
½ teaspoon cracked black peppercorns	
1 tablespoon all-purpose flour	2 cups diced red bell pepper
½ cup dry white wine (see Tip, left)	½ cup finely chopped fresh basil
1 can (14.5 ounces) diced tomatoes, including juice	

1. In a large skillet, heat oil over medium heat for 30 seconds. Add onions and cook, stirring, until softened, about 3 minutes. Add garlic, herbes de Provence, salt, and peppercorns; cook, stirring, for 1 minute. Add flour and cook, stirring, for 1 minute. Add wine and cook, stirring, for 1 minute. Add tomatoes and their juice and broth; bring to a boil. Stir in artichoke hearts and remove the pan from the heat.

2. Arrange chicken pieces evenly over the bottom of the slow cooker stoneware and cover with the tomato mixture. Cover and cook on Low for 6 hours or on High for 3 hours, or until juices run clear when chicken is pierced with a fork. Stir in bell pepper and basil. Cover and cook on High for 30 minutes, or until bell pepper is tender.

NUTRIENTS PER SERVING

Calories	153
Carbohydrate	8 g
Fiber	2 g
Protein	18 g
Fat, total	6 g
Fat, saturated	1 g
Sodium	339 mg
Cholesterol	69 mg

EXCHANGES PER SERVING

1½	Vegetable
2	Lean Meat

Balsamic Braised Chicken with Olives

Makes 12 servings (1 piece of chicken with sauce per serving)

This recipe can be partially prepared in advance. Complete Step 1. Cover and refrigerate the tomato mixture for up to 2 days. When you're ready to finish the recipe, continue with Step 2.

Note: *The suggested accompaniments for this recipe are not included in the nutrients or exchanges per serving. Whether you keep track of exchanges or count carbohydrates, remember to account for what these additional foods contribute.*

Here's a tasty Mediterranean-inspired dish that is simple yet elegant. For a delectable meal, serve it over creamy Basic Polenta (page 257) or hot whole grain couscous.

● **Works best in a large (minimum 5-quart) slow cooker**

1 tablespoon olive oil	½ cup lower-sodium chicken broth
2 onions, finely chopped	2 tablespoons balsamic vinegar
4 cloves garlic, minced	3 pounds skinless bone-in chicken thighs (about 12 thighs)
½ teaspoon salt	
½ teaspoon cracked black peppercorns	2 tablespoons drained capers
½ teaspoon dried thyme	2 tablespoons chopped pitted black olives
2 cups chopped peeled tomatoes, including juice, if canned	

1. In a large skillet, heat oil over medium heat for 30 seconds. Add onions and cook, stirring, until softened, about 3 minutes. Add garlic, salt, peppercorns, and thyme; cook, stirring, for 1 minute. Add tomatoes and their juice, broth, and vinegar; bring to a boil.

2. Arrange chicken on the bottom of the slow cooker stoneware and cover with the vegetable mixture. Cover and cook on Low for 6 hours or on High for 3 hours, or until juices run clear when chicken is pierced with a fork. Add capers and olives; stir well. Serve immediately.

NUTRIENTS PER SERVING

Calories	123
Carbohydrate	4 g
Fiber	1 g
Protein	15 g
Fat, total	5 g
Fat, saturated	1 g
Sodium	226 mg
Cholesterol	53 mg

EXCHANGES PER SERVING

2	Lean Meat

Chicken Cacciatore with Broccoli

Makes 12 servings (1 piece of chicken with vegetables per serving)

• If you can find them, use Italian San Marzano tomatoes when making this recipe because they have more flavor than domestic varieties. Otherwise, add 1 tablespoon tomato paste along with the tomatoes.

Note: *The suggested accompaniment for this recipe is not included in the nutrients or exchanges per serving. Whether you keep track of exchanges or count carbohydrates, remember to account for what these additional foods contribute.*

This dish is a classic because it's so tasty. The addition of broccoli to the traditional ingredients adds flavor as well as nutrients. Serve it over Basic Polenta (page 257) or whole grain pasta for a delicious meal.

• **Large (minimum 5-quart) slow cooker**

2 tablespoons olive oil	1 can (28 ounces) diced tomatoes, including juice (see Tip, left)
2 onions, finely chopped	
4 cloves garlic, minced	
1 teaspoon dried oregano	3 pounds skinless bone-in chicken thighs (about 12 thighs)
½ teaspoon salt	
½ teaspoon cracked black peppercorns	2 dried red chile peppers (optional)
8 ounces cremini mushrooms, trimmed and sliced	1 green bell pepper, diced
1 cup dry white wine or lower-sodium chicken broth	4 cups broccoli florets, blanched

1. In a large skillet, heat 1 tablespoon of the oil over medium heat for 30 seconds. Add onions and cook, stirring, until softened, about 3 minutes. Add garlic, oregano, salt, and peppercorns; cook, stirring, for 1 minute. Add mushrooms and toss to coat. Add wine and tomatoes and their juice; bring to a boil.

2. Arrange chicken over bottom of the slow cooker stoneware. Cover with the tomato sauce. Cover and cook on Low for 6 hours or on High for 3 hours, or until juices run clear when chicken is pierced with a fork. Using a slotted spoon, transfer chicken to a heatproof serving dish and keep warm in the oven.

3. In a skillet, heat remaining oil over medium heat for 30 seconds. Add chile peppers, if using, and cook, stirring, for 1 minute. Add bell pepper and cook, stirring, until softened, about 3 minutes. Add tomato sauce from the slow cooker and bring to a boil. Reduce the heat and simmer until slightly reduced and thickened, about 10 minutes. Add broccoli and cook until heated through. Combine sauce with chicken and serve.

NUTRIENTS PER SERVING

Calories	159
Carbohydrate	7 g
Fiber	2 g
Protein	18 g
Fat, total	7 g
Fat, saturated	1 g
Sodium	273 mg
Cholesterol	69 mg

EXCHANGES PER SERVING

1½	Vegetable
2½	Lean Meat

Everyone's Favorite Chicken Cacciatore

Makes 5 servings (2 pieces per serving, with sauce)

TIP

• Sun-dried tomatoes sold dry in packages are more economical than those packed in oil. To reconstitute, place in a bowl and cover with boiling water. Or cover with cold water and microwave on High for 2 minutes, or until just boiling. Let stand until softened, about 10 minutes; drain and chop.

Note: *The suggested accompaniments for this recipe are not included in the nutrients or exchanges per serving. Whether you keep track of exchanges or count carbohydrates, remember to account for what these additional foods contribute.*

To survive the 6 o'clock weeknight rush, batch-cook stews and sauce-based meals on weekends, and keep them in the fridge for up to 3 days or freeze for easy reheating. When you breeze through the door at night, you simply have to decide whether you'll serve the stew with pasta or rice—and dinner's on the table.

3 tablespoons all-purpose flour	½ cup white wine or reduced-sodium chicken broth
½ teaspoon salt	1 can (14.5 ounces) tomatoes, including juice, chopped
½ teaspoon freshly ground black pepper	⅓ cup chopped reconstituted sun-dried tomatoes (see Tip, left)
2 pounds skinless chicken thighs (about 10)	¼ cup chopped fresh basil or parsley or a mixture of both
3 tablespoons olive oil	
3 cups sliced mushrooms	
1 small onion, chopped	
2 cloves garlic, minced	

1. In a large zip-top plastic bag, shake together flour, salt, and pepper. In batches, toss chicken to coat, shaking off excess flour mixture.

2. In a Dutch oven or large saucepan, heat 1 tablespoon of the oil over medium-high heat. Brown half of the chicken on all sides; transfer to a plate. Add another 1 tablespoon of the oil and brown remaining chicken; transfer to the plate. Add remaining 1 tablespoon oil to the pan. Add mushrooms, onion, and garlic; cook, stirring, until softened, about 5 minutes. Stir in wine.

3. Return chicken and any juices to the pan along with tomatoes and their juice and sun-dried tomatoes. Bring to a boil; reduce the heat, cover, and simmer for 35 minutes, or until chicken is tender. Stir in basil and season with additional pepper to taste.

NUTRIENTS PER SERVING

Calories	313
Carbohydrate	14 g
Fiber	3 g
Protein	28 g
Fat, total	15 g
Fat, saturated	4 g
Sodium	580 mg
Cholesterol	95 mg

EXCHANGES PER SERVING

2½	Vegetable
3½	Lean Meat
1	Fat

The Captain's Curry

Makes 12 servings (1 piece of chicken with sauce per serving)

TIP

● Count ½ cup cooked rice as a Starch Exchange.

MAKE AHEAD

This recipe can be partially prepared in advance. Complete Step 1. Cover and refrigerate the onion mixture for up to 2 days. When you're ready to finish the recipe, continue with Steps 2 and 3.

This style of curry, made with a creamed curry sauce, was popular in the great American seaports during the 19th century. It gets its name from sea captains involved in the spice trade, who brought their wares to cities such as Charleston. Today we associate coconut milk with our current interest in Asian foods, but citizens of the old South were quite familiar with this ingredient, which they made themselves using fresh coconuts from the West Indies.

● **Works best in a large (minimum 5-quart) slow cooker**

1 tablespoon olive oil	1 cup lower-sodium chicken broth
2 onions, finely chopped	
2 stalks celery, thinly sliced	3 pounds skinless bone-in chicken thighs (about 12 thighs)
2 cloves garlic, minced	
½ teaspoon ground allspice	1 cup coconut milk
½ teaspoon freshly grated nutmeg	1 tablespoon curry powder
1 piece (3") cinnamon stick	½ teaspoon cayenne pepper
1 bay leaf	Hot white rice (see Tip, left)
2 tablespoons all-purpose flour	

1. In a large skillet, heat oil over medium heat for 30 seconds. Add onions and celery; cook, stirring, until celery is softened, about 5 minutes. Add garlic, allspice, nutmeg, cinnamon stick, and bay leaf; cook, stirring, for 1 minute. Sprinkle flour over mixture and cook, stirring, for 1 minute. Add broth, bring to a boil, and cook, stirring, until thickened.

2. Arrange chicken over the bottom of the slow cooker stoneware and cover with the vegetable mixture. Cover and cook on Low for 6 hours or on High for 3 hours, or until juices run clear when chicken is pierced with a fork.

3. In a small bowl, whisk ¼ cup of the coconut milk with the curry powder and cayenne. Add to the slow cooker. Stir in remaining ¾ cup coconut milk and cook on High for 30 minutes, or until flavors meld. Discard cinnamon stick and bay leaf. Serve over hot white rice.

NUTRIENTS PER SERVING

Calories	161
Carbohydrate	4 g
Fiber	1g
Protein	15 g
Fat, total	10
Fat, saturated	5 g
Sodium	99 mg
Cholesterol	53 mg

EXCHANGES PER SERVING

2	Medium-fat Meat

Indian-Style Chicken with Puréed Spinach

Makes 16 servings (1 piece of chicken with sauce per serving)

• If you don't have a 14.5-oz can of diced tomatoes, use 2 cups canned tomatoes with juice, coarsely chopped.

• If using fresh spinach, be sure to remove the stems, and if it has not been prewashed, rinse it thoroughly in a basin of lukewarm water. You will need to push the spinach well down in the blender or food processor before puréeing in batches, if necessary. If using frozen spinach, thaw it first and squeeze the water out.

• One chile produces a medium-hot result. Add a second chile only if you're a true heat seeker.

• When handling hot peppers, wear rubber gloves to avoid skin irritation.

NUTRIENTS PER SERVING

Calories	124
Carbohydrate	5 g
Fiber	2 g
Protein	14
Fat, total	6 g
Fat, saturated	1 g
Sodium	214 mg
Cholesterol	48 mg

EXCHANGES PER SERVING

1	Vegetable
2	Lean Meat

This mouthwatering dish is an adaptation of a recipe from Suneeta Vaswani's terrific book Easy Indian Cooking. *It makes a fine centerpiece for a meal, accompanied by rice and/or whole wheat chapati, the Indian flat bread.*

• **Large (minimum 5-quart) oval slow cooker**

4 pounds bone-in, skinless chicken thighs (about 16 thighs)	½ teaspoon salt
¼ cup fresh lemon juice	1 can (14.5 ounces) diced tomatoes, including juice (see Tips, left)
1 tablespoon cumin seeds	2 packages (10 ounces each) fresh or frozen spinach (see Tips, left)
2 teaspoons coriander seeds	
2 tablespoon olive oil	1 cup lower-sodium chicken broth
2 medium onions, thinly sliced on the vertical	1 to 2 long red or green chile peppers, chopped (see Tips, left)
1 tablespoon minced garlic	Juice of 1 lime or lemon
1 tablespoon minced fresh ginger	
1 teaspoon turmeric	
1 teaspoon cracked black peppercorns	

1. Rinse chicken under cold running water and pat dry. In a large bowl, combine chicken and ¼ cup lemon juice. Toss well and set aside for 20 to 30 minutes.

2. In a large dry skillet over medium heat, toast cumin and coriander seeds, stirring, until fragrant and just beginning to brown, about 3 minutes. Immediately transfer to a mortar or spice grinder and grind. Set aside.

This dish can be partially prepared in advance. Complete Step 1. Cover and refrigerate the chicken. Complete Steps 2 and 3. Cover and refrigerate tomato mixture separately from the chicken. The next day, continue with Steps 4 and 5.

Note: *The suggested accompaniments for this recipe are not included in the nutrients or exchanges per serving. Whether you keep track of exchanges or count carbohydrates, remember to account for what these additional foods contribute.*

3. In the same skillet, heat oil over medium-high heat for 30 seconds. Add onions and cook, stirring, until they just begin to color, about 5 minutes. Reduce the heat to medium and cook, stirring, until onions are golden, about 12 minutes. Add reserved cumin and coriander, garlic, ginger, turmeric, peppercorns, and salt; cook, stirring, for 1 minute. Stir in tomatoes and their juice and bring to a boil. Remove the pan from the heat.

4. Arrange marinated chicken evenly over the bottom of the slow cooker stoneware. Pour tomato mixture over the top. Cover and cook on Low for 6 hours or on High for 3 hours, or until juices run clear when chicken is pierced with a fork.

5. In a blender or food processor, combine spinach, broth, and chile(s). Pulse until spinach is puréed. Add to chicken and stir well. Cover and cook on High for 20 minutes, or until mixture is bubbly. Just before serving, stir in juice of 1 lime.

MINDFUL MORSELS

The spinach in this recipe provides more than 100 percent of the daily value of vitamin K, which is found in many leafy greens and some vegetable oils, such as olive oil. Vitamin K is an important blood-clotting agent and also plays a role in bone health.

Sage and Onion Chicken with Cranberry Rice

Makes 12 servings (1 piece of chicken with rice per serving)

TIPS

• Packaged mixtures of wild and several varieties of brown rice are available in most supermarkets. You can make your own mixture by combining ¾ cup of each, or use plain brown rice instead.

• You should have 4 cups of broth and orange juice in total. To make sure you have enough liquid, squeeze the orange juice into a 1-cup measure and add enough broth to make up the 1 cup, if necessary.

Simple but tasty, this dish has all the flavors of a Christmas turkey dinner without all the work. Add a tossed green salad or some marinated roasted peppers to complete the meal.

● **Works best in a large (minimum 5-quart) slow cooker**

CHICKEN AND RICE

| 1 tablespoon olive oil
| 2 medium onions, finely chopped
| 4 cloves garlic, minced
1½ teaspoons dried sage
½ teaspoon cracked black peppercorns
½ teaspoon salt
| 1 pound mushrooms, sliced
1½ cups brown and wild rice mixture, rinsed (see Tips, left)
| 1 cup dried cranberries
| 3 cups lower-sodium chicken broth

Grated zest and juice of 1 orange (see Tips, left)
3 pounds skinless bone-in chicken thighs (about 12 thighs)

TOPPING

1 tablespoon butter
1 tablespoon olive oil
1 cup fresh whole wheat bread crumbs (see Tips, page 253)
2 tablespoon toasted sliced almonds

1. Lightly coat the slow cooker stoneware with cooking spray.

2. **Make the chicken and rice:** In a large skillet, heat oil over medium heat for 30 seconds. Add onions and cook, stirring, until softened, about 3 minutes. Add garlic, sage, peppercorns, and salt; cook, stirring, for 1 minute. Add mushrooms and stir to coat. Add rice and stir to coat. Stir in cranberries. Add broth and orange zest and juice; bring to a boil.

NUTRIENTS PER SERVING

Calories	275
Carbohydrate	32g
Fiber	4g
Protein	18 g
Fat, total	9 g
Fat, saturated	2 g
Sodium	301 mg
Cholesterol	55 mg

EXCHANGES PER SERVING

2	Starch
2	Lean Meat

This dish can be partially prepared in advance. Complete Steps 1 and 2. Cover and refrigerate the rice mixture overnight. The next morning, continue with Steps 3 through 5.

Note: *The suggested accompaniments for this recipe are not included in the nutrients or exchanges per serving. Whether you keep track of exchanges or count carbohydrates, remember to account for what these additional foods contribute.*

3. Spoon half of the rice mixture evenly over bottom of the prepared slow cooker. Arrange chicken pieces evenly on top. Cover with remaining rice mixture.

4. Place 2 clean tea towels, each folded in half (so you will have 4 layers), over the top of the stoneware to absorb moisture. Cover and cook on Low for 6 hours or on High for 3 hours, or until juices run clear when chicken is pierced with a fork.

5. **Make the topping:** In a large skillet, heat butter and oil over medium heat. Add bread crumbs and toss until evenly coated. Cook, stirring, until golden, about 5 minutes. Stir in almonds. Spoon topping evenly over cooked chicken and rice and serve immediately.

MINDFUL MORSELS

Cranberries (along with cherries, blueberries, and other red, purple, and blue fruits) are particularly good sources of anthocyanins and other antioxidants that protect all the cells in the body.

Chicken Curry with Bell Peppers

Makes 4 servings

Note: *The suggested accompaniments for this recipe are not included in the nutrients or exchanges per serving. Whether you keep track of exchanges or count carbohydrates, remember to account for what these additional foods contribute.*

In the time it takes to cook an accompaniment of rice or pasta, this streamlined dish is ready to serve.

1 cup reduced-sodium chicken broth

2 teaspoons cornstarch

¼ teaspoon salt

4 teaspoons vegetable oil

1 pound boneless, skinless chicken breasts, cut into thin strips

2 cloves garlic, minced

1 tablespoon mild curry paste or powder

1 tablespoon minced fresh ginger

2 large red bell peppers, cut into thin strips

4 scallions, sliced

1. In a cup, combine broth, cornstarch, and salt; set aside.

2. In a large nonstick skillet, heat 2 teaspoons of the oil over medium-high heat. Add chicken and cook, stirring often, for 5 minutes, or until no longer pink inside. Transfer to a plate.

3. Reduce the heat under the pan to medium and add remaining 2 teaspoons oil. Add garlic, curry paste, and ginger. Cook, stirring, for 1 minute. Add peppers; cook, stirring, for 2 minutes. Stir reserved broth mixture and pour into the skillet; bring to a boil. Cook, stirring, until thickened. Add chicken and scallions; cook, stirring, for 2 minutes, or until heated through.

NUTRIENTS PER SERVING

Calories	234
Carbohydrate	9 g
Fiber	2 g
Protein	29 g
Fat, total	8 g
Fat, saturated	1 g
Sodium	460 mg
Cholesterol	71 mg

EXCHANGES PER SERVING

1½	Vegetable
3½	Lean Meat

Oven French Toast (page 2)

Creamy Morning Millet with Apples (page 4)

Caponata (page 34)

Smoked Salmon Mousse (page 35)

Butternut Apple Soup with Swiss Cheese (page 69)

Cheese-Smothered Onion Soup (page 73)

Creamy Onion Soup with Kale (page 74)

Quick Bistro-Style Steak (page 84)

Old-Fashioned Beef Stew (page 88)

Country Stew with Fennel (page 96)

Tex-Mex Cobbler with Cornbread Crust (page 98)

Moroccan-Spiced Beef (page 100)

Veal Goulash (page 104)

Company Pork Roast with Fruit Stuffing (page 108)

Thyme-Roasted Chicken with Garlic Gravy (page 123)

Yummy Parmesan Chicken Fingers (page 124)

Chicken Paprika with Noodles

Makes 4 servings

Note: *The suggested accompaniments for this recipe are not included in the nutrients or exchanges per serving. Whether you keep track of exchanges or count carbohydrates, remember to account for what these additional foods contribute.*

Ground meats provide versatile options for the harried cook. Serve this tasty ground chicken dish with a salad or green vegetable such as broccoli. Dinner is ready in about 30 minutes.

2 teaspoons vegetable oil

1 pound extra-lean ground chicken or turkey

1 onion, chopped

8 ounces mushrooms, sliced

1 tablespoon paprika

2 tablespoons all-purpose flour

1⅓ cups reduced-sodium chicken broth

½ cup light sour cream

2 tablespoons chopped fresh dill or parsley

Freshly ground black pepper

8 ounces fettuccine or broad egg noodles

1. Bring a large pot of water to a boil.

2. In a large nonstick skillet heat 1 teaspoon of the oil over medium-high heat. Add chicken and cook, breaking it up with a wooden spoon, until no longer pink, about 5 minutes. With a slotted spoon, transfer chicken to a plate lined with a paper towel. Drain fat from the skillet.

3. Heat remaining 1 teaspoon oil in the same skillet. Add onion, mushrooms, and paprika; cook, stirring often, for 3 minutes, or until vegetables are softened.

4. Sprinkle mushroom mixture with flour, stir in broth, and return chicken to skillet. Bring to a boil and cook, stirring, until thickened. Reduce the heat, cover, and simmer for 5 minutes. Remove the pan from the heat and stir in sour cream (it may curdle if added over the heat) and dill; season with pepper to taste.

5. While chicken is simmering, cook pasta in boiling water following package directions until tender but firm. Drain well. Return to the pot, add chicken mixture, and toss to combine. Serve immediately.

NUTRIENTS PER SERVING

Calories	468
Carbohydrate	53 g
Fiber	6 g
Protein	32 g
Fat, total	14 g
Fat, saturated	3 g
Sodium	520 mg
Cholesterol	156 mg

EXCHANGES PER SERVING

3	Starch
1	Vegetable
3	Lean Meat
½	Fat

Mexican-Style Chicken with Cilantro and Lemon

Makes 12 servings (1 piece of chicken with sauce per serving)

With a sauce of pumpkin seeds, cumin seeds, oregano, and cilantro, this dish conjures images of warm evening dinners in the courtyard of a charming Mexican hacienda. Mexicans have been thickening sauces with pumpkin seeds since long before the Spanish arrived; today, every cook has his or her own recipe for mole, one of the world's great culinary concoctions. Serve this with rice and fresh corn on the cob.

• **Works in slow cookers from 3½ to 6 quarts**

¼ cup raw pumpkin seeds	½ cup lower-sodium chicken broth
2 teaspoons cumin seeds	2 tablespoons fresh lemon juice
1 tablespoon olive oil	
2 onions, sliced	1 tablespoon grated lemon zest, plus grated lemon zest for garnish
4 cloves garlic, minced	
2 tablespoons tomato paste	
1 teaspoon salt	3 pounds bone-in, skinless chicken thighs (about 12 thighs)
1 teaspoon cracked black peppercorns	
1 teaspoon dried oregano	1 to 2 jalapeño peppers, chopped (see Tips, left)
¼ teaspoon ground cinnamon	
1 cup coarsely chopped cilantro, stems and leaves, plus finely chopped cilantro, for garnish	Finely chopped scallions, for garnish

1. In a large skillet, toast pumpkin and cumin seeds over medium-high heat, stirring constantly, until pumpkin seeds are popping and cumin is fragrant, about 3 minutes. Transfer to a small bowl and set aside.

2. In the same skillet, heat oil over medium heat for 30 seconds. Add onions and cook, stirring, until softened, about 3 minutes. Add garlic, tomato paste, salt, peppercorns, oregano, and cinnamon; cook, stirring, for 1 minute. Transfer to a blender or food processor. Add coarsely chopped cilantro, broth, lemon juice, 1 tablespoon of the zest, and reserved seeds; process until smooth.

NUTRIENTS PER SERVING

Calories	126
Carbohydrate	4 g
Fiber	1 g
Protein	15 g
Fat, total	5 g
Fat, saturated	1 g
Sodium	271 mg
Cholesterol	53 mg

EXCHANGES PER SERVING

2	Lean Meat

This dish can be partially prepared in advance. Complete Steps 1 and 2. Cover and refrigerate puréed sauce overnight. The next morning, continue with Step 3.

Note: *The suggested accompaniments for this recipe are not included in the nutrients or exchanges per serving. Whether you keep track of exchanges or count carbohydrates, remember to account for what these additional foods contribute.*

3. Arrange chicken on the bottom of the slow cooker stoneware. Top with vegetable mixture. Cover and cook on Low for 6 hours or on High for 3 hours, or until juices run clear when chicken is pierced with a fork. Stir in jalapeño(s). When ready to serve, garnish with finely chopped cilantro, grated lemon zest, and scallions.

MINDFUL MORSELS

Culinary herbs do more than add color and flavor to a dish—they also have health benefits. USDA researchers have found that many culinary herbs, such as sage, dill, thyme, and rosemary, are loaded with antioxidants, a group of nutrients that protect your body against the harmful effects of free radicals, much like rust proofing protects your car from rust. Recent research suggests that the best way to consume antioxidants is in food, where they work together as part of the whole food. Some studies have shown that taking antioxidants as supplements does not produce similar benefits.

Turkey Mole

Makes 8 servings

In many parts of Mexico, no special occasion is complete without turkey cooked in mole poblano. Since the authentic version is quite a production, We've simplified this slow cooker version, which is delicious nonetheless. Serve with hot tortillas, fluffy rice, and creamed corn.

• **Works best in a large (minimum 5-quart) slow cooker**

1 tablespoon plus 2 teaspoons olive oil	1 cup lower-sodium chicken broth
1 skin-on turkey breast (about 2 pounds)	2 dried ancho, New Mexico, or guajillo chiles
2 onions, sliced	2 cups boiling water
4 cloves garlic, sliced	½ cup coarsely chopped cilantro stems and leaves
1 piece (2") cinnamon stick	1 tablespoon chili powder
4 whole cloves	1 to 2 jalapeño peppers, chopped (see Tip, left)
1 teaspoon salt	3 tablespoon diced mild green chiles (optional)
1 teaspoon cracked black peppercorns	
1 can (28 ounces) tomatillos, drained	
½ ounce unsweetened chocolate, broken into pieces	

1. In a large skillet, heat 1 tablespoon of the oil over medium-high heat for 30 seconds. Add turkey and brown on all sides. Transfer turkey to the slow cooker stoneware.

2. Reduce the heat under the pan to medium. Add remaining 2 teaspoons oil and onions; cook, stirring, until softened, about 3 minutes. Add garlic, cinnamon stick, cloves, salt, and peppercorns; cook, stirring, for 1 minute. Transfer mixture to a blender. Add tomatillos, chocolate, and ½ cup of the broth; process until smooth.

NUTRIENTS PER SERVING

Calories	239
Carbohydrate	10 g
Fiber	2 g
Protein	25 g
Fat, total	11 g
Fat, saturated	3 g
Sodium	418 mg
Cholesterol	58 mg

EXCHANGES PER SERVING

2	Vegetable
3	Lean Meat

This dish can be partially prepared before cooking. Make the sauces in Steps 2 and 4, heating 1 tablespoon oil in the pan before softening the onions. Cover and refrigerate the puréed sauces separately for up to 2 days, being aware that the chile mixture will lose some of its vibrancy if held for this long. When you're ready to finish the recipe, brown the turkey (Step 1), or remove the skin from the turkey, omit browning, and place the turkey directly in the slow cooker. Continue with Steps 3 and 4.

3. Pour sauce over turkey, cover, and cook on Low for 8 hours or on High for 4 hours, or until juices run clear when turkey is pierced with a fork or a meat thermometer reads 170°F.

4. Half an hour before turkey has finished cooking, in a heatproof bowl, soak dried chiles in boiling water for 30 minutes, weighing down with a cup to ensure they remain submerged. Drain, discarding soaking liquid and stems, and chop coarsely. Transfer to a blender. Add cilantro, chili powder, jalapeño(s), and remaining ½ cup broth; purée. Add to the slow cooker along with green chiles, if using, and stir gently to combine. Cover and cook on High for 30 minutes, or until flavors meld.

MINDFUL MORSELS

Turkey is an excellent source of complete protein because, once the skin is removed, it is a very lean meat. In addition to being rich in protein, turkey is a good source of important B vitamins—niacin, B_6, and B_{12}—as well as zinc, which helps to keep your immune system strong. Turkey is also a good source of the trace mineral selenium, which acts as an antioxidant.

Peppery Turkey Casserole

Makes 8 servings

• For convenience, use jarred roasted red peppers, or, if you prefer, roast your own.

• When handling hot peppers, wear rubber gloves to avoid skin irritation.

• Some quinoa has a resinous coating called saponin, which needs to be rinsed off. To ensure your quinoa is saponin free, before cooking, fill a bowl with warm water and swish the kernels around, then transfer to a strainer and rinse thoroughly under cold running water.

NUTRIENTS PER SERVING

Calories	256
Carbohydrate	31 g
Fiber	4 g
Protein	22 g
Fat, total	5 g
Fat, saturated	1 g
Sodium	385 mg
Cholesterol	37 mg

EXCHANGES PER SERVING

1½	Starch
1	Vegetable
2	Lean Meat

With five different kinds of peppers, this dish is a testament to the depth and variety of this useful ingredient. The dish also features quinoa, a nutritious grain that isn't commonly included in the North American diet. Here, it is stirred in after the dish has finished cooking to make a casserole, but if you prefer, serve it on the side.

• **Works in slow cookers from 3½ to 6 quarts**

1 tablespoon olive oil	2 green bell peppers, diced
2 onions, finely chopped	1 roasted red bell pepper, diced (see Tips, left)
4 cloves garlic, minced	1 jalapeño pepper, finely chopped (see Tips, left)
2 teaspoons dried oregano	
½ teaspoon cracked black peppercorns	2 teaspoons sweet paprika, dissolved in 2 tablespoons water
1 can (14.5 ounces) diced tomatoes, including juice	3 cups water
1 cup dry white wine	1½ cups quinoa, rinsed (see Tips, left)
2 cups lower-sodium chicken broth	
1½ pounds bone-in turkey breast, skin removed, cut into ½" cubes (about 2½ cups)	

1. In a large skillet, heat oil over medium heat for 30 seconds. Add onions and cook, stirring, until softened, about 3 minutes. Add garlic, oregano, and peppercorns; cook, stirring, for 1 minute. Add tomatoes and their juice and wine; bring to a boil. Transfer to the slow cooker stoneware. Add broth and stir well.

2. Add turkey and stir well. Cover and cook on Low for 6 hours or on High for 3 hours, or until turkey is tender.

3. Add bell peppers, roasted bell pepper, jalapeño, and paprika solution to the slow cooker; stir well. Cover and cook on High for 30 minutes, or until peppers are tender.

Peppery Turkey Stew
Omit the quinoa. Serve the stew over mashed potatoes.

This dish can be partially prepared in advance. Complete Step 1. Cover and refrigerate the tomato mixture overnight or for up to 2 days. When you're ready finish the recipe, continue with Steps 2 through 5.

4. Meanwhile, in a large saucepan, bring water to a boil. Add quinoa in a steady stream, stirring to prevent lumps from forming, and return to a boil. Cover, reduce the heat to low, and simmer until quinoa is tender and liquid is absorbed, about 15 minutes. Set aside.

5. When peppers are tender, add cooked quinoa to the slow cooker and stir well. Serve immediately.

MINDFUL MORSELS

A serving of this dish provides about 30 percent of the daily value of vitamin B_6. Bell peppers and turkey are excellent sources of this vitamin, which is best known for keeping skin healthy. In addition, B_6 plays a role in keeping your mind sharp, and it boosts serotonin, which helps to keep depression at bay. The vitamin also helps your body make new cells to produce infection-fighting antibodies and may lower the risk of colon cancer, one of the most common cancers in North America.

Best-Ever Turkey Breast

Makes 8 servings (about 2½ ounces turkey with sauce per serving)

MAKE AHEAD

This dish can be partially prepared in advance. Complete Steps 1 and 3. Cover and refrigerate the bacon and vegetable mixture separately for up to 2 days. When you're ready to finish the dish, heat 1 tablespoon oil in the skillet and brown the turkey breast (Step 2), or, if you're pressed for time, remove the skin, omit browning, and place the turkey directly in the slow cooker. Continue with Step 4.

Note: *The suggested accompaniments for this recipe are not included in the nutrients or exchanges per serving. Whether you keep track of exchanges or count carbohydrates, remember to account for what these additional foods contribute.*

NUTRIENTS PER SERVING

Calories	201
Carbohydrate	10 g
Fiber	2 g
Protein	24 g
Fat, total	7 g
Fat, saturated	2 g
Sodium	404 mg
Cholesterol	59 mg

EXCHANGES PER SERVING

2	Vegetable
3	Lean Meat

If you want to celebrate a holiday with turkey but don't feel like cooking an entire bird, try this tasty alternative. Accompany the turkey with roasted or mashed potatoes, Brussels sprouts, and cranberry ketchup for a festive meal.

● **Works best in a large (minimum 5-quart) slow cooker**

2 slices bacon	1 teaspoon ground sage
2 tablespoons olive oil	6 whole cloves or allspice
1 skin-on turkey breast (about 2 pounds)	1 teaspoon salt
2 tablespoons brandy or cognac (optional)	½ teaspoon cracked black peppercorns
4 carrots, peeled and diced	¼ cup all-purpose flour
2 onions, finely chopped	¾ cup dry white wine or lower-sodium chicken broth
4 stalks celery, diced	
2 cloves garlic, minced	

1. In a large skillet, cook bacon over medium-high heat until crisp. Remove from the pan and drain on a paper towel. Crumble and set aside. Drain fat from the pan. Add oil.

2. Add turkey breast to the pan and brown on all sides. Turn turkey skin side up and carefully sprinkle with brandy, if using. Transfer turkey to the slow cooker stoneware.

3. Reduce the heat under the pan to medium. Add carrots, onions, and celery; cook, stirring, until vegetables are softened, about 7 minutes. Add garlic, sage, cloves, salt, and peppercorns; cook, stirring, for 1 minute. Sprinkle flour over mixture and cook, stirring, for 1 minute. Stir in wine and reserved bacon; cook, stirring, until mixture is thickened.

4. Spoon sauce over turkey. Cover and cook on Low for 6 hours or on High for 3 hours, or until turkey is tender and no longer pink inside or an instant-read meat thermometer reads 170°F. Transfer turkey to a warm platter, spoon sauce on top, and serve piping hot.

One-Pot Italian Sausages Braised with Potatoes

Makes 4 servings

This rustic dish is perfect with a glass of red wine on a chilly Friday night. Do give the fennel a try; when raw, this vegetable has an assertive anise taste. However, when cooked, it's much more mellow and inviting.

1 pound lean mild or hot Italian-style turkey sausages (see Tip, left)	4 potatoes, peeled and cubed (about 1½ pounds)
2 tablespoons water (approximately)	1 can (14.5 ounces) tomatoes, including juice, chopped
2 teaspoons olive oil	½ cup reduced-sodium beef broth
1 large onion, halved lengthwise, sliced	½ teaspoon salt
1 large bulb fennel, trimmed, cored, and cut into strips	¼ teaspoon freshly ground black pepper
2 cloves garlic, minced	2 tablespoons chopped fresh parsley
1 teaspoon dried oregano	

1. With a fork, prick sausages all over and place in a large saucepan over medium-high heat. Add water and cook, turning sausages often and adding more water as needed (to prevent sausages from sticking), until browned and no longer pink in center, 10 to 12 minutes. Transfer to a cutting board. Let cool slightly, then cut into slices.

2. Drain fat from the pan. Add oil, onion, fennel, garlic, and oregano; cook, stirring, until vegetables are softened, about 3 minutes. Add potatoes, tomatoes and their juice, broth, salt, and pepper; bring to a boil. Reduce the heat to medium, cover, and cook for 15 minutes, or until potatoes are almost tender. Return sausage to the pan, cover, and cook for 8 minutes, or until potatoes are tender. Sprinkle with parsley and serve.

NUTRIENTS PER SERVING

Calories	222
Carbohydrate	25 g
Fiber	4 g
Protein	16 g
Fat, total	6 g
Fat, saturated	2 g
Sodium	725 mg
Cholesterol	81 mg

EXCHANGES PER SERVING

1	Starch
½	Other Carbohydrate
2	Lean Meat

Turkey Meat Loaf

Makes 6 servings

VARIATION

Mini Turkey Meat Loaves
Divide meat loaf mixture into 12 balls; lightly press into muffin pan cups. Bake at 400°F for 20 minutes, or until no longer pink in the center. Drain off juice before serving 2 meatballs per person.

Note: *The suggested accompaniments for this recipe are not included in the nutrients or exchanges per serving. Whether you keep track of exchanges or count carbohydrates, remember to account for what these additional foods contribute.*

Serve this family-favorite meat loaf accompanied with fluffy mashed potatoes and Lemon-Glazed Baby Carrots (page 287) for a delicious, economical supper.

2 teaspoons olive oil	1 large egg
1 onion, finely chopped	1 teaspoon grated lemon zest
1 large clove garlic, minced	1½ pounds lean ground turkey or chicken
½ teaspoon dried thyme or marjoram	½ cup seasoned dried bread crumbs (see Tip, page 81)
1 teaspoon salt	2 tablespoons finely chopped fresh parsley
¼ teaspoon freshly ground black pepper	
¼ cup reduced-sodium chicken broth	

1. Preheat the oven to 350°F.

2. In a large nonstick skillet, heat oil over medium heat. Add onion, garlic, thyme, salt, and pepper; cook, stirring often, for 3 minutes, or until softened. Let cool slightly.

3. In a large bowl, beat together broth, egg, and zest. Stir in onion mixture, turkey, bread crumbs, and parsley. Using a wooden spoon, gently mix until evenly combined.

4. Press mixture lightly into a 9" × 5" loaf pan. Bake for 1 hour, or until a meat thermometer registers 170°F. Let stand for 5 minutes. Drain pan juices, turn meat loaf out onto a plate, and cut into 6 slices.

NUTRIENTS PER SERVING

Calories	219
Carbohydrate	9 g
Fiber	1 g
Protein	25 g
Fat, total	9 g
Fat, saturated	3 g
Sodium	580 mg
Cholesterol	99 mg

EXCHANGES PER SERVING

½	Starch
3½	Very Lean Meat
1	Fat

FISH & SHELLFISH

Cod Provençal

What to do with fresh cod from the market and ripe tomatoes plucked from your garden? Add some briny olives and pungent capers, and make this delicious fish dish that bursts with the sunny flavors of the Mediterranean.

1 pound cod or halibut, cut into 4 pieces

Freshly ground black pepper

2 ripe tomatoes, diced

¼ cup kalamata olives, rinsed, cut into slivers

2 scallions, sliced

2 tablespoons chopped fresh parsley or basil

1 tablespoon capers, drained and rinsed

1 clove garlic, minced

Pinch of red pepper flakes (optional)

1 tablespoon olive oil

1. Preheat the oven to 425°F.

2. Arrange cod in a single layer in a shallow baking dish. Season with black pepper.

3. In a medium bowl, combine tomatoes, olives, scallions, parsley, capers, garlic, and red pepper flakes, if using; season with black pepper to taste. Spoon tomato-olive mixture over fish fillets; drizzle with oil.

4. Bake for 15 to 20 minutes, or until fish flakes easily when tested with a fork. Serve in warmed shallow bowls with pan juices spooned over the top.

NUTRIENTS PER SERVING

Calories	140
Carbohydrate	4 g
Fiber	1 g
Protein	21 g
Fat, total	4 g
Fat, saturated	1 g
Sodium	140 mg
Cholesterol	49 mg

EXCHANGES PER SERVING

1	Vegetable
3	Very Lean Meat

Salmon with Lemon-Ginger Sauce

Makes 4 servings

• To store ginger, peel it, place it in a glass jar, and add white wine or sherry to cover. As a bonus, you can use the ginger-infused wine or sherry to flavor other fish or chicken dishes or stir-fries.

• One of the best uses for the microwave is for quickly cooking fish. Arrange the fish and sauce in a shallow baking dish and cover with microwave-safe plastic wrap; turn back 1 corner to vent. Microwave on Medium for 4 minutes. Turn the fish over and re-cover; microwave on Medium for 3 to 5 minutes longer, or until the salmon turns opaque.

Fresh ginger gives a sparkling flavor to salmon—or any fish, for that matter. Dried ground ginger just doesn't come close to imparting the same crisp taste as fresh, available in most supermarkets and produce stores.

4 salmon fillets (5 ounces each)	1 clove garlic, minced
MARINADE	1 tablespoon fresh lemon juice
2 scallions	1 teaspoon grated lemon zest
1½ teaspoons minced fresh ginger	1 teaspoon sesame oil
2 tablespoons reduced-sodium soy sauce	1 teaspoon sugar

1. Preheat the oven to 425°F.

2. Place salmon fillets in a single layer in a shallow baking dish.

3. **Marinade:** Chop white and green parts of scallions; set aside chopped green tops for garnish. In a small bowl, combine white part of scallions, ginger, soy sauce, garlic, lemon juice, zest, sesame oil, and sugar.

4. Pour marinade over salmon; let stand at room temperature for 15 minutes or in the refrigerator for up to 1 hour.

5. Bake, uncovered, for 13 to 15 minutes, or until salmon turns opaque. Arrange on serving plates, spoon sauce on top, and sprinkle with reserved scallion greens.

NUTRIENTS PER SERVING

Calories	286
Carbohydrate	3 g
Fiber	0 g
Protein	29 g
Fat, total	17 g
Fat, saturated	3 g
Sodium	320 mg
Cholesterol	80 mg

EXCHANGES PER SERVING

4	Lean Meat
1	Fat

Salmon Loaf

Makes 6 servings

● If you prefer and you have a large oval slow cooker, you can make this in an 8" × 4" loaf pan lightly coated with cooking spray. You won't need the foil strip, but you will need to cover the pan tightly with foil after filling it with the salmon mixture. Then the foil covering should be secured with a string or elastic band. Place the pan in the slow cooker and pour in enough boiling water to come 1" up the sides. Cover and cook on Low for 6 hours or on High for 3 hours, or until the loaf is set.

This tasty loaf, accompanied by a tossed green salad, will become a favorite weekday meal. If you don't have tomato sauce, homemade chili sauce or another tomato-based relish also makes a nice finish. Or try a yogurt-based sauce such as tzatziki.

● **Works in slow cookers from 3½ to 6 quarts**

1 tablespoon olive oil	2 tablespoons fresh lemon juice
4 stalks celery, finely chopped (about 1½ cups)	2 cans (7½ ounces each) wild salmon, including bones and juice, skin removed, if desired
1 large onion, finely chopped (about 1½ cups)	
8 ounces mushrooms, thinly sliced	¾ cup dried bread crumbs (see Tip, page 81)
½ teaspoon dried tarragon	½ cup finely chopped parsley
½ teaspoon freshly ground black pepper	Basic Tomato Sauce (page 212), warmed (optional)
3 large eggs	

1. In a large skillet, heat oil over medium heat for 30 seconds. Add celery, onion, and mushrooms; cook, stirring, until celery is tender, about 5 minutes. Add tarragon and pepper; cook, stirring, for 1 minute. Remove the pan from the heat and set aside.

2. In a bowl large enough to accommodate salmon and vegetables, beat eggs with lemon juice. Add salmon with bones and juice and break into small pieces with a fork. Add reserved mushroom mixture, bread crumbs, and parsley; mix until well blended. If mixture seems wet, add more bread crumbs, 1 tablespoon at a time, until liquid is absorbed.

NUTRIENTS PER SERVING

Calories	247
Carbohydrate	15 g
Fiber	2 g
Protein	18 g
Fat, total	13 g
Fat, saturated	3 g
Sodium	467 mg
Cholesterol	111 mg

EXCHANGES PER SERVING

1	Starch
2	Lean Meat
1½	Fat

This dish can be prepared in advance. Complete Steps 1 through 3. Cover and refrigerate the salmon mixture overnight. When you're ready to finish the recipe, continue with the end of Step 3 and Step 4.

Dill Salmon Loaf: Substitute ½ teaspoon dried dill or thyme for the tarragon and ½ cup of chopped dill for the parsley.

Note: The suggested accompaniments for this recipe are not included in the nutrients or exchanges per serving. Whether you keep track of exchanges or count carbohydrates, remember to account for what these additional foods contribute.

3. Fold a 2-foot piece of foil in half lengthwise. Place on the bottom and up the sides of the slow cooker stoneware (see Tip, left). Shape salmon mixture into a loaf and place in the middle of the foil strip on the bottom of the slow cooker.

4. Cover and cook on Low for 4 to 5 hours or on High for 2 to 2½ hours, or until loaf is set. Slide loaf off the foil onto a platter and cut into 6 slices. Top each slice with a dollop of tomato sauce, if using.

MINDFUL MORSELS

Every cell in our bodies needs omega-3 fatty acids to build strong cell membranes. And studies indicate that these fatty acids, found primarily in coldwater fish and some vegetable oils, also appear to reduce the risk of coronary heart disease and other chronic diseases. Salmon is one of the best sources of omega-3 fatty acids.

Poached Salmon

Makes 15 servings (one 2½-ounce piece per serving)

• Make sure that the salmon is completely covered with the poaching liquid. If you do not have sufficient liquid, add water to cover.

• When the salmon is cooked, it should feel firm to the touch, and the skin should peel off easily.

You can make the poaching liquid (Step 1) in advance. Cover and refrigerate for up to 2 days.

Although salmon is delicious cooked almost any way, poaching produces the moistest result. The problem is, a large piece of salmon usually requires a fish poacher, a piece of kitchen equipment that's relatively costly, cumbersome to store, and rarely used. A large oval slow cooker offers the ideal solution, producing great results with little fuss. Serve poached salmon, warm or cold, as the focus of an elegant buffet or dinner, attractively garnished with sliced lemon and sprigs of parsley or dill and accompanied with your favorite sauce.

• **Works best in a large (minimum 5-quart) oval slow cooker**

POACHING LIQUID

6 cups	water
½ cup	white wine or fresh lemon juice
1	onion, chopped
2	stalks celery, chopped, or ½ teaspoon celery seeds
4	sprigs parsley
8	whole black peppercorns
1	bay leaf

SALMON

1	fillet of salmon (about 3 pounds)
	Lemon slices, for garnish
	Sprigs of fresh parsley or dill, for garnish

1. **Poaching liquid:** In a large saucepan, combine water, wine, onion, celery, parsley, peppercorns, and bay leaf; bring to a boil. Reduce the heat to medium and simmer for 30 minutes. Strain liquid into a bowl and discard solids.

2. **Salmon:** Preheat the slow cooker stoneware on High for 15 minutes. Fold a 2-foot piece of foil in half lengthwise. Place on the bottom and up the sides of the slow cooker, allowing it to overhang the casing a bit. Place salmon over the foil strip.

3. Return the poaching liquid to the saucepan and bring to a boil; pour over salmon (see Tips, left). Cover and cook on High for 1 hour. Carefully remove the stoneware from the slow cooker. Allow salmon to cool in the stoneware for 20 minutes.

4. If serving salmon chilled, place the stoneware in the refrigerator and allow salmon to chill in its liquid, then lift out and transfer to a platter. If serving hot, immediately transfer to the platter. Garnish with lemon slices and sprigs of parsley and serve.

NUTRIENTS PER SERVING

Calories	151
Carbohydrate	0 g
Fiber	0 g
Protein	16 g
Fat, total	9 g
Fat, saturated	2 g
Sodium	45 mg
Cholesterol	46 mg

EXCHANGES PER SERVING

2	Medium-fat Meat

Stuffed Sole

Makes 6 servings

NUTRIENTS PER SERVING

Calories	154
Carbohydrate	4 g
Fiber	1 g
Protein	22 g
Fat, total	5 g
Fat, saturated	2 g
Sodium	120 mg
Cholesterol	70 mg

EXCHANGES PER SERVING

½	Vegetable
3	Very Lean Meat
½	Fat

Want to wow your guests? Put this on your menu. Tender sole fillets with vibrant red pepper stuffing marry well in a light wine and cream sauce. It makes an attractive fish dish that never fails to impress.

1 tablespoon butter	6 skinned sole fillets (about 1½ pounds)
1 cup chopped mushrooms	Freshly ground white pepper
1 red bell pepper, cut into very thin 1" strips	⅓ cup white wine or fish broth
¼ cup chopped scallions	2 teaspoons cornstarch
1 teaspoon dried tarragon	⅓ cup half-and-half

1. Preheat the oven to 425°F.

2. In a large nonstick skillet, heat butter over medium heat. Add mushrooms, bell pepper, scallions, and tarragon; cook, stirring, until vegetables are softened, about 3 minutes. Remove the pan from the heat and let cool.

3. Place fillets, skinned side down, on a work surface with the smaller tapered ends closest to you; season with white pepper. Spoon a generous tablespoonful of vegetable mixture on bottom ends of fillets. Roll up and place seam side down in an 8" × 8" baking dish. Pour wine on top.

4. To bake, cover baking dish with a lid or foil. Bake for 16 to 20 minutes, or until fish turns opaque.

5. Using a slotted spoon, remove fillets and arrange on a serving plate; cover and keep warm.

6. Strain fish juices through a fine strainer into a medium saucepan. Bring to a boil over high heat and reduce to about ½ cup.

7. Meanwhile, in a small bowl, blend cornstarch with 1 tablespoon cold water; stir in half-and-half. Pour into saucepan, whisking constantly, until sauce comes to a boil and thickens. Season with white pepper to taste. Spoon sauce over fish and serve.

Crispy Almond Baked Fish

Makes 4 servings

TIP

● To defrost a package of frozen fish fillets, remove the package wrapping and place the fish on a plate. Microwave on Medium for 3 minutes. Microwave at Defrost for 3 minutes longer, or until the fish separates into fillets. Let stand for 10 minutes to complete defrosting. Pat dry with paper towels to absorb excess moisture.

This easy, practical method is an excellent way to cook white fish fillets, such as sole, haddock, or turbot. Unlike many stovetop methods, in which fish must be cooked in more than 1 batch, all the fish is cooked (and ready) at the same time.

½ cup soft bread crumbs (see Tips, page 253)	1 pound white fish fillets, such as sole, haddock, or turbot
⅓ cup sliced blanched almonds	Freshly ground black pepper
½ teaspoon dried tarragon or basil	Lemon wedges
½ teaspoon grated orange or lemon zest	

1. Preheat the oven to 425°F. Coat a baking sheet with cooking spray.

2. In a food processor, combine bread crumbs, almonds, tarragon, and zest. Pulse until almonds are finely chopped.

3. Wrap fillets in paper towels to absorb any excess moisture. Arrange fillets on the prepared baking sheet in a single layer. Season with pepper. Sprinkle crumb mixture over fish and pat in lightly.

4. Bake for 8 to 10 minutes, or until fish flakes easily when tested with a fork. (The baking time depends on thickness of fish; increase time accordingly.) Serve with lemon wedges.

NUTRIENTS PER SERVING

Calories	166
Carbohydrate	4 g
Fiber	1 g
Protein	24 g
Fat, total	6 g
Fat, saturated	1 g
Sodium	125 mg
Cholesterol	60 mg

EXCHANGES PER SERVING

2½	Very Lean Meat
1	Lean Meat

Creamy Tuna Casserole

Makes 8 servings

In this family-friendly dish, tuna is combined with pasta, mushrooms, and other vegetables in a delectable creamy base. The crispy crumb topping adds crunch and a bit of punch in the form of Parmesan cheese. Serve with a tossed green salad for a tasty and nutritious meal.

- **Works in slow cookers from 3½ to 6 quarts**

CASSEROLE

8 ounces	small tubular pasta, such as penne
1 tablespoon	olive oil
1	onion, minced
4 stalks	celery, diced
8 ounces	mushrooms, sliced
½ teaspoon	dried tarragon or thyme
½ teaspoon	cracked black peppercorns
1 can (10 ounces)	reduced-sodium condensed cream of mushroom soup, undiluted
2 tablespoons	light cream cheese, softened
2 cans (6 ounces each)	solid white tuna, drained and flaked

CRISPY CRUMB TOPPING

1 tablespoon	butter
½ teaspoon	salt
2 cups	fresh bread crumbs (see Tips, page 253)
2 tablespoons	freshly grated Parmesan cheese

1. Coat the slow cooker stoneware with cooking spray. Bring a large pot of water to a boil.

2. Cook pasta in boiling water according to package directions until al dente. Drain and transfer to the prepared slow cooker.

3. While pasta is cooking, in a large skillet, heat oil over medium heat for 30 seconds. Add onion, celery, and mushrooms; cook, stirring, until celery is softened, about 6 minutes. Add tarragon and peppercorns; stir well. Gradually add soup, stirring to dissolve any lumps. Add cream cheese and cook, stirring, until melted and incorporated into sauce. Stir in tuna. Transfer to the slow cooker; Stir well.

4. Cover and cook on Low for 4 to 5 hours or on High for 2 to 2½ hours, or until hot and bubbly.

5. **Make the topping:** In a large skillet, melt butter with salt over medium heat. Add bread crumbs and cook, stirring, until they start to brown, about 5 minutes. Remove the pan from the heat and stir in Parmesan cheese. Spread topping evenly over the cooked casserole and serve.

NUTRIENTS PER SERVING

Calories	259
Carbohydrate	35 g
Fiber	3 g
Protein	15 g
Fat	7 g
Fat, saturated	2 g
Sodium	229 mg
Cholesterol	22 mg

EXCHANGES PER SERVING

2	Starch
1	Vegetable
1	Lean Meat

New World Bouillabaisse

Makes 12 servings

TIP

● If you don't have fresh thyme, you can use ½ teaspoon dried. Add it to the recipe in Step 2, along with the garlic.

Traditional bouillabaisse contains a wide variety of Mediterranean fish, which leads many to conclude that it can be made only in proximity to the Mediterranean Sea. But this belief elevates the dish to a status that defies its origins. Bouillabaisse was originally a one-pot meal fishermen made from their daily catch. This simple stew is distinguished by the addition of saffron and a rapid reduction of the broth, which intensifies the flavor and emulsifies the olive oil. Serve this delicious meal-in-a-bowl in soup plates, followed by a simple salad and fresh fruit for dessert.

● **Works best in a large (minimum 5-quart) slow cooker**

BOUILLABAISSE

1 teaspoon fennel seeds

3 tablespoons olive oil

1 pound halibut, cut into 1" cubes

1 pound uncooked medium shrimp, peeled and deveined

2 onions, chopped

2 carrots, peeled and diced

1 large bulb fennel, cored and thinly sliced on the vertical

6 cloves garlic, minced

1 teaspoon salt

½ teaspoon cracked black peppercorns

1 can (28 ounces) diced tomatoes, including juice

2 potatoes, peeled and diced

4 cups water

2 cups dry white wine

2 pounds fish trimmings

4 sprigs parsley

2 sprigs fresh thyme (see Tips, left)

2 bay leaves

1 teaspoon saffron threads, dissolved in 1 tablespoon boiling water

24 mussels, cleaned

Crostini, optional (see Tips, opposite)

ROUILLE (optional)

¼ cup light mayonnaise

1 roasted red pepper, peeled and chopped (see Tips, page 56)

2 cloves garlic minced

Pinch of cayenne pepper

NUTRIENTS PER SERVING

Calories	176
Carbohydrate	12 g
Fiber	2 g
Protein	19 g
Fat, total	6 g
Fat, saturated	1 g
Sodium	471 mg
Cholesterol	77 mg

EXCHANGES PER SERVING

2	Vegetable
2½	Very Lean Meat
½	Fat

1. **Make the bouillabaisse:** In a large dry skillet over medium heat, toast fennel seeds, stirring, until fragrant, about 3 minutes. Immediately transfer to a mortar or spice grinder and grind. Set aside.

2. In a large bowl, combine 2 tablespoons of the olive oil and reserved fennel seeds. Add halibut and shrimp; toss until coated. Cover and refrigerate for 2 hours or overnight, stirring occasionally.

● To make crostini, if using: Preheat the broiler. Brush baguette slices on both sides with olive oil and toast under the broiler, turning once.

● If you are using the crostini and rouille, count 2 pieces of crostini and 1 tablespoon of Rouille as 1 Starch Exchange plus 1 Free Food.

Note: *The suggested accompaniments for this recipe are not included in the nutrients or exchanges per serving. Whether you keep track of exchanges or count carbohydrates, remember to account for what these additional foods contribute.*

3. In the same skillet, heat remaining 1 tablespoon oil over medium heat for 30 seconds. Add onions, carrots, and fennel; cook, stirring, until carrots are softened, about 7 minutes. Add garlic, salt, and peppercorns; cook, stirring, for 1 minute. Add tomatoes and their juice; bring to a boil. Transfer to the slow cooker stoneware.

4. Add potatoes, water, and wine to the slow cooker and stir well. In a large square of cheesecloth, tie fish trimmings, parsley, thyme, and bay leaves. Place in the slow cooker, ensuring all or most of the cheesecloth is submerged in the sauce. Cover and cook on Low for 8 to 10 hours or on High for 4 to 5 hours, or until vegetables are very tender. Remove packet of fish trimmings and discard.

5. Place a colander over a large saucepan and pour in the soup. Transfer solids from the colander to a food processor and purée. Bring liquids in the saucepan to a boil over medium-high heat and cook until reduced by about one-third, about 10 minutes. Stir in dissolved saffron and then add the mussels; cook until mussels open, about 5 minutes. Discard any mussels that do not open. Add shrimp and halibut; cook until fish is tender, about 3 minutes. Add reserved puréed solids and cook until heated through.

6. **Make the rouille, if using:** In a mini-chopper, combine mayonnaise, red pepper, garlic, and cayenne. Process until smooth.

7. To serve bouillabaisse, spread crostini with rouille [if using], place in the bottom of a bowl, and ladle soup over them.

Cioppino

Makes 10 servings

This zesty stew originated on the San Francisco pier, where it was prepared using whatever was bountiful in the catch that day. The rouille adds flavor and richness. Serve this with a crusty country-style bread, such as ciabatta, and a green salad.

● **Large (minimum 5-quart) slow cooker**

CIOPPINO

1 tablespoon olive oil

2 onions, finely chopped

1 fennel bulb, cored and chopped

6 cloves garlic, minced

4 anchovy fillets, finely chopped

1 teaspoon cracked black peppercorns

½ teaspoon fennel seeds, toasted (see Tips, left)

1 tablespoon tomato paste (see Tips, left)

1 can (28 ounces) diced tomatoes, including juice

1 cup dry white wine

2 cups bottled clam juice

2 cups water

1 pound skinless firm white fish, such as snapper, cut into bite-size pieces

8 ounces cooked crabmeat

8 ounces cooked medium shrimp, peeled and deveined (see Tips, left)

1 red bell pepper, diced

1 long red chile pepper, diced, optional (see Tips, opposite)

EASY ROUILLE (optional)

⅓ cup mayonnaise

2 cloves garlic, puréed

1 tablespoon extra virgin olive oil

1 teaspoon fresh lemon juice

¼ teaspoon hot or regular paprika

1. **Make the cioppino:** In a large skillet, heat oil over medium heat for 30 seconds. Add onions and fennel; cook, stirring, until vegetables are softened, about 3 minutes. Add garlic, anchovies, peppercorns, and fennel seeds; cook, stirring, for 1 minute. Stir in tomato paste. Add tomatoes and their juice and wine; bring to a boil. Transfer to the slow cooker stoneware.

NUTRIENTS PER SERVING

Calories	152
Carbohydrate	9 g
Fiber	2 g
Protein	22 g
Fat, total	3 g
Fat, saturated	1 g
Sodium	612 mg
Cholesterol	70 mg

EXCHANGES PER SERVING

2	Vegetable
2½	Very Lean Meat

● When handling hot peppers, wear rubber gloves to avoid skin irritation.

● If you are using the Easy Rouille, count 1 tablespoon as 1 Fat Exchange.

This dish can be partially prepared in advance. Complete Step 1. Cover and refrigerate the tomato mixture overnight or for up to 2 days. When you're ready to finish the recipe, continue with Steps 2 through 4.

Note: *The suggested accompaniments for this recipe are not included in the nutrients or exchanges per serving. Whether you keep track of exchanges or count carbohydrates, remember to account for what these additional foods contribute.*

2. Add clam juice and water; stir well. Cover and cook on Low for 6 to 8 hours or on High for 3 to 4 hours. Add fish, crabmeat, shrimp, bell pepper, and chile pepper, if using; stir well. Cover and cook on High for 20 minutes, or until fish flakes easily when pierced with a fork.

3. **Make the rouille, if using:** In a small bowl, combine mayonnaise, garlic, oil, lemon juice, and paprika. Mix until thoroughly blended.

4. To serve, ladle cioppino into warm bowls and garnish each serving with a dollop of rouille, if using.

MINDFUL MORSELS

Cooking with fennel is a good way to vary your diet and increase your intake of beneficial antioxidants. Like celery, fennel is a member of the parsley family and low in calories. But it is more nutritious than celery. One cup of chopped fennel is a source of fiber, folate, and potassium.

Seafood Jambalaya

Makes 12 servings

TIPS

● Large cans of tomatoes come in 28-ounce and 35-ounce sizes. For convenience, this recipe calls for the 28-ounce size. If you happen to have the 35-ounce size, drain off 1 cup of the juice before adding to the recipe.

● When handling hot peppers, wear rubber gloves to avoid skin irritation.

Like its Spanish relative, paella, jambalaya is an ever-changing mixture depending upon the cook's whim and the available ingredients. This recipe uses Italian sausage instead of the more traditional ham or andouille (a Louisiana smoked sausage) and produces a medium-spicy result, but you can use andouille if you prefer. Since andouille is quite strongly flavored, use only 8 ounces and add without browning along with the shrimp. For even more heat, add a hot pepper along with the shrimp.

● **Works best in a large (minimum 5-quart) slow cooker**

1 tablespoon olive oil	1 bay leaf
1 pound mild Italian sausages, casings removed	8 ounces boneless, skinless chicken breasts or thighs, cut into 1" cubes
2 onions, finely chopped	
2 stalks celery, cut into ¼" dice	2 cups long-grain rice, preferably parboiled
4 cloves garlic, minced	1 pound medium cooked shrimp, peeled and deveined (see Tips, page 178)
½ teaspoon salt	
1 teaspoon dried oregano	
1 teaspoon dried thyme	
½ teaspoon cracked black peppercorns	2 tablespoons Worcestershire sauce
1 can (28 ounces) diced tomatoes, including juice (see Tips, left)	1 hot banana pepper or long red or green chile, finely chopped, optional (see Tips, left)
2 cups lower-sodium chicken broth	

1. In a large skillet, heat oil over medium-high heat for 30 seconds. Add sausages and cook, breaking up with a spoon, until no longer pink, about 10 minutes. Using a slotted spoon, transfer to the slow cooker stoneware. Drain all but 1 tablespoon fat from the pan.

2. Reduce the heat under the pan to medium. Add onions and celery; cook, stirring, until celery is softened, about 5 minutes. Add garlic, salt, oregano, thyme, and peppercorns; cook, stirring, for 1 minute. Add tomatoes and their juice, broth, and bay leaf; bring to a boil. Transfer to the slow cooker.

NUTRIENTS PER SERVING

Calories	280
Carbohydrate	31 g
Fiber	2 g
Protein	19 g
Fat, total	8 g
Fat, saturated	3 g
Sodium	623 mg
Cholesterol	86 mg

EXCHANGES PER SERVING

2	Starch
2	Lean Meat

This dish can be partially prepared in advance. Complete Steps 1 and 2. Cover and refrigerate the sausage and vegetable mixtures separately for up to 2 days. Cook, peel, and devein the shrimp and refrigerate overnight. The next day, combine the sausage and vegetables in the slow cooker and continue with Step 3.

3. Add chicken and rice to the slow cooker; stir well. Place 2 clean tea towels, each folded in half (so you will have 4 layers), across the top of the stoneware to absorb moisture. Cover and cook on Low for 6 to 8 hours or on High for 3 to 4 hours. Stir in shrimp, Worcestershire sauce, and hot pepper, if using. Cover and cook on High for 20 to 30 minutes, or until shrimp are heated through. Discard bay leaf and serve.

MINDFUL MORSELS

To increase the nutritional value of this dish, substitute long-grain brown rice for the white. Brown rice contains much more fiber than white rice—½ cup of white rice contains 0.3 grams of dietary fiber, whereas you'll get 1.5 grams from the same quantity of brown rice.

Louisiana Seafood Stew with Chicken and Sausage

Makes 10 servings

This tasty dish is a variation on gumbo, with less broth and minus the heavy roux for thickening. Gumbo is a bit of a grab bag—within the flavor profile, you can add just about anything. The more health-conscious you are, the more you should downplay sausage and emphasize seafood. This is a rich dish—it just needs rice and a simple green salad to complete the meal.

● **Large (minimum 5-quart) slow cooker**

1 to 2 tablespoons olive oil (approximately)	8 ounces medium cooked shrimp, peeled and deveined (see Tips, page 178)
3 ounces sweet Italian sausage, casings removed and meat crumbled (about 1 sausage)	1 can (5 ounces) clams, drained
2 onions, diced	1 green bell pepper, diced
4 stalks celery, diced	1 red bell pepper, diced
4 cloves garlic, minced	½ cup finely chopped parsley leaves
1 teaspoon dried oregano	
1 teaspoon dried thyme	1 teaspoon chili powder (see Tips, left)
½ teaspoon cracked black peppercorns	Pinch of cayenne pepper
1 tablespoon tomato paste	8 ounces sea scallops, halved
1 tablespoon all-purpose flour	1 tablespoon butter
3 cups lower-sodium chicken broth	1 tablespoon filé powder, optional (see Tips, left)
1 can (14.5 ounces) diced tomatoes, including juice	Hot pepper sauce
1 pound boneless, skinless chicken thighs, cut into bite-size pieces (about 8 thighs)	

1. In a large skillet, heat 1 tablespoon of the oil over medium heat. Add sausage and cook, stirring, until no longer pink inside, about 4 minutes. Transfer to the slow cooker stoneware.

NUTRIENTS PER SERVING

Calories	198
Carbohydrate	9 g
Fiber	2 g
Protein	22 g
Fat, total	8 g
Fat, saturated	2 g
Sodium	418 mg
Cholesterol	94 mg

EXCHANGES PER SERVING

1	Vegetable
3	Lean Meat

This dish can be partially prepared in advance. Complete Steps 1 and 2. Cover and refrigerate the tomato mixture overnight or for up to 2 days. When you're ready to finish the recipe, continue with Steps 3 through 5.

Note: *The suggested accompaniments for this recipe are not included in the nutrients or exchanges per serving. Whether you keep track of exchanges or count carbohydrates, remember to account for what these additional foods contribute.*

2. Add remaining 1 tablespoon oil to the pan, if necessary. Add onions and celery; cook, stirring, until celery is tender, about 5 minutes. Add garlic, oregano, thyme, and peppercorns; cook, stirring, for 1 minute. Stir in tomato paste. Add flour and cook, stirring, for 1 minute. Add broth and tomatoes and their juice; bring to a boil. Cook, stirring, until slightly thickened, about 3 minutes. Transfer to the slow cooker.

3. Add chicken to the slow cooker and stir well. Cover and cook on Low for 6 hours or on High for 3 hours, or until juices run clear when chicken is pierced with a fork. Add shrimp, clams, green bell pepper, red bell pepper, and parsley; stir well. Cover and cook on High for 30 minutes, or until peppers are tender and shrimp are heated through.

4. Meanwhile, combine chili powder and cayenne in a large zip-top plastic bag. Add scallops and toss until coated with mixture.

5. In a large skillet, melt butter over medium heat. Add scallops and cook, stirring, just until they become opaque, about 4 minutes. Add to the slow cooker and stir well. Add filé powder, if using, and stir well. Serve immediately. Pass hot pepper sauce at the table.

Sweet Potato Coconut Curry with Shrimp

Makes 6 servings

MAKE AHEAD

This dish can be partially prepared before it is cooked. Complete Step 1. Cover and refrigerate the onion mixture or for up to 2 days. When you're ready finish the recipe, continue with Steps 2 and 3.

Note: *The suggested accompaniments for this recipe are not included in the nutrients or exchanges per serving. Whether you keep track of exchanges or count carbohydrates, remember to account for what these additional foods contribute.*

NUTRIENTS PER SERVING

Calories	232
Carbohydrate	22 g
Fiber	2 g
Protein	18 g
Fat, total	8 g
Fat, saturated	4 g
Sodium	355 mg
Cholesterol	147 mg

EXCHANGES PER SERVING

1	Starch
1	Vegetable
2	Very Lean Meat
1	Fat

You'll love the combination of sweet and spicy flavors in this luscious dish. Serve the curry over brown basmati rice, and add a platter of steamed spinach lightly sprinkled with toasted sesame seeds to complete the meal.

● **Works in slow cookers from 3½ to 6 quarts**

1 tablespoon olive oil or extra virgin coconut oil	1 tablespoon fresh lime juice
2 onions, finely chopped	1 pound medium cooked shrimp, peeled and deveined (see Tips, page 178)
4 cloves garlic, minced	½ cup coconut milk
1 tablespoon minced fresh ginger	¼ cup toasted slivered almonds, optional (see Tip, left)
1 cup lower-sodium vegetable broth	¼ cup finely chopped cilantro leaves
2 medium sweet potatoes, peeled and cut into 1" cubes	
2 teaspoons Thai green curry paste	

1. In a skillet, heat oil over medium heat for 30 seconds. Add onions and cook, stirring, until softened, about 3 minutes. Add garlic and ginger and cook, stirring, for 1 minute. Stir in broth. Transfer mixture to the slow cooker stoneware.

2. Add sweet potatoes to the slow cooker and stir well. Cover and cook on Low for 6 to 8 hours or on High for 3 to 4 hours, or until sweet potatoes are tender.

3. In a small bowl, combine curry paste and lime juice. Add to the slow cooker and stir well. Stir in shrimp and coconut milk. Cover and cook on High for 20 minutes, or until shrimp are hot. Transfer to a serving dish. Garnish with almonds, if using, and cilantro.

Seafood Supreme

Makes 6 servings

TIPS

• Cooked lobster can replace part of the shellfish.

• For a less expensive version, omit the scallops and shrimp and increase the amount of sole (or haddock or cod) to 1½ pounds.

• The moisture content of fresh and frozen seafood differs and may result in a finished sauce that's too thick or too thin. To eliminate this problem, be sure to cook the uncooked seafood first in the broth and wine.

Note: *The suggested accompaniments for this recipe are not included in the nutrients or exchanges per serving. Whether you keep track of exchanges or count carbohydrates, remember to account for what these additional foods contribute.*

Do you pine for the days when elegant luncheons were in fashion? Here's a special dish that calls to mind white-gloved ladies at lunch. Serve this richly flavored seafood over rice, or toss with pasta.

1 cup fish stock or reduced-sodium chicken broth (approximately)
½ cup dry white wine or vermouth
8 ounces sole or other white fish, cut into 1" cubes
8 ounces small scallops
8 ounces small cooked shrimp, peeled and deveined (see Tips, page 178)

3 tablespoons butter
¾ cup diced red bell pepper
⅓ cup finely chopped scallions
¼ cup all-purpose flour
½ cup half-and-half
   Freshly ground white pepper
2 tablespoons chopped fresh dill or parsley

1. In a large saucepan, bring broth and wine to a boil over medium heat. Add sole and cook for 2 minutes (start timing when fish is added to broth). Add scallops and cook for 1 to 2 minutes longer, or until seafood is opaque. Using a slotted spoon, transfer seafood to a medium bowl. Add shrimp to the bowl and set aside.

2. Strain cooking liquid into large glass measure; there should be 2 cups. Add water, if necessary, to make 2 cups; set aside.

3. In a large saucepan, melt butter over medium heat. Add bell pepper and scallions; cook, stirring, until softened, about 3 minutes. Stir in flour, then pour in reserved cooking liquid. Bring to a boil, stirring, until sauce is very thick and smooth. Stir in half-and-half and bring to a boil.

4. Add reserved seafood and heat through. Season with pepper to taste, then stir in dill. Serve immediately.

NUTRIENTS PER SERVING

Calories	217
Carbohydrate	8 g
Fiber	1 g
Protein	23 g
Fat, total	9 g
Fat, saturated	5 g
Sodium	330 mg
Cholesterol	112 mg

EXCHANGES PER SERVING

½	Other Carbohydrate
3½	Lean Meat

Easy Curried Fish Stew

Makes 4 servings

Note: *The suggested accompaniments for this recipe are not included in the nutrients or exchanges per serving. Whether you keep track of exchanges or count carbohydrates, remember to account for what these additional foods contribute.*

Ginger adds a vibrant flavor to this stew. Serve steaming bowls with chunks of crusty whole-grain bread. It's a complete meal!

2 teaspoons vegetable oil	1½ cups thinly sliced carrots
1 small onion, finely chopped	1 tablespoon cornstarch
1 tablespoon minced fresh ginger	2 tablespoons water
	Freshly ground black pepper
2 teaspoons mild curry paste or powder	1 pound fresh or frozen haddock or cod fillets, cut into chunks
2¼ cups fish broth or reduced-sodium chicken broth	1½ cups snow peas, ends trimmed, halved
2 cups diced peeled potatoes	

1. In a large saucepan, heat oil over medium heat. Add onion, ginger and curry paste; cook, stirring, until softened, about 2 minutes. Add broth, potatoes, and carrots; bring to a boil. Reduce heat, cover, and simmer for 10 to 12 minutes, or until vegetables are just tender.

2. In a small bowl, blend cornstarch and water. Add to stew and cook, stirring, until thickened. Season with pepper to taste. Stir in fish and snow peas; cover and cook for 2 to 3 minutes, or until snow peas are crisp-tender and fish is opaque. Serve hot.

NUTRIENTS PER SERVING

Calories	258
Carbohydrate	26 g
Fiber	5 g
Protein	26 g
Fat, total	5 g
Fat, saturated	1 g
Sodium	470 mg
Cholesterol	65 mg

EXCHANGES PER SERVING

1	Starch
2	Vegetable
3	Very Lean Meat

Snapper Vera Cruz

Makes 8 servings

This traditional Mexican recipe has many variations. Most often, filleted fish is fried and covered with a sauce that is cooked separately. For this slow cooker version, the fish is sliced very thinly and cooked in the sauce during the last 20 minutes. For an authentic Mexican touch, serve the snapper with hot tortillas to soak up the sauce. Feel free to use any firm white fish you prefer instead of snapper.

● **Works in slow cookers from 3½ to 6 quarts**

1 tablespoon olive oil	1½ pounds skinless snapper fillets, cut in half lengthwise and sliced as thinly as possible on the horizontal
1 onion, finely chopped	
2 cloves garlic, minced	
½ teaspoon dried oregano	1 to 2 jalapeño peppers, finely chopped (see Tips, left)
¼ teaspoon ground cinnamon	
⅛ teaspoon ground cloves	2 tablespoons fresh lemon juice
1 can (28 ounces) diced tomatoes, drained (see Tips, left)	1 tablespoon drained capers
	10 olives, pitted and thinly sliced
½ cup fish stock or bottled clam juice	Hot whole wheat tortillas (optional)

1. In a large skillet, heat oil over medium heat for 30 seconds. Add onion and cook, stirring, until softened, about 3 minutes. Add garlic, oregano, cinnamon, and cloves; cook, stirring, for 1 minute. Add tomatoes and stock and bring to a boil. Transfer to the slow cooker stoneware.

2. Cover and cook on Low for 6 hours or on High for 3 hours, or until hot and bubbly. Stir in fish, jalapeño, and lemon juice. Cover and cook on High for 20 minutes, or until fish is cooked through. Stir in capers and pour mixture onto a deep platter. Sprinkle with olives and serve with hot tortillas, if desired.

NUTRIENTS PER SERVING

Calories	127
Carbohydrate	5 g
Fiber	1 g
Protein	18 g
Fat, total	4 g
Fat, saturated	1 g
Sodium	251 mg
Cholesterol	31 mg

EXCHANGES PER SERVING

1	Vegetable
2½	Very Lean Meat

Caribbean Fish Stew

Makes 10 servings

• One Scotch bonnet pepper is probably enough for most people, but if you're a heat seeker, use 2. You can also use habanero pepper equally sparingly instead. To avoid skin irritation, be sure to wear rubber gloves when cutting these extremely hot peppers.

Note: *The suggested accompaniments for this recipe are not included in the nutrients or exchanges per serving. Whether you keep track of exchanges or count carbohydrates, remember to account for what these additional foods contribute.*

The allspice and superhot Scotch bonnet peppers add a distinctive island tang to this delicious stew. For a delicious finish, be sure to include the dill. Serve this stew with crusty rolls to soak up the sauce, a fresh green salad, and some crisp white wine.

• **Works in slow cookers from 3½ to 6 quarts**

2 teaspoons cumin seeds	2 cups fish stock
6 whole allspice	2 cups sliced okra (¼" slices)
1 tablespoon olive oil	1½ pounds skinless grouper fillets, cut into bite-size pieces
2 onions, finely chopped	
4 cloves garlic, minced	8 ounces cooked shrimp, peeled and deveined (see Tips, page 178)
1 tablespoon grated orange or lime zest	
2 teaspoons dried thyme	1 to 2 Scotch bonnet peppers, minced (see Tip, left)
1 teaspoon turmeric	
½ teaspoon cracked black peppercorns	½ cup finely chopped dill (optional)
1 can (28 ounces) diced tomatoes, including juice	

1. In a large dry skillet, toast cumin seeds and allspice over medium heat, stirring, until fragrant and just beginning to brown, about 3 minutes. Immediately transfer to a mortar or spice grinder and grind. Set aside.

2. In the same skillet, heat oil over medium heat for 30 seconds. Add onions and cook, stirring, until softened, about 3 minutes. Add garlic, zest, thyme, turmeric, peppercorns, and reserved cumin and allspice; cook, stirring, for 1 minute. Add tomatoes and their juice and stock; bring to a boil. Transfer to the slow cooker stoneware.

3. Cover and cook on Low for 6 hours or on High for 3 hours. Add okra, fish, shrimp, and peppers. Cover and cook on High for 20 minutes, or until fish flakes easily with a fork and okra is tender. Stir in dill, if using, just before serving.

NUTRIENTS PER SERVING

Calories	138
Carbohydrate	8 g
Fiber	2 g
Protein	19 g
Fat, total	3 g
Fat, saturated	1 g
Sodium	294 mg
Cholesterol	51 mg

EXCHANGES PER SERVING

1½	Vegetable
2½	Very Lean Meat

PASTA DISHES

Big-Batch Tomato Sauce

Makes 14 servings (½ cup per serving)

• In summer, instead of buying canned tomatoes, make this sauce with 5 pounds of fresh ripe tomatoes, preferably the plum variety. Remove the tomato stems. Cut an × in the bottom of each. Plunge into boiling water for 30 seconds to loosen the skins, then chill in cold water and drain. Slip off the skins, cut the tomatoes in half cross-wise, and squeeze out the seeds. Finely chop.

• Instead of using dried basil and oregano, replace dried herbs with ⅓ cup chopped fresh basil; add it toward the end of cooking.

• To save time, chop the vegetables in the food processor.

Here's an indispensable sauce you should always have handy in the freezer to use as a base for your family's favorite pasta dishes. This versatile sauce is used in any number of ways throughout this book.

1 tablespoon olive oil	½ teaspoon freshly ground black pepper
1 onion, finely chopped	1 bay leaf
2 carrots, peeled and finely chopped	2 cans (28 ounces) plum tomatoes, including juice, chopped
1 stalk celery, including leaves, finely chopped	1 can (5½ ounces) tomato paste
4 cloves garlic, minced	¼ cup finely chopped fresh parsley
1 tablespoon dried basil	
1½ teaspoons dried oregano	
1 teaspoon sugar	

1. In a large Dutch oven or saucepan, heat oil over medium-high heat. Add onion, carrots, celery, garlic, basil, oregano, sugar, pepper, and bay leaf; cook, stirring often, for 5 minutes, or until vegetables are softened.

2. Stir in tomatoes and their juice, tomato paste, and 1 tomato-paste can full of water; bring to a boil. Reduce the heat and simmer, partially covered, for 35 to 40 minutes, stirring occasionally, or until slightly thickened. Remove bay leaf and stir in parsley. Let cool and refrigerate or freeze.

NUTRIENTS PER SERVING

Calories	57
Carbohydrate	11 g
Fiber	2 g
Protein	2 g
Fat, total	1 g
Fat, saturated	0 g
Sodium	210 mg
Cholesterol	0 mg

EXCHANGES PER SERVING

2	Vegetable

Basil Pesto

Makes 8 servings (1 tablespoon per serving)

Pesto keeps well for up to a week in the refrigerator, or you can pack it into a small airtight container and freeze it for up to 1 month.

1½ cups lightly packed fresh basil leaves	¼ cup olive oil (approximately)
2 cloves garlic, coarsely chopped	¼ cup freshly grated Parmesan cheese
2 tablespoons pine nuts or lightly toasted walnuts	Freshly ground black pepper

1. In a food processor, combine basil, garlic, and pine nuts. While the machine is running, add oil in a steady stream and process until smooth. Add a little more oil if pesto appears dry.

2. Transfer basil to a small bowl and stir in cheese; season with pepper to taste. Transfer to a small covered container, cover with a thin layer of oil, and refrigerate. If you want to freeze it, make pesto without adding cheese. When you're ready to use it, thaw and stir in cheese.

NUTRIENTS PER SERVING

Calories	89
Carbohydrate	1 g
Fiber	0 g
Protein	2 g
Fat, total	9 g
Fat, saturated	2 g
Sodium	60 mg
Cholesterol	2 mg

EXCHANGES PER SERVING

2	Fat

Sun-Dried Tomato Pesto

Makes 12 servings (1 tablespoon per serving)

For a fast dinner, toss this pesto with 8 ounces pasta, cooked according to package directions, or swirl it into soup for a wonderful burst of flavor.

½ cup sun-dried tomatoes	⅓ cup vegetable broth
½ cup lightly packed fresh basil leaves (see Tips, left)	2 tablespoons olive oil
½ cup lightly packed fresh parsley	⅓ cup freshly grated Parmesan cheese
1 large clove garlic	½ teaspoon freshly ground black pepper

1. In a small bowl, cover sun-dried tomatoes with boiling water; let stand until softened, about 10 minutes. Drain and pat dry; chop coarsely.

2. In a food processor, combine rehydrated tomatoes, basil, parsley, and garlic. With the motor running, add broth and oil in a steady stream. Transfer to a small bowl and stir in cheese and pepper. Transfer to a small covered container, cover with a thin layer of oil, and refrigerate. If you want to freeze it, make it without adding the cheese. When you're ready to use it, thaw and stir in the cheese.

NUTRIENTS PER SERVING

Calories	41
Carbohydrate	2 g
Fiber	0 g
Protein	2 g
Fat, total	3 g
Fat, saturated	1 g
Sodium	115 mg
Cholesterol	2 mg

EXCHANGES PER SERVING

½	Fat

Easy One-Pot Macaroni and Cheese

Makes 6 servings

TIPS

● For a speedy meal-in-one dinner, add 3 to 4 cups small broccoli florets to the pot of boiling pasta for the last 3 minutes of cooking; drain with the pasta.

● To reheat any leftovers on the stovetop or in the microwave, stir in additional milk until sauce is creamy.

This streamlined mac and cheese is as easy to assemble as the packaged version.

2 tablespoons all-purpose flour	1 teaspoon Dijon mustard
1½ cups low-fat milk	Cayenne pepper
1½ cups shredded light Cheddar cheese	2 cups elbow macaroni
¼ cup freshly grated Parmesan cheese	

1. Bring a large pot of water to a boil.

2. In a large saucepan, whisk flour with ¼ cup of the milk to make a smooth paste; stir in remaining milk until smooth. Place over medium heat and cook, stirring, until mixture comes to a boil and thickens. Reduce the heat to low; stir in Cheddar, Parmesan, and mustard. Cook, stirring, until cheeses are melted. Season with a pinch of cayenne; remove from the heat and keep warm.

3. Cook pasta in boiling water according to package directions until al dente. Drain well and return to the pan. Add cheese mixture and cook over medium heat for 1 minute, or until sauce coats the pasta. Transfer to serving bowls and serve immediately.

NUTRIENTS PER SERVING

Calories	269
Carbohydrate	32 g
Fiber	2 g
Protein	15 g
Fat, total	8 g
Fat, saturated	5 g
Sodium	460 mg
Cholesterol	24 mg

EXCHANGES PER SERVING

2	Starch
1½	High-fat Meat

Spaghetti with Meatballs

Makes 6 servings

This dish is the essence of Italian cooking—comforting, hearty, and sure to please.

3 cups Big-Batch Tomato Sauce (page 190)	12 ounces spaghetti or other strand pasta
24 Basic Meatballs (½ recipe; see page 212)	⅓ cup freshly grated Parmesan cheese

1. Bring a large pot of water to a boil.

2. In a large saucepan, combine tomato sauce and meatballs; bring to a boil. Reduce the heat, cover, and simmer for 15 minutes.

3. Cook pasta in boiling water according to package directions until al dente; drain well. Return to the pan, add meatballs and sauce, and toss to coat. Transfer to serving bowls and sprinkle with cheese.

HOW TO COOK PASTA

You can ruin a good pasta dish if you don't cook the pasta properly. The most common error is not using enough water to boil the pasta, which then cooks unevenly and sticks together.

To cook 8 to 12 ounces of pasta: Using a large pot, bring 12 cups of water to a full rolling boil. Add up to 1 teaspoon salt and all the pasta at once. (Do not add oil.) Stir immediately to prevent pasta from sticking. Cover with a lid to return water quickly to a full boil, then uncover and stir occasionally. Taste to see if pasta is al dente, or firm to the bite. Drain immediately. Unless directed otherwise, never rinse pasta—this chills it and removes the coating of starch that helps sauce cling to pasta. Return the pasta to the cooking pot or place it in a large warmed serving bowl; add the sauce and toss until well coated. Serve immediately.

NUTRIENTS PER SERVING

Calories	436
Carbohydrate	60 g
Fiber	5 g
Protein	25 g
Fat, total	11 g
Fat, saturated	4 g
Sodium	575 mg
Cholesterol	52 mg

EXCHANGES PER SERVING

3	Starch
2	Vegetable
2	Medium-fat Meat

Kids' Favorite Spaghetti Pie

Makes 4 servings

TIP

● It's easy to turn this recipe into a vegetarian dish—just omit the meat. The broccoli can be replaced by zucchini, bell peppers, or whatever vegetable you have on hand (and your kids like).

Leftover pasta is perfect for this pizzalike supper dish that's especially appealing to the younger set.

8 ounces lean ground beef or chicken

2 cups sliced mushrooms

1 small onion, chopped

1 large clove garlic, minced

1½ teaspoons dried oregano

2 cups Big-Batch Tomato Sauce (page 190) or commercial tomato-based pasta sauce

2 cups small broccoli florets

3 cups cooked spaghetti or other strand pasta (6 ounces uncooked)

1½ cups shredded part-skim mozzarella cheese

1. Preheat the oven to 350°F. Coat a 9" or 10" glass pie plate with cooking spray.

2. In a medium saucepan over medium-high heat, cook beef, breaking it up with a wooden spoon, until no longer pink, about 4 minutes. Drain in a strainer to remove any fat.

3. Return meat to the pan. Add mushrooms, onion, garlic, and oregano; cook over medium-high heat, stirring, until vegetables are softened, about 3 minutes. Add tomato sauce, cover, reduce the heat to medium-low, and simmer for 10 minutes.

4. Rinse broccoli and place in a covered casserole dish. Microwave on High for 2 to 2½ minutes, or until bright green and almost tender. Rinse under cold running water to chill, and drain.

5. Spread spaghetti in the prepared pie plate. Spread with meat sauce, top with broccoli, and sprinkle with mozzarella. Bake for 25 to 30 minutes or until cheese is melted. Cut into wedges and serve.

NUTRIENTS PER SERVING

Calories	455
Carbohydrate	47 g
Fiber	6 g
Protein	32 g
Fat, total	16 g
Fat, saturated	8 g
Sodium	760 mg
Cholesterol	59 mg

EXCHANGES PER SERVING

2	Starch
1	Other Carbohydrate
3½	Lean Meat
1	Fat

Spaghetti with Garlic Tomato Sauce

Makes 6 servings

TIP

● Improvise if you don't have any fresh herbs by using 1 teaspoon each of dried basil and dried oregano instead of the fresh basil and parsley.

Even when your pantry is almost empty, chances are you'll have a can of tomatoes and dried pasta on hand to whip up this easy supper dish.

1 tablespoon olive oil	Pinch granulated sugar
3 cloves garlic, thinly sliced, then coarsely chopped	12 ounces spaghetti
¼ teaspoon red pepper flakes	2 tablespoons chopped fresh basil leaves or chives
1 can (28 ounces) plum tomatoes, including juice, chopped	2 tablespoons chopped fresh parsley
Freshly ground black pepper	

1. Bring a large pot of water to a boil.

2. In a large saucepan, heat oil over medium heat; stir in garlic and red pepper flakes. Reduce heat to low and cook, stirring, until garlic is light golden, about 1 minute. (Do not let garlic brown or sauce will be bitter.)

3. Add tomatoes and their juice; season with pepper and sugar to taste. Bring to a boil, reduce heat, and simmer, partially covered, stirring occasionally, for 15 minutes.

4. Cook pasta in boiling water according to package directions until al dente. Drain well and return to the pot. Add tomato sauce, basil, and parsley; toss well. Add pepper to taste. Serve immediately.

NUTRIENTS PER SERVING

Calories	279
Carbohydrate	52 g
Fiber	4 g
Protein	9 g
Fat, total	4 g
Fat, saturated	1 g
Sodium	385 mg
Cholesterol	0 mg

EXCHANGES PER SERVING

3	Starch
1	Vegetable

Spaghetti with Meat Sauce

Makes 6 servings

Instead of ground beef, use half veal and half pork or a combination of all three.

Intensely flavored, thanks to the addition of red wine, this easy pasta dish suits those nights when you crave something simple but satisfying.

12 ounces lean ground beef

½ cup red wine or reduced-sodium beef broth

3 cups Big-Batch Tomato Sauce (page 190)

Freshly ground pepper

Red pepper flakes

12 ounces spaghetti

½ cup freshly grated Parmesan cheese

1. Bring a large pot of water to a boil.

2. In a large nonstick skillet over medium-high heat, cook beef, breaking it up with a wooden spoon, until no longer pink, about 5 minutes. Drain in a strainer to remove any fat.

3. Return meat to the pan, add wine, and cook over medium-high heat until partly reduced. Stir in tomato sauce and season with black pepper and red pepper flakes to taste. Reduce the heat to medium-low, cover, and simmer for 15 minutes.

4. Cook pasta in boiling water according to package directions until al dente; drain well, return to the pan, and toss with sauce. Transfer to serving bowls and sprinkle with cheese.

NUTRIENTS PER SERVING

Calories	416
Carbohydrate	58 g
Fiber	5 g
Protein	24 g
Fat, total	9 g
Fat, saturated	3 g
Sodium	400 mg
Cholesterol	32 mg

EXCHANGES PER SERVING

3	Starch
2	Vegetable
1½	Medium-fat Meat

FREEZING AND REFRIGERATING PASTA

Here are some general guidelines for making pasta dishes ahead and refrigerating or freezing.

- Make pasta sauces up to 2 days ahead and refrigerate, or freeze for up to 2 months. If assembling a pasta dish ahead: Cook pasta and chill under cold water; drain. Toss the cold pasta with cold sauce and spoon into a casserole dish. It's best to assemble the casserole no more than a few hours ahead to prevent the pasta from absorbing too much of the sauce.

- When freezing sauce, do not add the cheese topping (it gets rubbery when frozen). Cover with plastic wrap, then with foil. Freeze for up to 2 months. Let the dish defrost in the refrigerator overnight. Increase the baking time by about 10 minutes.

Fast Fusilli with Mushrooms and Peas

Makes 4 servings

You can prepare this 5-minute pasta sauce the day ahead and refrigerate. Reheat on the stovetop or in a microwave before tossing with hot cooked pasta.

Fusilli works well in this recipe because the sauce clings nicely to the corkscrew-shaped pasta, but feel free to use whatever pasta you have in your pantry.

2 teaspoons butter	½ cup low-fat milk
2 cups sliced mushrooms	⅓ cup freshly grated Parmesan cheese
2 scallions, sliced	
1 package (4 ounces) light herb-and-garlic cream cheese	8 ounces fusilli, penne, or other pasta
1 cup frozen peas	Freshly ground black pepper

1. Bring a large pot of water to a boil.

2. In a large saucepan, melt butter over medium heat. Add mushrooms and scallions; cook, stirring, until softened, about 3 minutes. Add cream cheese, peas, milk, and Parmesan; cook, stirring, for 2 minutes, or until piping hot.

3. Cook pasta in boiling water according to package directions until al dente. Drain well. Stir into mushroom mixture and toss to coat well. Season with pepper to taste. Transfer to warm bowls and serve immediately.

NUTRIENTS PER SERVING

Calories	398
Carbohydrate	56 g
Fiber	5 g
Protein	17 g
Fat, total	12 g
Fat, saturated	6 g
Sodium	580 mg
Cholesterol	31 mg

EXCHANGES PER SERVING

3½	Starch
½	Vegetable
½	Medium-fat Meat
1½	Fat

Fettuccine with Seared Scallops, Lemon, and Garlic

Makes 6 servings

TIP

● When to use curly versus flat-leaf parsley? While they are interchangeable in many recipes, flat-leaf has a more assertive taste that is ideal in recipes such as this one, where it is a vital ingredient and balances nicely with the lemon and garlic.

When you crave a rich and creamy pasta dish, this is it. Since this recipe requires very little preparation time, assemble all of the ingredients before you start.

1 pound large scallops	¼ cup fish stock or reduced-sodium chicken broth
¼ teaspoon salt	1 tablespoon fresh lemon juice
Freshly ground black pepper	1 tablespoon grated lemon zest
12 ounces fettuccine pasta	¾ cup heavy cream
2 tablespoons butter	¼ cup chopped fresh flat-leaf parsley (see Tip, left)
3 cloves garlic, minced	
½ cup dry white wine	

1. Bring a large pot of water to a boil.

2. Pat scallops dry with paper towels. Halve horizontally and season with the salt and pepper to taste; set aside.

3. Cook pasta in boiling water according to package directions until al dente.

4. About halfway through pasta cooking time, heat a large nonstick skillet over high heat. Add butter and heat until foamy and butter starts to brown. Add reserved scallops and cook for 1 minute, or until lightly browned. Turn and cook on second side for about 30 seconds. Do not overcook. Transfer to a plate.

5. Reduce the heat to medium. Add garlic and cook, stirring, for 30 seconds, or until fragrant. Stir in wine, stock, lemon juice, and zest; bring to a boil. Add cream and cook, stirring, until sauce boils and is slightly reduced.

6. Add parsley and season with salt and pepper to taste. Return scallops to the pan and cook for 1 minute, or just until heated through. Do not overcook. Remove from the heat.

7. Drain pasta and return to the pan. Pour scallops and sauce over pasta and toss until well coated. Spoon pasta into warm bowls and serve immediately.

NUTRIENTS PER SERVING

Calories	420
Carbohydrate	46 g
Fiber	3 g
Protein	21 g
Fat, total	16 g
Fat, saturated	9 g
Sodium	440 mg
Cholesterol	74 mg

EXCHANGES PER SERVING

3	Starch
2	Medium-fat Meat
½	Fat

Roasted Vegetable Lasagna with Spicy Tomato Sauce

Makes 8 servings

TIP

• Bottled pasta sauces can be very high in sodium. Compare labels and choose a lower-sodium variety.

Today's store-bought tomato sauces and packaged shredded cheeses ease the making of traditional lasagna. This updated version serves a crowd and replaces ground meat with plenty of healthy vegetables.

ROASTED VEGETABLES

1 large fennel bulb, diced

1 large red bell pepper, diced

2 small zucchini, diced

1 red onion, cut into thin wedges

1 tablespoon dried oregano

½ teaspoon freshly ground black pepper

2 tablespoons olive oil

CHEESE FILLING

2 large eggs

½ teaspoon freshly ground black pepper

1½ cups light ricotta cheese

1 cup crumbled light feta cheese (about 4 ounces)

¼ cup chopped fresh parsley

PASTA AND SAUCE

12 lasagna noodles

1 jar (26 ounces) spicy tomato sauce with roasted red peppers

1 can (7½ ounces) tomato sauce

⅓ cup chopped kalamata olives (optional)

MOZZARELLA TOPPING

1½ cups shredded part-skim mozzarella cheese

1. Preheat the oven to 400°F. Coat a 13" × 9" baking dish with cooking spray. Bring a large pot of water to a boil.

2. **Make the vegetables:** In a large bowl, combine fennel, bell pepper, zucchini, onion, oregano, and black pepper; drizzle with oil and toss to coat. Spread vegetables on 2 baking sheets. Roast, stirring occasionally, for 20 to 25 minutes, or until tender. Remove from the oven and set aside. Reduce the oven temperature to 350°F.

NUTRIENTS PER SERVING

Calories	414
Carbohydrate	44 g
Fiber	5 g
Protein	24 g
Fat, total	16 g
Fat, saturated	8 g
Sodium	995 mg
Cholesterol	82 mg

EXCHANGES PER SERVING

2	Starch
2	Vegetable
2	High-fat Meat

To make ahead, cover and refrigerate the finished dish for up to 2 days, or cover completely with heavy-duty foil and freeze for up to 2 months. Let thaw completely in the refrigerator for 24 hours before reheating.

3. **Make the cheese filling:** In a medium bowl, beat eggs with pepper. Stir in ricotta, feta, and parsley.

4. **Prepare the pasta:** Cook noodles in boiling water for 8 minutes, or until almost tender. Drain; chill under cold running water. Arrange in single layer on a damp tea towel.

5. **Make the sauce:** In a large bowl, combine jarred and canned tomato sauces. Reserve ¾ cup of the sauce in a small bowl. Stir reserved vegetables and olives, if using, into remaining sauce.

6. **Assemble dish:** Spread reserved ¾ cup sauce in the bottom of the prepared baking dish. Top with 3 of the noodles. Spread with one-quarter of the vegetable sauce, and top with one-third of the cheese filling. Repeat the layers twice. Top with remaining noodles and spread with remaining sauce. Sprinkle the top with mozzarella.

7. Cover pan loosely with foil. Bake for 30 minutes, uncover, and bake for 20 to 25 minutes longer, or until bubbly and top is golden. Let stand for 5 minutes before cutting.

Easy Lasagna

Makes 8 servings

• Lasagna freezes well for up to 2 months. Transfer to a freezer-proof container and cover with plastic wrap, then with foil. Let defrost in the refrigerator overnight before baking.

Everyone loves lasagna, but who has time to make it from scratch? Try this uncomplicated version that makes even a noncook look like a pro in the kitchen. It's also the perfect recipe for young cooks, since there's no chopping involved. Once you assemble the ingredients, it takes a mere 15 minutes to prepare, and the lasagna is ready for the oven.

2 cups light ricotta cheese	¼ teaspoon freshly ground black pepper
2 large eggs, beaten	1 jar (26 ounces) tomato sauce
⅓ cup freshly grated Parmesan cheese	12 oven-ready lasagna noodles
¼ teaspoon freshly grated nutmeg	1½ cups shredded part-skim mozzarella cheese

1. Preheat the oven to 350°F. Coat a 13" × 9" baking dish with cooking spray.

2. In a large bowl, combine ricotta, eggs, Parmesan, nutmeg, and pepper.

3. Place tomato sauce in a medium bowl. Depending on thickness of the tomato sauce, add about ¾ cup water to thin the sauce. (Precooked noodles absorb extra moisture while cooking.)

4. Spoon ½ cup of the sauce into the bottom of the prepared baking dish. Top with 3 of the lasagna noodles. Spread with ¾ cup of the sauce and then one-third of the ricotta mixture. Repeat with 2 more layers of noodles, sauce, and ricotta. Top with remaining noodles and sauce. Sprinkle with mozzarella.

5. Bake, uncovered, for 45 minutes, or until cheese is melted and sauce is bubbly.

NUTRIENTS PER SERVING

Calories	332
Carbohydrate	31 g
Fiber	2 g
Protein	21 g
Fat, total	13 g
Fat, saturated	7 g
Sodium	670 mg
Cholesterol	82 mg

EXCHANGES PER SERVING

1½	Starch
½	Other Carbohydrate
2½	Medium-fat Meat

Tuna Noodle Bake
with Cheddar Crumb Topping

Makes 6 servings

MAKE AHEAD

To make the casserole up to 2 days in advance, cook the noodles, rinse under cold running water to chill, and drain. Combine the cold noodles and the cold sauce; spoon into the casserole dish, cover, and refrigerate. Add the crumb topping just before baking to prevent it from getting soggy. Add 10 minutes to the baking time.

Note: *The suggested accompaniment for this recipe is not included in the nutrients or exchanges per serving. Whether you keep track of exchanges or count carbohydrates, remember to account for what these additional foods contribute.*

NUTRIENTS PER SERVING

Calories	407
Carbohydrate	48 g
Fiber	5 g
Protein	23 g
Fat, total	14 g
Fat, saturated	7 g
Sodium	630 mg
Cholesterol	82 mg

EXCHANGES PER SERVING

3	Starch
1	Vegetable
1½	Medium-fat Meat
½	Fat

This recipe takes an old standby to new heights. What's great, too, is that it keeps well in the fridge for up to 2 days before baking. For an effortless meal, just pop it in the oven when you get home from work. Serve with a crisp green salad.

TUNA AND NOODLES

1 tablespoon butter

8 ounces mushrooms, sliced

¾ cup chopped scallions

2 tablespoons all-purpose flour

1 can (10 ounces) chicken broth, undiluted

1 cup low-fat milk

4 ounces light cream cheese, softened

1 can (6½ ounces) solid white tuna, drained and flaked

1 cup frozen peas

8 ounces broad egg noodles

CHEDDAR CRUMB TOPPING

1 cup shredded light Cheddar cheese

½ cup dried bread crumbs (see Tip, page 81)

1. Preheat the oven to 350°F. Coat a 13" × 9" casserole dish with cooking spray. Bring a large pot of water to a boil.

2. **Make the tuna and noodles:** In a large saucepan, melt butter over medium heat. Add mushrooms and scallions; cook, stirring, until softened, about 3 minutes. Blend in flour, then stir in broth and milk. Bring to a boil, stirring constantly, until slightly thickened. Stir in cream cheese until melted. Add tuna and peas; cook for 2 minutes longer, or until heated through. Remove the pan from the heat.

3. Cook noodles according to package directions until al dente. Drain well. Add noodles to sauce and coat well. Spoon mixture into the prepared dish.

4. **Make the topping:** In a medium bowl, toss cheese with bread crumbs. Just before baking, sprinkle topping over noodles.

5. Bake for 30 minutes, or until top is golden.

Baked Penne with Italian Sausage and Sweet Peppers

Makes 6 servings

TIPS

● Not all turkey sausages are the same. Check labels carefully, and look for those that contain no more than 10 grams of fat per 3½ ounces.

● For fresher flavor and less sodium, replace canned tomatoes with 4 large ripe tomatoes. Remove the tomato stems. Cut an × in the bottom of each. Plunge into boiling water for 30 seconds to loosen the skins, then chill in cold water and drain. Slip off the skins, cut the tomatoes in half crosswise, and squeeze out the seeds. Finely chop.

This hearty pasta dish, brimming with chunks of tasty sausage and colorful peppers, makes a delicious feast for any occasion.

8 ounces hot or mild lean turkey Italian sausages

1 tablespoon olive oil

3 bell peppers (assorted colors)

1 large onion, halved lengthwise and thinly sliced

2 cloves garlic, minced

1 teaspoon dried basil

1 teaspoon dried oregano

½ teaspoon red pepper flakes, or to taste

1 can (28 ounces) plum tomatoes, including juice, chopped

¼ cup chopped fresh parsley

12 ounces penne or other small tube-shaped pasta

1 cup shredded part-skim mozzarella cheese

½ cup freshly grated Parmesan cheese

1. Preheat the oven to 350°F. Coat a 13" × 9" baking dish with cooking spray. Bring a large pot of water to a boil.

2. Prick skins of sausages with a fork. In a large Dutch oven or saucepan, heat oil over medium-high heat; add sausages and cook until browned on all sides, about 5 minutes. (Sausages will not be cooked through.) Remove from the pan, cut into slices, and reserve.

NUTRIENTS PER SERVING

Calories	432
Carbohydrate	60 g
Fiber	5 g
Protein	24 g
Fat, total	11 g
Fat, saturated	4 g
Sodium	675 mg
Cholesterol	57 mg

EXCHANGES PER SERVING

3	Starch
1	Other Carbohydrate
2	Lean Meat
½	Fat

Vegetarian Penne with Sweet Peppers Omit the sausages, and add ⅓ cup small pitted black olives to the sauce along with the parsley for an added dimension of flavor.

3. Drain fat from the pan. Add peppers, onion, garlic, basil, oregano, and red pepper flakes; cook, stirring often, until vegetables are softened, about 7 minutes.

4. Return sausage slices to the pan along with canned tomatoes with their juice; bring to a boil. Reduce the heat to medium-low, cover, and simmer, stirring occasionally, for 20 minutes. Stir in parsley.

5. While tomatoes are cooking, cook pasta in boiling water according to package directions until al dente. Drain well. Place half of the cooked pasta in the prepared baking dish. Pour in half of the sauce. Top with remaining pasta and remaining sauce.

6. In a medium bowl, combine mozzarella and Parmesan; sprinkle over top of casserole. Bake, uncovered, for 30 to 35 minutes, or until cheese is melted and lightly colored.

Spinach and Ricotta Cannelloni

Makes 6 servings (2 cannelloni per serving)

• To defrost spinach, remove the packaging and place the spinach in a 4-cup casserole dish. Cover and microwave on High, stirring once, for 6 to 8 minutes, or until defrosted and hot. Place in a strainer and press out excess moisture.

• The major difference between fresh and dried pasta is that fresh pasta contains egg and most dried pasta does not. Look for fresh lasagna noodles at larger supermarkets and specialty food stores.

NUTRIENTS PER SERVING

Calories	254
Carbohydrate	26 g
Fiber	3 g
Protein	7 g
Fat, total	9 g
Fat, saturated	5 g
Sodium	510 mg
Cholesterol	58 mg

EXCHANGES PER SERVING

1	Starch
1½	Vegetable
1½	Medium-fat Meat
½	Fat

To streamline this one-dish pasta meal, choose one of the convenient bottled tomato pasta sauces sold in supermarkets. Check labels and select one with less sodium. If you have the time to make a sauce from scratch, try Big-Batch Tomato Sauce (page 190).

1 tablespoon olive oil	⅓ cup chopped fresh parsley
1 package (10 ounces) frozen chopped spinach, thawed, squeezed dry	¼ teaspoon freshly ground nutmeg
4 scallions, sliced	¼ teaspoon salt
2 cloves garlic, minced	¼ teaspoon freshly ground black pepper
1 large egg	6 sheets (9" × 6" each) fresh lasagna noodles
2 cups ricotta cheese	3 cups tomato pasta sauce
1½ cups shredded light provolone cheese, divided	½ cup chicken broth
½ cup freshly grated Parmesan cheese, divided	

1. Preheat the oven to 350°F. Coat a 13" × 9" baking dish with cooking spray. Bring a large pot of water to a boil.

2. In a large nonstick skillet, heat oil over medium-high heat. Add spinach, scallions, and garlic; cook, stirring, until softened, about 3 minutes. Remove the pan from the heat.

To make ahead and freeze, cover the cannelloni with plastic wrap, then with heavy-duty foil. Freeze for up to 1 month. Thaw in the refrigerator. Add 15 minutes to the baking time.

3. In a medium bowl, beat egg. Stir in ricotta, ½ cup of the provolone, ¼ cup of the Parmesan, the parsley, nutmeg, salt, and pepper. Stir in spinach mixture until combined.

4. Cook lasagna noodles in boiling water until al dente, about 3 minutes. Drain and chill under cold running water. Cut each sheet in half crosswise. Place on a damp kitchen towel.

5. In a medium bowl, combine pasta sauce and broth. Spread 1 cup of the tomato sauce in the bottom of the prepared baking dish.

6. Working one lasagna sheet at a time, spoon ⅓ cup of the ricotta filling along a short edge of each sheet. Roll up and place in the baking dish, making 2 rows. Cover with remaining tomato sauce; sprinkle with remaining 1 cup provolone and ¼ cup Parmesan. Bake for 40 to 45 minutes, or until sauce is bubbly.

Company Chicken Tetrazzini

Makes 6 servings

With leftover cooked chicken or turkey, you can make a wonderful pasta dish that's great for company and can be assembled ahead of time (see Make Ahead, left).

MAKE AHEAD

To prepare the dish in advance, cook the sauce, cover, and refrigerate. Boil the pasta, rinse under cold water, and chill. Combine the cold sauce and pasta up to 4 hours before the dish goes into the oven. (This prevents the pasta from absorbing too much of the sauce.) Add 10 minutes to the baking time, or cook until piping hot in the center.

8 ounces broad egg noodles
1 tablespoon butter
8 ounces mushrooms, sliced
4 scallions, finely chopped
1 teaspoon dried basil
¼ cup all-purpose flour
2 cups reduced-sodium chicken broth

2 cups cubed cooked chicken or turkey
½ cup half-and-half
¼ cup medium-dry sherry
½ cup freshly grated Parmesan cheese
Freshly ground black pepper

1. Preheat the oven to 350°F. Coat a 13" × 9" baking dish with cooking spray. Bring a large pot of water to a boil.

2. Cook noodles in boiling water according to package directions until al dente.

3. Meanwhile, in a large saucepan, melt butter over medium-high heat. Add mushrooms, scallions, and basil; cook until softened, about 4 minutes.

4. In a medium bowl, blend flour with ⅓ cup of the broth to make a smooth paste; stir in remaining broth. Add broth mixture to the saucepan; bring to a boil, stirring, until thickened. Add chicken, half-and-half, and sherry. Reduce the heat to medium and cook for 2 to 3 minutes, or until heated through. Remove the pan from the heat. Stir in ¼ cup of the cheese and season with pepper to taste.

5. When noodles are cooked, drain well and return to the pot. Add chicken mixture and toss to coat well.

6. Spoon noodle mixture into prepared baking dish. Sprinkle with remaining ¼ cup cheese. Bake for 30 to 35 minutes, or until heated through.

NUTRIENTS PER SERVING

Calories	376
Carbohydrate	39 g
Fiber	4 g
Protein	26 g
Fat, total	12 g
Fat, saturated	5 g
Sodium	590 mg
Cholesterol	99 mg

EXCHANGES PER SERVING

2½	Starch
2½	Lean Meat
½	Fat

Spicy Noodles with Vegetables and Peanut Sauce

Makes 6 servings

TIP

● Cut vegetables into uniform 2" lengths. This colorful pasta dish takes only a few minutes to cook, so have the ingredients assembled before you start.

Vegetarians in your household will request this dish often and think of it as a comfort food. Its vibrant combination of Asian flavors tastes terrific and is nourishing, too. Any leftovers make a great next-day lunch.

¼ cup light peanut butter	2 small Italian eggplants, cut into thin strips (about 2 cups)
⅓ cup water	
2 tablespoons reduced-sodium soy sauce	1 leek, white and light green parts only, cleaned and cut into matchstick strips (see Tip, page 42)
2 tablespoons fresh lime juice	
2 tablespoons packed brown sugar	1 tablespoon minced fresh ginger
¼ teaspoon red pepper flakes, or to taste	2 cloves garlic, minced
1 tablespoon sesame oil	2 bell peppers (assorted colors), cut into thin strips
12 ounces linguine, broken into thirds	½ cup chopped fresh cilantro or parsley
1 tablespoon vegetable oil	

1. Bring a large pot of water to a boil.

2. In a small saucepan, combine peanut butter, water, soy sauce, lime juice, brown sugar, red pepper flakes, and sesame oil. Cook over medium heat, stirring, until mixture is warm and smooth. Set aside.

3. Cook linguine in boiling water according to package directions until al dente.

4. Meanwhile, in a wok or large skillet, heat vegetable oil over high heat. Add eggplants, leek, ginger, and garlic; cook, stirring, for 2 minutes. Add peppers; cook, stirring, for 1 minute longer, or until vegetables are just crisp-tender. Add reserved peanut sauce and cook, stirring, until heated through.

5. Drain pasta and return to the pot. Add vegetables and peanut sauce to pasta and toss until pasta is well coated; stir in cilantro. Serve warm or at room temperature.

NUTRIENTS PER SERVING

Calories	378
Carbohydrate	63 g
Fiber	6 g
Protein	12 g
Fat, total	9 g
Fat, saturated	1 g
Sodium	390 mg
Cholesterol	0 mg

EXCHANGES PER SERVING

3	Starch
1	Vegetable
1	Other Carbohydrate
1	Fat

Singapore Noodles

Makes 4 servings

TIP

● Other pasta such as angel hair can be substituted for the vermicelli. Cook the noodles according to package directions before adding to the recipe.

Here's a popular noodle dish you'll spot on many restaurant menus—it's easy to re-create in your home kitchen.

6 ounces rice vermicelli	5 scallions, sliced
2 tablespoons reduced-sodium soy sauce	2 large cloves garlic, minced
2 teaspoons mild curry paste or powder	3 cups bean sprouts, rinsed and dried
4 teaspoons vegetable oil	12 ounces cooked baby shrimp, peeled
1 red or green bell pepper, cut into thin strips	

1. Bring a large pot of water to a boil.

2. Cook noodles in boiling water for 3 minutes. Drain, chill under cold running water, and drain well. Using scissors, cut noodles into 3" lengths; set aside.

3. In a small bowl, combine soy sauce and curry paste; set aside.

4. Heat a wok or large skillet over high heat until very hot; add 2 teaspoons of the oil, tilting the wok, if using, to coat the sides. Add pepper, scallions, and garlic; cook for 1 minute, stirring constantly. Add bean sprouts and shrimp; cook for 1 to 2 minutes, stirring constantly, or until vegetables are crisp-tender. Transfer to a medium bowl.

5. Add remaining 2 teaspoons oil to the pan; when very hot, add noodles and soy sauce mixture. Cook for 1 minute, stirring constantly, or until heated through. Return vegetable-shrimp mixture to the pan and cook, stirring constantly, for 1 minute longer. Serve immediately.

NUTRIENTS PER SERVING

Calories	351
Carbohydrate	46 g
Fiber	3 g
Protein	25 g
Fat, total	7 g
Fat, saturated	1 g
Sodium	570 mg
Cholesterol	143 mg

EXCHANGES PER SERVING

2½	Starch
2	Vegetable
2	Very Lean Meat
½	Fat

MEATLESS
MAINS

Basic Tomato Sauce

Makes about 8 cups (1 cup per serving)

● If you are in a hurry, you can soften the vegetables on the stovetop. Heat the oil in a skillet for 30 seconds. Add the onions and carrots and cook, stirring, until the carrots are softened, about 7 minutes. Add the garlic, thyme, and peppercorns and cook, stirring, for 1 minute. Transfer to the slow cooker. Add the tomatoes with their juice and continue with Step 2.

Not only is this sauce tasty and easy to make, it is also much lower in sodium than prepared sauces. It keeps covered for up to 1 week in the refrigerator and can be frozen for up to 6 months.

● **Works in slow cookers from 3½ to 6 quarts**

2 onions, finely chopped	½ teaspoon cracked black peppercorns
2 carrots, diced	2 cans (each 28 ounces) diced tomatoes, including juice
1 tablespoon olive oil	
4 cloves garlic, minced	
1 teaspoon dried thyme	

1. In the slow cooker stoneware, combine onions, carrots, and oil. Stir well to coat with oil. Cover and cook on High for 1 hour, or until vegetables are softened. Add garlic, thyme, and peppercorns; stir well. Stir in tomatoes and their juice.

2. Place a tea towel folded in half (so you have 2 layers) over the top of the stoneware to absorb moisture. Cover and cook on Low for 6 to 8 hours or on High for 3 to 4 hours, or until sauce is thickened and flavors are melded.

MINDFUL MORSELS

One advantage to making your own tomato sauce is that it is much lower in sodium than prepared versions. One-half cup of prepared tomato sauce, a typical serving size when used in a recipe, may contain as much as 700 milligrams of sodium, compared with 155 milligrams in ½ cup of this sauce with no added salt. If you want to reduce the sodium even further, use canned tomatoes with no salt added, which are now widely available.

NUTRIENTS PER SERVING

Calories	75
Carbohydrate	14 g
Fiber	3 g
Protein	3 g
Fat, total	2 g
Fat, saturated	0 g
Sodium	311 mg
Cholesterol	0 mg

EXCHANGES PER SERVING

1	Vegetable
½	Other Carbohydrate
½	Fat

Mushroom Tomato Sauce

Makes 6 servings

MAKE AHEAD

For an easy and delicious meal, make this sauce ahead of time and refrigerate. Prepare a batch of Basic Polenta, and just before it is ready to serve, reheat the Mushroom Tomato Sauce. To serve, spoon the polenta onto a warm plate and top with the sauce.

Note: *The suggested accompaniments for this recipe are not included in the nutrients or exchanges per serving. Whether you keep track of exchanges or count carbohydrates, remember to account for what these additional foods contribute.*

Add variety to your diet by expanding the kinds of grains you use with sauces traditionally served with pasta. For example, try this classic sauce over Basic Polenta (page 257) or whole wheat pasta. Accompanied by a tossed green salad, it makes a great weeknight meal.

● **Works in slow cookers from 3½ to 6 quarts**

1 tablespoon olive oil	½ cup dry white wine or lower-sodium chicken or vegetable broth
1 onion, finely chopped	
2 stalks celery, diced	1 tablespoon tomato paste
4 cloves garlic, minced	1 can (28 ounces) diced tomatoes, including juice
1 tablespoon finely chopped fresh rosemary or 2 teaspoons dried	Crushed red pepper flakes (optional)
½ teaspoon salt	Freshly grated Parmesan cheese (optional)
½ teaspoon cracked black peppercorns	
8 ounces cremini mushrooms, sliced	

1. In a large skillet, heat oil over medium heat for 30 seconds. Add onion and celery; cook, stirring, until celery is softened, about 5 minutes. Add garlic, rosemary, salt, and peppercorns; cook, stirring, for 1 minute. Add mushrooms and toss to coat. Add wine and cook for 1 minute. Stir in tomato paste and tomatoes and their juice; bring to a boil. Transfer to the slow cooker stoneware.

2. Place a tea towel folded in half (so you will have 2 layers) over top of the stoneware to absorb moisture. Cover and cook on Low for 6 hours or on High for 3 hours, or until hot and bubbly. Stir in red pepper flakes, if using. Serve over cooked whole wheat pasta, polenta, or grits. Sprinkle with cheese to taste, if using.

NUTRIENTS PER SERVING

Calories	67
Carbohydrate	11 g
Fiber	2 g
Protein	3 g
Fat, total	3 g
Fat, saturated	0 g
Sodium	403 mg
Cholesterol	0 mg

EXCHANGES PER SERVING

2	Vegetable
½	Fat

Artichoke, Sun-Dried Tomato, and Goat Cheese Strata

Makes 8 servings

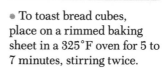

TIP

• To toast bread cubes, place on a rimmed baking sheet in a 325°F oven for 5 to 7 minutes, stirring twice.

Note: *The suggested accompaniment for this recipe is not included in the nutrients or exchanges per serving. Whether you keep track of exchanges or count carbohydrates, remember to account for what these additional foods contribute.*

This is a great brunch dish. Round it out with a green salad.

• **Large (minimum 5-quart) slow cooker**

8 cups cubed (½") toasted sourdough or whole wheat bread (see Tip, left)	4 to 6 oil-packed sun-dried tomatoes, drained and finely chopped
1 can (14 ounces) artichoke hearts, drained and chopped	4 large eggs
8 ounces soft goat cheese, crumbled	2 cups 2% evaporated milk
1 cup sliced scallions, white part with just a bit of green	½ teaspoon salt
	½ teaspoon cracked black peppercorns

1. Coat the slow cooker stoneware with cooking spray.

2. In the prepared slow cooker, combine bread, artichokes, 4 ounces of the cheese, scallions, and tomatoes. Toss well.

3. In a medium bowl, whisk together eggs, milk, salt, and peppercorns. Pour over bread mixture. Sprinkle remaining cheese evenly on top.

4. Place 2 clean tea towels, each folded in half (so you will have 4 layers) over the top of the stoneware to absorb moisture. Cover and cook on Low for 6 hours or on High for 3 hours, or until strata is set and edges are browning.

NUTRIENTS PER SERVING

Calories	280
Carbohydrate	28 g
Fiber	3 g
Protein	17 g
Fat, total	11 g
Fat, saturated	6 g
Sodium	663 mg
Cholesterol	111 mg

EXCHANGES PER SERVING

1	Starch
1	Vegetable
½	Low-fat Milk
1	Lean Meat
1	Fat

Pumpkin and Rice Casserole with Mushrooms

Makes 12 servings

TIP

● Chipotle peppers are smoked and dried jalapeño peppers. They typically come canned in adobo sauce, which is made from tomatoes, garlic, vinegar, salt, and spices (you can use a little of the sauce or rinse it off). Freeze what you don't use in a zip-top plastic bag.

Note: *The suggested accompaniments for this recipe are not included in the nutrients or exchanges per serving. Whether you keep track of exchanges or count carbohydrates, remember to account for what these additional foods contribute.*

This simple casserole makes a nice weeknight dinner. Serve it with a green salad or sliced tomatoes, in season.

● **Large (minimum 5-quart) slow cooker**

1 tablespoon olive oil	1 can (28 ounces) diced tomatoes, including juice
2 onions, diced	2 cups lower-sodium vegetable broth
2 carrots, diced	4 cups cubed (½") peeled pumpkin, or orange or yellow squash
2 stalks celery, diced	
2 cloves garlic, minced	
1 teaspoon dried thyme	1 chipotle pepper in adobo sauce, minced (see Tip, left)
½ teaspoon salt	2 cups shredded light Monterey Jack cheese
½ teaspoon cracked black peppercorns	
12 ounces cremini mushrooms, trimmed and quartered	
2 cups long-grain brown rice	

1. In a large skillet, heat oil over medium heat for 30 seconds. Add onions, carrots, and celery; cook, stirring, until carrots are softened, about 7 minutes. Add garlic, thyme, salt, and peppercorns; cook, stirring, for 1 minute. Add mushrooms and toss to coat. Add rice and toss to coat. Add tomatoes and their juice and broth; bring to a boil. Transfer to the slow cooker stoneware. Stir in pumpkin.

2. Place a clean tea towel, folded in half (so you will have 2 layers), across the top of the stoneware to absorb moisture. Cover and cook on Low for 7 to 8 hours or on High for 4 hours, or until rice is tender and liquid is absorbed. Remove the towel. Stir in chipotle pepper and sprinkle cheese on top of mixture. Cover and cook on High for 20 to 25 minutes, or until flavors meld and cheese is melted.

NUTRIENTS PER SERVING

Calories	231
Carbohydrate	34 g
Fiber	4 g
Protein	10 g
Fat, total	7 g
Fat, saturated	3 g
Sodium	409 mg
Cholesterol	12 mg

EXCHANGES PER SERVING

2	Starch
1	Medium-fat Meat

Mushroom and Chickpea Stew with Roasted Red Pepper Coulis

Makes 6 servings

TIPS

• Large cans of tomatoes come in 28-ounce and 35-ounce sizes. For convenience, the recipe calls for the 28-ounce size. If you're using the 35-ounce size, drain off 1 cup of the liquid before adding to the recipe.

• For convenience, use jarred roasted red peppers, or, if you prefer, roast your own. (see Tips, page 56)

This delicious stew will appeal to vegetarians and nonvegetarians alike. Topped with the luscious coulis, it is quite divine. Add whole grain rolls and a green salad or steamed asparagus, in season.

• **Works in slow cookers from 3½ to 6 quarts**

MUSHROOM AND CHICKPEA STEW

1 tablespoon cumin seeds

1 tablespoon olive oil

2 onions, finely chopped

2 carrots, peeled and diced

4 stalks celery, thinly sliced, or 1 bulb fennel, trimmed, cored, and vertically sliced

4 cloves garlic, minced

1 teaspoon turmeric

¼ teaspoon salt

½ teaspoon cracked black peppercorns

8 ounces cremini mushrooms, thinly sliced

1 can (28 ounces) diced tomatoes, including juice (see Tips, left)

1 can (14 ounces) chickpeas, drained and rinsed, or 1 cup dried chickpeas, soaked, cooked, and drained (see Basic Beans Variation, page 236)

RED PEPPER COULIS

2 roasted red bell peppers (see Tips, left)

3 oil-packed sun-dried tomatoes, drained and chopped

2 tablespoons extra virgin olive oil

1 tablespoon balsamic vinegar

10 fresh basil (optional)

1. **Make the stew:** In a large dry skillet, toast cumin seeds over medium heat, stirring, until fragrant and just beginning to brown, about 3 minutes. Immediately transfer to a mortar or spice grinder and grind. Set aside.

NUTRIENTS PER SERVING

Calories	202
Carbohydrate	31 g
Fiber	7 g
Protein	7 g
Fat, total	8 g
Fat, saturated	1 g
Sodium	558 mg
Cholesterol	0 mg

EXCHANGES PER SERVING

1½	Starch
2	Vegetable
1	Fat

This dish can be partially prepared in advance. Complete Steps 1 and 2. Cover and refrigerate the vegetable mixture overnight or for up to 2 days. When you're ready to finish the recipe, continue with Steps 3 through 5.

Note: *The suggested accompaniments for this recipe are not included in the nutrients or exchanges per serving. Whether you keep track of exchanges or count carbohydrates, remember to account for what these additional foods contribute.*

2. In the same skillet, heat oil over medium heat for 30 seconds. Add onions, carrots, and celery; cook, stirring, until vegetables are tender, about 7 minutes. Add garlic, turmeric, salt, peppercorns, and reserved cumin; cook, stirring, for 1 minute. Add mushrooms and toss until coated. Add tomatoes and their juice; bring to a boil. Transfer to the slow cooker stoneware.

3. Add chickpeas and stir well. Cover and cook on Low for 6 hours or on High for 3 hours, or until hot and bubbly.

4. **Make the coulis:** In a food processor, combine peppers, sun-dried tomatoes, oil, vinegar, and basil, if using. Process until smooth.

5. Ladle stew into bowls and top with coulis.

MINDFUL MORSELS

Most of the sodium in a serving of this recipe comes from the canned tomatoes, the canned chickpeas (135 milligrams), and, of course, the salt. There are several ways you can reduce the amount of sodium from these ingredients in any recipe: Use tomatoes and/or chickpeas canned without salt; use fresh tomatoes in season; prepare homemade stock from scratch without salt; and cut back on added salt.

Tagine of Squash and Chickpeas with Mushrooms

Makes 6 servings

TIPS

● This dish has a strong gingery flavor. If you're ginger-averse, reduce the amount.

● Large cans of tomatoes come in 28-ounce and 35-ounce sizes. For convenience, the recipe calls for the 28-ounce size. If you're using the 35-ounce size, drain off 1 cup of the liquid before adding to the recipe.

The unusual combination of flavorings in this dish melds beautifully in the slow cooker. The taste of the cinnamon and ginger really comes through, and the bittersweet combination of lemon and honey adds a perfect finish. Serve this over whole grain couscous to complete the Middle Eastern flavors and provide vegetarians with a complete protein. Add a leafy green vegetable, such as spinach or Swiss chard, to round out the meal.

● **Works in slow cookers from 3½ to 6 quarts**

1 tablespoon olive oil	1 can (28 ounces) diced tomatoes, including juice (see Tips, left)
1 onion, finely chopped	
2 carrots, diced (about 1 cup)	3 cups cubed (1") peeled butternut squash or pumpkin
4 cloves garlic, minced	
2 tablespoons minced ginger (see Tips, left)	2 cups cooked dried chickpeas (see Basic Beans Variation, page 236) or canned chickpeas, drained and rinsed
1 teaspoon turmeric	
½ teaspoon salt	
½ teaspoon cracked black peppercorns	1 tablespoon honey
1 piece (2") cinnamon stick	1 tablespoon fresh lemon juice
8 ounces cremini mushrooms, stemmed and halved	

1. In a large skillet, heat oil over medium heat for 30 seconds. Add onion and carrots; cook, stirring, until carrots are softened, about 7 minutes. Add garlic, ginger, turmeric, salt, peppercorns, and cinnamon stick; cook, stirring, for 1 minute. Add mushrooms and toss until coated. Add tomatoes and their juice; bring to a boil. Transfer to the slow cooker stoneware.

2. Add squash and chickpeas; stir well. Cover and cook on Low for 8 hours or on High for 4 hours, or until vegetables are tender.

3. In a small bowl, combine honey and lemon juice. Add to the slow cooker and stir well.

NUTRIENTS PER SERVING

Calories	205
Carbohydrate	39 g
Fiber	7 g
Protein	8 g
Fat, total	4 g
Fat, saturated	1 g
Sodium	595 mg
Cholesterol	0 mg

EXCHANGES PER SERVING

2	Starch
1	Vegetable
½	Fat

This dish can be partially prepared in advance. Complete Step 1. Cover and refrigerate the mushroom mixture for up to 2 days. When you're ready to finish the recipe, continue with Steps 2 and 3.

Note: *The suggested accompaniments for this recipe are not included in the nutrients or exchanges per serving. Whether you keep track of exchanges or count carbohydrates, remember to account for what these additional foods contribute.*

MINDFUL MORSELS

Mushrooms team up well with numerous other ingredients. One cup of sliced raw mushrooms or $\frac{1}{2}$ cup cooked contains less than 20 calories and almost no fat, is a good source of the B vitamins pantothenic acid and riboflavin, and supplies the antioxidant mineral selenium. If you're adding mushrooms to an existing recipe (creminis offer intense, delicious flavor), count these amounts as a Free Food.

Tofu in Indian-Spiced Tomato Sauce

Makes 6 servings

MAKE AHEAD

This dish can be partially prepared in advance. Complete Step 1. Cover and refrigerate the tomato mixture for up to 2 days. When you're ready to cook, continue with Steps 2 through 4.

Note: *The suggested accompaniments for this recipe are not included in the nutrients or exchanges per serving. Whether you keep track of exchanges or count carbohydrates, remember to account for what these additional foods contribute.*

NUTRIENTS PER SERVING

Calories	130
Carbohydrate	14 g
Fiber	2 g
Protein	5 g
Fat, total	7 g
Fat, saturated	1 g
Sodium	614 mg
Cholesterol	0 mg

EXCHANGES PER SERVING

½	Starch
1	Vegetable
½	Lean Meat
1	Fat

This robust dish makes a lively and different meal. Serve it with fresh green beans and naan, an Indian bread, to soak up the sauce.

● **Works in slow cookers from 3½ to 6 quarts**

TOMATO SAUCE

1 tablespoon olive oil
2 onions, finely chopped
2 cloves garlic, minced
4 pods white or green cardamom
1 piece (2") cinnamon stick
1 teaspoon caraway seeds
½ teaspoon minced ginger
6 whole cloves
1 teaspoon salt
½ teaspoon cracked black peppercorns
1 can (28 ounces) diced tomatoes, including juice
1 long green chile pepper, seeded and finely chopped (see Tip, left)

TOFU

¼ cup all-purpose flour
1 teaspoon curry powder
¼ teaspoon cayenne pepper
8 ounces firm tofu, cut into 1" squares
1 tablespoon olive oil

1. **Make the tomato sauce:** In a large skillet, heat oil over medium heat for 30 seconds. Add onions and cook, stirring, until softened, about 3 minutes. Add garlic, cardamom pods, cinnamon stick, caraway seeds, ginger, cloves, salt, and peppercorns; cook, stirring, for 1 minute. Add tomatoes and their juice; bring to a boil. Transfer to the slow cooker stoneware.

2. Cover and cook on Low for 8 hours or on High for 4 hours, or until hot and bubbly. Stir in chile pepper.

3. **Make the tofu:** On a plate, mix together flour, curry powder, and cayenne. Turn pieces of tofu in mixture until lightly coated. Discard excess flour mixture.

4. In a large skillet, heat oil over medium-high heat for 30 seconds. Add dredged tofu and cook, stirring constantly, until nicely browned. Spoon tomato mixture into a serving dish. Discard cloves, cardamom pods, and cinnamon stick. Place tofu on top.

Winter Vegetable Casserole

Makes 8 servings

TIP

● Although pearl barley is more readily available, make an effort to find whole (also known as hulled) barley when making the recipes in this book. It contains more nutrients, including fiber, than its refined relative. Pot barley, which is more refined than whole barley, is also a preferable alternative to pearl barley because it maintains some of the bran.

Note: *The suggested accompaniments for this recipe are not included in the nutrients or exchanges per serving. Whether you keep track of exchanges or count carbohydrates, remember to account for what these additional foods contribute.*

NUTRIENTS PER SERVING

Calories	173
Carbohydrate	36 g
Fiber	6 g
Protein	4 g
Fat, total	3 g
Fat, saturated	0 g
Sodium	438 mg
Cholesterol	0 mg

EXCHANGES PER SERVING

1	Starch
4	Vegetable

Here's a great dish to make during the dark days of winter. This combination of root vegetables, seasoned with caraway seeds, produces a great-tasting dish that is seasonally appropriate. Imagine your pioneer ancestors sitting down to a similar meal. The casserole is delicious served with rye bread and steamed broccoli.

● **Large (minimum 5-quart) slow cooker**

1 large celery root, peeled and shredded	1 teaspoon caraway seeds
1 tablespoon fresh lemon juice	1 teaspoon salt
1 tablespoon olive oil	½ teaspoon cracked black peppercorns
4 carrots, sliced	1 can (14.5 ounces) diced tomatoes, including juice
4 parsnips, tough core removed, sliced	2 cups lower-sodium vegetable broth
2 leeks, white and light green parts only, cleaned and thinly sliced (see Tip, page 42)	½ cup whole (hulled) or pot barley (see Tip, left)
2 cloves garlic, minced	½ cup finely chopped parsley

1. In a medium bowl, toss celery root with lemon juice. Set aside.

2. In a large skillet, heat oil over medium heat for 30 seconds. Add carrots, parsnips, and leeks; cook, stirring, until vegetables have softened, about 7 minutes. Add garlic, caraway seeds, salt, and peppercorns; cook, stirring, for 1 minute. Add tomatoes and their juice, broth, and barley; bring to a boil.

3. Spread reserved celery root over the bottom of the slow cooker stoneware. Add vegetable mixture and stir well. Cover and cook on Low for 6 hours or on High for 3 hours, or until vegetables and barley are tender. Sprinkle with parsley and serve.

Vegetable Curry with Lentils and Spinach

Makes 8 servings

NUTRIENTS PER SERVING

Calories	252
Carbohydrate	50 g
Fiber	9 g
Protein	10 g
Fat, total	3 g
Fat, saturated	0 g
Sodium	253 mg
Cholesterol	0 mg

EXCHANGES PER SERVING

2½	Starch
2	Vegetable

Serve this delicious curry for dinner with warm Indian bread such as naan. It's a meal in itself.

● **Large (minimum 5-quart) slow cooker**

2 teaspoons cumin seeds	2 sweet potatoes, peeled and thinly sliced (about 1 pound)
1 teaspoon coriander seeds	1 cup brown or green lentils, picked over and rinsed
1 tablespoon olive oil or extra virgin coconut oil	1 long red chile pepper, finely chopped (see Tips, left), or ½ teaspoon cayenne pepper dissolved in 1 tablespoon lemon juice
4 carrots, thinly sliced (about 1 pound)	
4 parsnips, tough core removed, thinly sliced (about 1 pound)	1 pound fresh spinach, stems removed, or 1 package (10 ounces) spinach leaves, thawed and drained if frozen, coarsely chopped (see Tips, left)
2 onions, finely chopped	
4 cloves garlic, minced	
1 tablespoon minced ginger	
2 teaspoons turmeric	1 cup coconut milk, optional (see Mindful Morsels, below)
1 piece (2") cinnamon stick	
½ teaspoon cracked black peppercorns	
2 cups lower-sodium vegetable broth	

1. In a large dry skillet, toast cumin and coriander seeds over medium heat until fragrant and just beginning to brown, about 3 minutes. Immediately transfer to a mortar or spice grinder and grind. Set aside.

2. In the same skillet, heat oil over medium heat for 30 seconds. Add carrots, parsnips, and onions; cook, stirring, until vegetables are tender, about 6 minutes. Add garlic, ginger, turmeric, cinnamon stick, peppercorns, and reserved cumin and coriander; cook, stirring, for 1 minute. Add broth and bring to a boil. Transfer to the slow cooker stoneware. Add sweet potatoes and lentils and stir well.

This dish can be partially prepared in advance. Complete Steps 1 and 2. Cover and refrigerate the vegetable mixture overnight or for up to 2 days. When you're ready to finish the recipe, continue with Step 3.

Note: *The suggested accompaniments for this recipe are not included in the nutrients or exchanges per serving. Whether you keep track of exchanges or count carbohydrates, remember to account for what these additional foods contribute.*

3. Cover and cook on Low for 8 hours or on High for 4 hours, or until lentils are tender. Add chile pepper and stir well. Add spinach in batches, stirring after each batch is added, until all the leaves are submerged in the liquid. Add coconut milk, if using. Cover and cook on High for 20 minutes, or until spinach is wilted and flavors have blended. Discard cinnamon stick.

MINDFUL MORSELS

The coconut milk adds a pleasant nutty flavor and creaminess to the curry but is high in saturated fat. The curry is very tasty on its own, so omit the coconut milk if you prefer.

Vegetable Cobbler with Millet Crust

Makes 8 servings

Not only is this tasty cobbler loaded with flavor, the distinctive millet crust adds whole grain goodness to this delightfully different treat. Add a sliced tomato salad, in season, or a tossed green salad topped with shredded carrots to add color and nutrients.

● **Large (minimum 6-quart) slow cooker**

TOPPING

1 cup millet (see Tips, left)
3 cups water
   Freshly ground black pepper
½ cup freshly grated Parmesan cheese (optional)

COBBLER

1 tablespoon olive oil
4 carrots, diced
2 onions, finely chopped
4 stalks celery, diced
4 cloves garlic, minced
2 tablespoons finely chopped fresh rosemary
   or 1½ teaspoons dried

½ teaspoon cracked black peppercorns
1 can (28 ounces) diced tomatoes, including juice
1 can (14 to 19 ounces) white beans, drained and rinsed (see Tips, left), or 1 cup dried white beans, soaked, cooked, and drained (see Basic Beans, page 236)
12 ounces frozen sliced green beans (about 2 cups)

1. **Make the topping:** In a large saucepan, toast millet over medium heat, stirring constantly, until it crackles and releases its aroma, about 5 minutes. Add water and pepper to taste; bring to a boil. Reduce the heat to low, cover, and cook until millet is tender and all the water is absorbed, about 20 minutes. Stir in cheese, if using, and set aside.

NUTRIENTS PER SERVING

Calories	220
Carbohydrate	42 g
Fiber	8 g
Protein	8 g
Fat, total	3 g
Fat, saturated	1 g
Sodium	335 mg
Cholesterol	0 mg

EXCHANGES PER SERVING

2	Starch
2	Vegetable
½	Fat

Although it makes this dish unsuitable for vegetarians, adding a small bit of pancetta (Italian-style cured pork) imbues a tremendous amount of flavor. Dice a 3-ounce chunk and cook it in the olive oil until it becomes crispy, about 3 minutes. Then add the onions, carrots, and celery.

MAKE AHEAD

This dish can be partially prepared in advance. Complete Step 2. Cover and refrigerate the tomato mixture overnight or for up to 2 days. When you're ready to finish the recipe, continue with Steps 1 and 3.

Note: *The suggested accompaniments for this recipe are not included in the nutrients or exchanges per serving. Whether you keep track of exchanges or count carbohydrates, remember to account for what these additional foods contribute.*

2. **Make the cobbler:** Meanwhile, in a large skillet, heat oil over medium heat for 30 seconds. Add carrots, onions, and celery; cook, stirring, until vegetables are softened, about 7 minutes. Add garlic, rosemary, and peppercorns; cook, stirring, for 1 minute. Add tomatoes and their juice and bring to a boil. Transfer to the slow cooker stoneware.

3. Add white beans and green beans and stir well. Spread millet evenly over the top. Cover and cook on Low for 8 to 10 hours or on High for 4 to 5 hours, or until hot and bubbly.

Vegetable Stroganoff

Makes 8 servings

This robust stew makes a delicious dinner with a salad and crusty bread. You can also serve it over hot whole wheat fettuccine or brown rice noodles.

● **Works best in a large (minimum 5-quart) slow cooker**

1 tablespoon olive oil	1 pound portobello mushrooms, stems removed and caps sliced (see Tips, left)
2 large leeks, white part only, cleaned and thinly sliced (see Tip, page 42)	2 potatoes, peeled and cut into ½" cubes
4 stalks celery, thinly sliced	¼ cup heavy cream
2 cloves garlic, minced	2 ounces good-quality blue cheese such as Gorgonzola, crumbled, and at room temperature
1 teaspoon dried thyme	
1 teaspoon cracked black peppercorns	
½ teaspoon salt	
1 can (28 ounces) diced tomatoes, including juice	
1 cup lower-sodium vegetable broth	

1. In a large skillet, heat oil over medium heat. Add leeks and celery; cook, stirring, until vegetables are softened, about 5 minutes. Add garlic, thyme, peppercorns, and salt; cook, stirring, for 1 minute. Add tomatoes and their juice and broth; bring to a boil. Transfer to the slow cooker stoneware.

2. Stir in mushrooms and potatoes. Cover and cook on Low for 8 to 10 hours or on High for 4 to 5 hours, or until potatoes are tender. Stir in cream and cheese. Cover and cook on High for 15 minutes, or until cheese is melted into sauce and mixture is hot and bubbly.

NUTRIENTS PER SERVING

Calories	142
Carbohydrate	18 g
Fiber	4 g
Protein	5 g
Fat, total	7 g
Fat, saturated	3 g
Sodium	494 mg
Cholesterol	15 mg

EXCHANGES PER SERVING

½	Starch
2	Vegetable
1½	Fat

RICE, BEANS & GRAINS

Spanish Vegetable Paella

Makes 6 servings

TIP

• Try a variety of different vegetables, including bite-size pieces of broccoli, cauliflower, asparagus, green beans, bell peppers, and zucchini.

Traditional paella is made in a wide shallow pan, but today's nonstick skillet makes a very good substitute and reduces the amount of oil needed for this dish.

4 cups assorted prepared vegetables (see Tip, left)	2 tablespoons olive oil
3½ cups reduced-sodium chicken broth or vegetable broth	4 scallions, chopped
¼ teaspoon saffron threads, crushed	3 large cloves garlic, minced
Pinch of red pepper flakes	1½ cups short-grain white rice, such as Arborio

1. Preheat the oven to 375°F. Bring a large saucepan of water to a boil.

2. Cook vegetables (except peppers and zucchini, if using) in boiling water for 1 minute. Rinse under cold running water to chill; drain well.

3. In the same saucepan, bring broth to a boil. Add saffron and red pepper flakes. Remove from the heat and keep warm.

4. In a large ovenproof skillet, heat oil over medium-high heat. Add scallions and garlic; cook, stirring, for 1 minute. Add vegetables to the skillet; cook, stirring often, until lightly colored, about 4 minutes. Stir in rice and broth mixture. Reduce the heat so rice cooks at a gentle boil. Cook, uncovered, without stirring, for 10 minutes, or until most of the liquid is absorbed.

5. Cover the skillet with a lid or foil. (If the skillet handle is not ovenproof, wrap it in a double layer of foil.) Bake for 15 minutes, or until all liquid is absorbed and rice is tender. Remove from the oven and let stand, covered, for 5 minutes before serving.

NUTRIENTS PER SERVING

Calories	255
Carbohydrate	46 g
Fiber	3 g
Protein	6 g
Fat, total	5 g
Fat, saturated	1 g
Sodium	295 mg
Cholesterol	0 mg

EXCHANGES PER SERVING

2½	Starch
1	Vegetable
½	Fat

Skillet Shrimp and Rice Creole

Makes 6 servings

TIP

● Today, supermarkets stock frozen shrimp already peeled and deveined—a convenient option for this recipe. You don't have to defrost before adding the shrimp.

Attractive and colorful, this classic Southern specialty relies on the flavors of tomato, celery, thyme, and bay leaf. It's a spicy one-dish meal that takes only 30 minutes to cook.

1 tablespoon vegetable oil	1 cup fish stock or reduced-sodium chicken broth
1 large onion, chopped	Pinch of cayenne pepper
2 cloves garlic, minced	2 small zucchini, halved lengthwise and thinly sliced
2 stalks celery, chopped	1 pound large uncooked shrimp, peeled and deveined, tails left on
½ teaspoon dried thyme	
1 bay leaf	
1 cup long-grain white rice	
1 red bell pepper, diced	
1 can (14.5 ounces) tomatoes, including juice, chopped	

1. In a large nonstick skillet, heat oil over medium heat. Add onion, garlic, celery, thyme, and bay leaf; cook, stirring, until onion is softened, about 5 minutes.

2. Stir in rice and bell pepper; cook for 2 minutes. Add tomatoes and their juice, stock, and a generous pinch of cayenne. Bring to a boil; reduce the heat, cover, and simmer for 15 minutes.

3. Stir in zucchini; bury shrimp in rice. Cover and cook for 8 minutes, or until zucchini are tender and shrimp are pink and firm.

NUTRIENTS PER SERVING

Calories	229
Carbohydrate	33 g
Fiber	2 g
Protein	16 g
Fat, total	3 g
Fat, saturated	0 g
Sodium	335 mg
Cholesterol	112 mg

EXCHANGES PER SERVING

2	Starch
½	Vegetable
1	Very Lean Meat

Vegetable Fried Rice

Makes 6 servings

VARIATION

Chicken or Pork Fried Rice Cut 8 ounces of chicken breasts or lean boneless pork loin into thin strips. In a large skillet, heat 1 table-spoon oil over medium-high heat; cook the meat, stirring, for 5 minutes, or until no longer pink. Remove from the pan and keep warm. Continue with the recipe as directed. Return the meat to the skillet with the bean sprouts and heat through.

Use this recipe as a guide for creating your own versions of fried rice, depending on what type of veggies you have in the fridge. With rice cooked ahead, it takes no time to prepare.

1 tablespoon vegetable oil	½ red bell pepper, cut into thin 1½" strips
3 scallions, chopped	
1½ teaspoons minced fresh ginger	2 tablespoons reduced-sodium soy sauce
1 clove garlic, minced	1 teaspoon mild curry paste or powder (optional)
3 cups cold cooked rice	
1 cup frozen peas	2 cups bean sprouts

1. In a large nonstick skillet, heat oil over high heat until hot but not smoking. Add scallions, ginger, and garlic; cook, stirring, until fragrant, about 15 seconds. Add rice, peas, and pepper; cook, stirring often, until rice is heated through and vegetables are tender, 5 to 7 minutes.

2. In a small bowl, combine soy sauce and curry paste, if using; stir into rice mixture along with bean sprouts. Cook, stirring, for 1 to 2 minutes, or until heated through. Serve immediately.

NUTRIENTS PER SERVING

Calories	164
Carbohydrate	30 g
Fiber	2 g
Protein	5 g
Fat, total	3 g
Fat, saturated	0 g
Sodium	515 mg
Cholesterol	0 mg

EXCHANGES PER SERVING

1½	Starch
1	Vegetable
½	Fat

Herbed Rice Pilaf

Makes 8 servings

To save time, make ahead and reheat in the microwave before serving.

Saffron Rice Pilaf Substitute ¼ teaspoon crushed saffron threads for the thyme.

This herb-infused rice makes the perfect accompaniment to a wide range of dishes. Try it with fish, chicken, beef, lamb, or pork.

1 tablespoon olive oil	3 cups reduced-sodium chicken broth or vegetable broth
1 small onion, finely chopped	
1 clove garlic, minced	1 small red bell pepper, finely diced
½ teaspoons dried thyme	
Freshly ground black pepper	¼ cup chopped fresh parsley
1½ cups long-grain white rice	

1. In a large saucepan, heat oil over medium heat. Add onion, garlic, thyme, and black pepper; cook, stirring often, until onion is softened, about 3 minutes.

2. Add rice and broth; bring to a boil. Reduce the heat to low; cover and simmer for 15 minutes, or until most of broth is absorbed.

3. Stir in bell pepper; cover and cook for 7 to 9 minutes longer, or until rice is tender. Stir in parsley; let stand, covered, for 5 minutes before serving.

NUTRIENTS PER SERVING

Calories	155
Carbohydrate	29 g
Fiber	1 g
Protein	4 g
Fat, total	2 g
Fat, saturated	0 g
Sodium	185 mg
Cholesterol	0 mg

EXCHANGES PER SERVING

2	Starch

Wild Rice with Mushrooms and Apricots

Makes 6 servings

TIPS

• You can purchase wild and brown rice mixtures in many supermarkets, or make your own by combining ½ cup of each.

• Check the Nutrition Facts on the label of the chutney you choose. Chutney usually contains 9 to 11 grams of carbohydrate per tablespoon, or ½ Other Carbohydrate Exchange.

Note: The suggested accompaniments for this recipe are not included in the nutrients or exchanges per serving. Whether you keep track of exchanges or count carbohydrates, remember to account for what these additional foods contribute.

This combination of wild and brown rice with dried apricots makes a tasty weeknight meal. Be sure to serve it with a good chutney alongside—tomato or spicy mango works very well. A grated carrot salad is a nice accompaniment.

• **Works in slow cookers from 3½ to 6 quarts**

1 tablespoon olive oil	1 tablespoon balsamic vinegar
1 onion, chopped	Freshly ground black pepper
4 stalks celery, diced	8 ounces portobello or cremini
1 cup wild rice and brown rice mixture, rinsed (see Tips, left)	mushrooms, stems removed and caps diced
2 cloves garlic, minced	¼ cup chopped dried apricots
2 cups lower-sodium vegetable broth	Chutney (see Tips, left)

1. Coat the slow cooker stoneware with cooking spray.

2. In a large skillet, heat oil over medium heat for 30 seconds. Add onion and celery; cook, stirring, until softened, about 5 minutes. Add rice and garlic; stir until coated. Add broth and vinegar; bring to a boil. Season to taste with pepper. Transfer to the prepared slow cooker.

3. Stir in mushrooms and apricots. Place 2 clean tea towels, each folded in half (so you will have 4 layers), over the top of the stoneware. Cover and cook on Low for 7 to 8 hours or on High for 3½ to 4 hours, or until rice is tender and liquid has been absorbed. Serve hot, accompanied by your favorite fruit chutney.

NUTRIENTS PER SERVING

Calories	181
Carbohydrate	34 g
Fiber	4 g
Protein	5 g
Fat, total	4 g
Fat, saturated	1 g
Sodium	182 mg
Cholesterol	0 mg

EXCHANGES PER SERVING

1½	Starch
1	Vegetable
½	Fruit

Rice and Bulgur Pilaf

Makes 8 servings

NUTRIENTS PER SERVING

Calories	192
Carbohydrate	38 g
Fiber	6 g
Protein	6 g
Fat, total	3 g
Fat, saturated	0 g
Sodium	188 mg
Cholesterol	0 mg

EXCHANGES PER SERVING

2	Starch
1½	Vegetable

Accompanied by a sliced tomato salad, shredded carrots in vinaigrette, or a simple green salad, this tasty pilaf makes a nice weekday meal or an interesting side. It keeps warm in the slow cooker and is perfect for those evenings when everyone is coming and going at different times and can help themselves.

• **Works best in a large (minimum 5-quart) slow cooker**

1 cup coarse bulgur (see Tip, left)	1 teaspoon dried thyme
3 cups boiling water	½ teaspoon cracked black peppercorns
1 tablespoon olive oil	1 cup brown and wild rice mixture, rinsed (see Tips, opposite)
2 large leeks, white part only, cut in half lengthwise, cleaned, and thinly sliced (see Tip, page 42)	¼ cup finely chopped reconstituted sun-dried tomatoes
2 medium carrots, peeled and diced	2 cups lower-sodium vegetable or chicken broth
2 stalks celery, diced	
4 cloves garlic, minced	

1. In a large bowl, combine bulgur and boiling water. Set aside until water is absorbed, about 20 minutes.

2. In a large skillet, heat oil over medium heat. Add leeks, carrots, and celery; cook, stirring, until carrots are softened, about 7 minutes. Add garlic, thyme, and peppercorns; cook, stirring, for 1 minute. Add rice and toss to coat. Add sun-dried tomatoes and stir well. Add broth, stirring, and bring to a boil.

3. Transfer rice mixture to the slow cooker stoneware. Stir in bulgur. Place a clean tea towel, folded in half (so you will have 2 layers), over the top of the stoneware to absorb moisture. Cover and cook on High for 3 hours or on Low for 6 hours, until rice is tender and liquid has been absorbed.

Leek and Barley Risotto

Makes 10 servings

MAKE AHEAD

This dish can be partially prepared the night before you want to finish it. Complete Step 1. Cover and refrigerate the leek mixture overnight. The next morning, continue with Step 2.

This slow cooker method for making risotto saves you from all that time-consuming stirring. Here it's made with barley, rather than arborio rice, for a nice change of pace.

● **Works in slow cookers from 3½ to 6 quarts**

1 tablespoon olive oil	½ teaspoon cracked black peppercorns
3 leeks, white part only, cleaned and thinly sliced (see Tip, page 42)	1 can (28 ounces) diced tomatoes, including juice
2 cups whole (hulled) pot or pearl barley, rinsed	3 cups lower-sodium vegetable broth or water
1 teaspoon salt	

1. In a large skillet, heat oil over medium heat for 30 seconds. Add leeks and cook, stirring, until softened, about 5 minutes. Add barley, salt, and peppercorns; cook, stirring, for 1 minute. Add tomatoes and their juice and broth; bring to a boil. Transfer to the slow cooker stoneware.

2. Cover and cook on Low for 8 hours or on High for 4 hours, or until barley is tender. Serve piping hot.

NUTRIENTS PER SERVING

Calories	160
Carbohydrate	34 g
Fiber	4 g
Protein	3 g
Fat, total	2 g
Fat, saturated	0 g
Sodium	427 mg
Cholesterol	0 mg

EXCHANGES PER SERVING

2	Starch
1	Vegetable

Wild Mushroom Risotto

Makes 10 servings

Risotto's creamy appeal makes it a modern comfort food. It may seem intimidating to make at home, but it's easy to do provided you don't wander away from the stove. Risotto waits for no one, so call everyone to the table as you add the last ladle of broth to the saucepan.

5 cups reduced-sodium chicken broth or vegetable broth (approximately)	1 tablespoon olive oil
1 tablespoon butter	1 small onion, finely chopped
1 pound assorted mushrooms, such as cremini, shiitake, and oyster, coarsely chopped	1½ cups short-grain rice, such as Arborio
2 cloves garlic, minced	½ cup white wine or additional broth
1 tablespoon chopped fresh thyme	⅓ cup freshly grated Parmesan cheese
¼ teaspoon freshly ground black pepper	2 tablespoons chopped fresh parsley

1. In a large saucepan, bring broth to a boil; reduce heat to low and keep hot.

2. In a heavy-bottomed medium saucepan, melt butter over medium heat. Add mushrooms, garlic, thyme, and pepper; cook, stirring often, until tender, 5 to 7 minutes. Remove the pan from the heat and set aside.

3. Add oil to the saucepan; add onion and cook, stirring, until softened, about 2 minutes. Add rice and stir for 1 minute. Add wine and stir until absorbed. Add 1 cup hot broth; adjust heat to a simmer so broth bubbles and is absorbed slowly. When absorbed, continue adding 1 cup broth at a time, stirring almost constantly, for 15 minutes. Add mushroom mixture; cook, stirring often, adding more broth when absorbed, until rice is just tender but slightly firm in the center. Mixture should be creamy; add more broth or water, if necessary. (Total cooking time will be 20 to 25 minutes.)

4. Add Parmesan cheese and adjust seasoning with additional pepper to taste. Spoon into warm shallow serving bowls. Sprinkle with parsley and serve immediately.

NUTRIENTS PER SERVING

Calories	179
Carbohydrate	30 g
Fiber	2 g
Protein	6 g
Fat, total	4 g
Fat, saturated	2 g
Sodium	320 mg
Cholesterol	6 mg

EXCHANGES PER SERVING

1½	Starch
1	Vegetable
½	Fat

Basic Beans

Makes about 2½ cups (½ cup per serving)

TIP

● This recipe may be doubled or tripled to suit the quantity of beans required for a recipe.

VARIATION

Substitute any dried bean (for instance, red kidney, pinto, or white navy) chickpeas, black-eyed peas, or split yellow peas for the white beans. Soybeans and chickpeas take longer than other legumes to cook; they'll likely take the full 12 hours on Low or about 6 hours on High.

DRIED LENTILS These instructions also work for dried lentils, with the following changes: Do not presoak, and reduce the cooking time to about 6 hours on Low.

NUTRIENTS PER SERVING

Calories	129
Carbohydrate	24 g
Fiber	8 g
Protein	9 g
Fat, total	0 g
Fat, saturated	0 g
Sodium	2 mg
Cholesterol	0 mg

EXCHANGES PER SERVING

1½	Starch
1	Very Lean Meat

Loaded with nutrition and high in fiber, dried beans are one of our most healthful edibles. And the slow cooker excels at transforming them into potentially sublime fare. It is also extraordinarily convenient. Put presoaked beans into the slow cooker before you go to bed, and in the morning they're ready for your recipe.

● **Works in slow cookers from 3½ to 6 quarts**

1 cup dried white beans	Bay leaves (optional)
3 cups water	Bouquet garni (optional)
Garlic (optional)	

Long soak: In a large bowl, combine beans and water. Soak for at least 6 hours or overnight. Drain and rinse thoroughly with cold water. Beans are now ready for cooking.

Quick soak: In a large saucepan, combine beans and water. Cover and bring to a boil. Boil for 3 minutes. Turn off the heat and soak in cooking liquid for 1 hour. Drain and rinse thoroughly under cold running water. Beans are now ready for cooking.

Cooking method: In the slow cooker stoneware, combine pre-soaked beans and 3 cups fresh cold water. If desired, season with garlic, or a bouquet garni made from your favorite herbs (typically fresh parsley, thyme, and bay leaf, tied with string). Cover and cook on Low for 10 to 12 hours or overnight or on High for 5 to 6 hours, or until beans are tender. Drain and rinse. If not using immediately, cover and refrigerate. The beans are now ready for use in your favorite recipe.

MINDFUL MORSELS

Beans prepared from scratch without salt contain almost no sodium. Half a cup of regular canned beans (even after draining and rinsing) contains about 300 milligrams of sodium.

Classic Chicken Stew (page 127)

Chicken-Vegetable Cobbler with Cheddar Biscuit Crust (page 128)

One-Pot Italian Sausages Braised with Potatoes (page 165)

Sweet Potato Coconut Curry with Shrimp (page 184)

Baked Penne with Italian Sausage and Sweet Peppers (page 204)

242
Mushroom and Chickpea Stew with Roasted Red Pepper Coulis (page 216)

Cheesy Butterbeans (page 255)

244   Brown Rice Chili (page 276)

Peas and Greens (page 292)

Raspberry Coffee Cake (page 319)

Frozen Strawberry Cake (page 320)

Bread Pudding with Caramelized Pears (page 329)

Cranberry Pear Brown Betty (page 332)

Fudgy Chocolate Brownies (page 336)

Classic Chocolate Chip Cookies (page 340)

Gingery Pears Poached in Green Tea (page 344)

Baked Italian White Beans

Makes 6 servings

A simple combo of beans and vegetables makes a terrific side dish or main course that will delight not only the vegetarians in the crowd but everyone else as well.

2 tablespoons olive oil	2 small zucchini, halved lengthwise, thickly sliced
2 cups chopped Spanish onion	1 red bell pepper, diced
3 cloves garlic, minced, plus 1 large clove garlic, minced	1 yellow bell pepper, diced
1 tablespoon balsamic vinegar	1 can (19 ounces) white kidney beans, drained and rinsed
5 medium tomatoes, seeded and diced	1 cup soft bread crumbs (see Tips, left)
1 tablespoon chopped fresh thyme	2 tablespoons chopped fresh parsley
1 bay leaf	
Freshly ground black pepper	

1. Preheat the oven to 350°F. Coat an 8-cup shallow baking dish with cooking spray.

2. In a large saucepan, heat 1 tablespoon of the oil over medium heat. Add onions and 3 cloves minced garlic, stirring often, until softened, about 5 minutes. Add vinegar and cook until evaporated. Add tomatoes, thyme, and bay leaf; season with black pepper to taste. Bring to a boil; reduce the heat, cover, and simmer for 20 minutes.

3. Add zucchini and red and yellow bell peppers; cook until vegetables are crisp-tender, 5 to 7 minutes. Gently stir in beans. Spoon mixture into the prepared baking dish.

4. In a bowl, combine bread crumbs, parsley, and remaining large clove minced garlic. Drizzle with remaining 1 tablespoon olive oil and toss to coat. Sprinkle bread crumb mixture over beans. Bake for 35 to 45 minutes, or until bubbly and top is golden.

NUTRIENTS PER SERVING

Calories	198
Carbohydrate	32 g
Fiber	9 g
Protein	8 g
Fat, total	6 g
Fat, saturated	1 g
Sodium	245 mg
Cholesterol	0 mg

EXCHANGES PER SERVING

1	Starch
1	Other Carbohydrate
½	Very Lean Meat
1	Fat

Molasses Baked Beans

Vegetarian Baked Beans
Omit the bacon, and cook
the onions and garlic in
2 tablespoons vegetable oil.

Note: The suggested accompaniments for this recipe are not included in the nutrients or exchanges per serving. Whether you keep track of exchanges or count carbohydrates, remember to account for what these additional foods contribute.

Here's an old-time favorite that stirs the spirit. This rustic dish is a winter standby and wonderful when served with home-baked bread.

1 pound dried great Northern or white pea beans, rinsed and picked over (about 2¼ cups)	⅓ cup fancy molasses
	¼ cup packed brown sugar
	2 tablespoons balsamic vinegar
6 slices lean smoky bacon, chopped	2 teaspoons dry mustard
	1 teaspoon salt
1 large onion, chopped	¼ teaspoon freshly ground black pepper
3 cloves garlic, minced	
1 can (8 ounces) tomato sauce	

1. Preheat the oven to 300°F.

2. In a Dutch oven or large saucepan, combine beans with 6 cups cold water. Bring to a boil over high heat; boil for 3 minutes. Remove from the heat, cover, and let stand for 1 hour.

3. Drain beans and cover with 8 cups of cold water. Bring to a boil; reduce the heat, cover, and simmer for 30 to 40 minutes, or until beans are just tender but still hold their shape. Drain, reserving 2 cups cooking liquid. Place beans in a 12-cup casserole dish or bean pot.

4. Meanwhile, in a large saucepan, cook bacon over medium heat, stirring often, until crisp, about 5 minutes. Drain fat from pan. Add onion and garlic; cook, stirring, until softened, about 3 minutes.

5. Add 2 cups of the reserved bean-cooking liquid, tomato sauce, molasses, brown sugar, vinegar, mustard, salt, and pepper. Stir into beans.

6. Cover casserole and bake for 2½ to 3 hours, or until most of the liquid has been absorbed.

NUTRIENTS PER SERVING

Calories	287
Carbohydrate	51 g
Fiber	11 g
Protein	15 g
Fat, total	3 g
Fat, saturated	1 g
Sodium	655 mg
Cholesterol	7 mg

EXCHANGES PER SERVING

2	Starch
1	Vegetable
1	Other Carbohydrate
1	Very Lean Meat

Cheesy Butterbeans

Makes 8 servings

This dish can be partially prepared before it is cooked. Complete Step 1. Cover and refrigerate the bean mixture overnight. The next morning, continue with Step 2.

Note: *The suggested accompaniments for this recipe are not included in the nutrients or exchanges per serving. Whether you keep track of exchanges or count carbohydrates, remember to account for what these additional foods contribute.*

Serve these tasty beans with grilled or roasted meat, or add a salad and enjoy them as a light main course.

● **Works in slow cookers from 3½ to 6 quarts**

4 cups frozen lima beans, thawed and drained	1 teaspoon salt
	Freshly ground black pepper
1 can (28 ounces) diced tomatoes, drained, ½ cup of the juice set aside	1 green bell pepper, chopped
	1 cup shredded light aged Cheddar cheese
½ cup chopped scallions	

1. In the slow cooker stoneware, combine beans, tomatoes and reserved juice, scallions, salt, and black pepper to taste.

2. Cover and cook on Low for 6 hours or on High for 3 hours, or until hot and bubbly. Stir in bell pepper and cheese. Cover and cook on High for 20 minutes, or until bell pepper is tender and cheese is melted.

NUTRIENTS PER SERVING

Calories	158
Carbohydrate	22 g
Fiber	5 g
Protein	10 g
Fat, total	4 g
Fat, saturated	2 g
Sodium	572 mg
Cholesterol	10 mg

EXCHANGES PER SERVING

1	Starch
1	Vegetable
1	Lean Meat

Bistro Lentils

Makes 6 servings

It's Friday night. You've worked hard all week—don't even bother setting the table. Here's a supper dish that's easy to balance on your lap while you relax in front of the TV.

3½ cups reduced-sodium chicken broth or vegetable broth (approximately)

1½ cups lentils, rinsed and sorted

½ teaspoon dried thyme

1 tablespoon olive oil

1 cup diced red onions

2 carrots, peeled and diced

1 cup diced fennel or celery

3 cloves garlic, minced

1 red bell pepper, diced

2 tablespoons balsamic vinegar

1 cup diced extra-lean kielbasa or lean ham (about 5 ounces)

Freshly ground black pepper

¼ cup chopped fresh parsley

1. In a large saucepan, bring broth to a boil over high heat. Add lentils and thyme; reduce the heat to medium-low, cover, and simmer, until lentils are just tender but still hold their shape, 20 to 25 minutes.

2. Meanwhile, heat oil in a large nonstick skillet over medium heat. Add onions, carrots, fennel, and garlic; cook, stirring often, for 8 minutes. Add bell pepper; cook, stirring, for 2 minutes longer, or until vegetables are just tender. Stir in vinegar.

3. Add vegetables and kielbasa to lentils in the saucepan; season with black pepper to taste. Cover and cook until sausage is heated through, 5 to 8 minutes. (Add more broth or water, if necessary, to prevent lentils from sticking.) Stir in parsley. Serve warm or at room temperature.

NUTRIENTS PER SERVING

Calories	261
Carbohydrate	37 g
Fiber	8 g
Protein	19 g
Fat, total	5 g
Fat, saturated	0 g
Sodium	530 mg
Cholesterol	0 mg

EXCHANGES PER SERVING

1	Starch
1½	Other Carbohydrate
2½	Very Lean Meat

Basic Polenta

Makes 8 servings

TIP

• You can cook polenta directly in the slow cooker stoneware or, if you prefer, in a 6-cup baking dish lightly coated with cooking spray. If you are cooking directly in the stoneware, use a small (maximum 3½-quart) slow cooker, lightly coated with cooking spray. If you are using a baking dish, you will need a large (minimum 5-quart) oval slow cooker.

MAKE AHEAD

This dish can be partially prepared before it is cooked. Complete Step 1. Transfer the polenta to a container, cover, and refrigerate overnight or for up to 2 days. When you're ready to finish the recipe, continue with Step 2 or 3.

Polenta, which is cornmeal cooked in seasoned liquid, is extremely nutritious and goes well with many different foods. It's usually served as a side dish. To add variety to your diet, consider topping polenta with sauces traditionally served with pasta. Here we provide two different methods of cooking it in the slow cooker.

• **Works in slow cookers from 3½ to 6 quarts**

4 cups lower-sodium vegetable or chicken broth or water	1¼ cups coarse yellow cornmeal, preferably stone-ground
½ teaspoon salt	
¼ teaspoon freshly ground black pepper	

1. In a saucepan over medium heat, bring broth, salt, and pepper to a boil. Add cornmeal in a thin stream, stirring constantly.

2. **Direct method:** Transfer mixture to the prepared slow cooker stoneware (see Tip, left). Cover and cook on Low for 1½ hours.

3. **Baking dish method:** Transfer mixture to a baking dish (see Tip, left). Cover with foil and secure with a string. Place the dish in the slow cooker stoneware and pour in enough boiling water to come 1" up the sides of the dish. Cover and cook on Low for 1½ hours.

NUTRIENTS PER SERVING

Calories	88
Carbohydrate	17 g
Fiber	2 g
Protein	3 g
Fat, total	1 g
Fat, saturated	0 g
Sodium	319 mg
Cholesterol	0 mg

EXCHANGES PER SERVING

1	Starch

Baked Garlic Polenta with Roasted Vegetables

Makes 10 servings

• If you've run out of homemade tomato sauce and have to buy a commercial pasta sauce, be aware that these sauces can have as much as 700 milligrams of sodium per ½ cup—be sure to check labels.

This impressive dish, which features plenty of vegetables, appeals to both vegetarians and meat eaters. You'll want to have Big-Batch Tomato Sauce (page 190) on hand.

GARLIC POLENTA

- 7 cups water
- 3 cloves garlic, minced
- ½ teaspoon salt
- 2 cups cornmeal
- ¼ cup freshly grated Parmesan cheese
- 1 tablespoon butter

VEGETABLES

- 1 small eggplant (about 1 pound)
- 2 medium zucchini
- 1 large red onion
- 1 red bell pepper
- 1 yellow bell pepper
- 2 tablespoons olive oil
- 1½ teaspoons dried rosemary, crushed
- ½ teaspoon freshly ground black pepper
- ¼ cup chopped fresh parsley
- 2 cups Big-Batch Tomato Sauce (page 190)
- 1¼ cups shredded part-skim mozzarella cheese
- ¼ cup freshly grated Parmesan cheese

1. **Make polenta:** Coat a baking sheet with cooking spray. In a large Dutch oven or saucepan, bring water, garlic, and salt to a boil; gradually whisk in cornmeal until thickened. Reduce the heat to low; cook, stirring often with a wooden spoon, until polenta is thick enough to mound on the spoon, 15 to 20 minutes. Stir in cheese and butter.

2. Spread polenta onto prepared baking sheet and cover with plastic wrap. Refrigerate for 30 minutes, or until firm.

NUTRIENTS PER SERVING

Calories	257
Carbohydrate	34 g
Fiber	5 g
Protein	11 g
Fat, total	9 g
Fat, saturated	4 g
Sodium	395 mg
Cholesterol	17 mg

EXCHANGES PER SERVING

1½	Starch
2	Vegetable
½	High-fat Meat
1	Fat

The dish can be prepared ahead up to the point of baking; cover and refrigerate for up to 2 days. It can also be baked, then covered and refrigerated for up to 1 day.

3. **Make vegetables:** Preheat the oven to 425°F. Coat two additional baking sheets with cooking spray. Coat a 13" × 9" baking dish with cooking spray.

4. Cut eggplant into ½" slices, then cut into 1½" pieces. Halve zucchini lengthwise and thickly slice. Cut onion into thin lengthwise wedges. Cut bell peppers into 1" pieces. Arrange vegetables on prepared baking sheets. Drizzle with oil, then sprinkle with rosemary and black pepper. Bake for 25 to 30 minutes, stirring occasionally, or until tender. Transfer vegetables to a large bowl; stir in parsley.

5. **Assemble the dish:** Reduce the oven temperature to 350°F. Cut prepared polenta in half crosswise; using 2 lifters, gently transfer 1 of the halves to a baking dish. Spread with half of the tomato sauce, then half of the vegetables, half of the mozzarella, and half of the Parmesan. Repeat layers. Bake for 50 to 60 minutes, or until piping hot in center and cheese is melted.

Creamy Polenta with Corn and Chiles

Makes 8 servings

Polenta is a quintessential comfort food. It's great as a side dish, particularly accompanying a robust stew. This version contains the luscious combination of corn and chiles.

● **Works best in a small (3½ quart) slow cooker**

3 cups fat-free milk	1 cup fresh or frozen corn kernels
2 cloves garlic, minced	1 cup shredded Monterey Jack cheese
1 teaspoon finely chopped fresh rosemary or ½ teaspoon dried	½ cup freshly grated Parmesan cheese
¼ teaspoon salt	1 can (4½ ounces) diced mild green chiles
Freshly ground black pepper	
¾ cup coarse yellow cornmeal, preferably stone-ground	

1. In a large saucepan over medium heat, bring milk, garlic, rosemary, salt, and pepper to taste to a boil. Gradually add polenta in a steady stream, whisking to remove all lumps. Continue whisking until mixture begins to thicken and bubbles like lava, about 5 minutes. Add corn, Monterey Jack, Parmesan, and chiles and mix well. Transfer to the slow cooker (see Tip, page 257).

2. Cover and cook on Low for 2 hours, or until mixture is firm and just beginning to brown around the edges.

NUTRIENTS PER SERVING

Calories	181
Carbohydrate	20 g
Fiber	1 g
Protein	11 g
Fat, total	7 g
Fat, saturated	4 g
Sodium	447 mg
Cholesterol	20 mg

EXCHANGES PER SERVING

1	Starch
½	Milk
½	Medium-fat Meat
1	Fat

CHILIES
FOR ALL
OCCASIONS

Dynamite Beanless Chili

Makes 12 servings

TIPS

- If you wish to add beans, omit the cornmeal. Add 2 cans (19 ounces each) red kidney beans, drained and rinsed, to the chili instead.

- When handling jalapeños and other hot peppers, wear gloves to avoid skin irritation.

Note: *The suggested accompaniments for this recipe are not included in the nutrients or exchanges per serving. Whether you keep track of exchanges or count carbohydrates, remember to account for what these additional foods contribute.*

This beanless chili has a hot kick to it, so reduce the amount of red pepper flakes if you prefer it on the tamer side. Ladle into bowls and have ready shredded light Cheddar cheese, sliced green onions, sour cream, and chopped cilantro so everyone can choose their fixings. It's terrific served with Cheddar Drop Biscuits (see page 13).

3 pounds lean ground beef	1 teaspoon salt
1 tablespoon olive oil	1 can (28 ounces) tomatoes, including juice, chopped
2 large onions, chopped	
6 cloves garlic, minced	2 cups reduced-sodium beef broth
5 to 6 jalapeño peppers, minced (see Tips, left)	$1\frac{1}{2}$ cups water
3 tablespoons chili powder	1 can ($5\frac{1}{2}$ ounces) tomato paste
1 tablespoon ground cumin	3 red or green bell peppers, diced
1 tablespoon dried oregano	
2 teaspoons red pepper flakes, or to taste	$\frac{1}{4}$ cup cornmeal
2 bay leaves	

1. In a Dutch oven or stockpot, cook beef over medium-high heat in 2 batches, breaking it up with a wooden spoon, until no longer pink, about 7 minutes. Transfer beef to a strainer and drain fat. Transfer to a large bowl; set aside.

2. Reduce the heat to medium and heat oil. Add onions, garlic, jalapeños, chili powder, cumin, oregano, red pepper flakes, bay leaves, and salt. Cook, stirring, until onions are softened, about 5 minutes.

3. Return meat to the pan. Add tomatoes and their juice, broth, $1\frac{1}{4}$ cups of the water, and tomato paste; bring to a boil. Reduce the heat and simmer, covered, for 30 minutes, stirring occasionally. Add bell peppers and cook for 30 minutes longer.

4. In a small bowl, stir together cornmeal and remaining $\frac{1}{4}$ cup water. Add to meat mixture and stir well. Cook until sauce is thickened, about 10 minutes. Remove bay leaves before serving.

NUTRIENTS PER SERVING

Calories	260
Carbohydrate	13 g
Fiber	3 g
Protein	23 g
Fat, total	13 g
Fat, saturated	5 g
Sodium	665 mg
Cholesterol	59 mg

EXCHANGES PER SERVING

2	Vegetable
3	Lean Meat
1	Fat

20-Minute Chili

Makes 6 servings

● Add just a pinch of red pepper flakes for a mild chili; if you want to turn up the heat, use the amount specified in the recipe.

● Bottled pasta sauces are great timesavers but can be very high in sodium. Compare labels and choose a lower-sodium variety.

Note: The suggested accompaniments for this recipe are not included in the nutrients or exchanges per serving. Whether you keep track of exchanges or count carbohydrates, remember to account for what these additional foods contribute.

Here's a streamlined version of chili that's a snap. Make a double batch and stash containers in the freezer for quick microwaveable meals. To serve, just ladle the chili into bowls and, if desired, top with shredded Monterey Jack cheese. Set out a basket of crusty bread—supper is that easy.

1 pound lean ground beef or turkey	1 teaspoon dried oregano
2 teaspoons vegetable oil	½ teaspoon red pepper flakes, or to taste
1 large onion, chopped	2 cups tomato pasta sauce
1 large green bell pepper, chopped	1⅓ cups reduced-sodium beef broth
2 large cloves garlic, minced	1 can (19 ounces) kidney or pinto beans, drained and rinsed
4 teaspoons chili powder	
1 tablespoon all-purpose flour	Freshly ground black pepper
1 teaspoon dried basil	

1. In a Dutch oven or large saucepan, cook beef over medium-high heat, breaking it up with a wooden spoon, until no longer pink, about 5 minutes. Transfer beef to a strainer and drain fat.

2. Reduce the heat to medium. Add oil, onion, bell pepper, garlic, chili powder, flour, basil, oregano, and red pepper flakes. Cook, stirring, until vegetables are softened, about 4 minutes.

3. Stir in tomato sauce and broth; bring to a boil. Cook, stirring, until sauce is thickened. Add beans and season with black pepper to taste. Reduce the heat and simmer, covered, for 10 minutes. Serve warm.

NUTRIENTS PER SERVING

Calories	291
Carbohydrate	29 g
Fiber	9 g
Protein	22 g
Fat, total	10 g
Fat, saturated	3 g
Sodium	640 mg
Cholesterol	40 mg

EXCHANGES PER SERVING

2	Vegetable
1	Other Carbohydrate
2½	Lean Meat
½	Fat

Chili con Carne

Makes 10 servings

TIPS

● This recipe includes a range of fresh peppers, but feel free to select those that suit your taste or are available. Poblano and Anaheim chiles are mildly hot. Green bell peppers, which can substitute, produce a milder but equally pleasant chili.

● When handling hot peppers, wear gloves to avoid skin irritation.

● Count 1 tablespoon of light sour cream as a Free Food.

NUTRIENTS PER SERVING

Calories	275
Carbohydrate	22 g
Fiber	7 g
Protein	24 g
Fat, total	10 g
Fat, saturated	3 g
Sodium	580 mg
Cholesterol	38 mg

EXCHANGES PER SERVING

1½	Starch
2½	Lean Meat

Because it contains beans, this slow-cooker chili doesn't qualify as a "Texas" version, but it is every bit as flavorful. It is also much more nutritious because it balances the quantity of red meat with other healthful ingredients such as onions, garlic, peppers, kidney beans, cumin, and oregano. Add a nutrient-dense garnish, such as strips of roasted red pepper, and be sure to keep the sour cream in check.

● **Works in slow cookers from 3½ to 6 quarts**

2 tablespoons cumin seeds	1 cup lager or pilsner beer
⅓ cup all-purpose flour	1 tablespoon ancho chili powder, or ½ teaspoon cayenne pepper dissolved in 2 tablespoons fresh lime juice
1 teaspoon salt	
2 pounds trimmed stewing beef, cut into 1" cubes	
3 tablespoons olive oil (approximately)	2 poblano or Anaheim chiles or green bell peppers, diced (see Tips, left)
2 onions, finely chopped	
4 cloves garlic, minced	1 jalapeño pepper or 1 chipotle pepper in adobo sauce, minced (see Tips, left)
1 tablespoon dried oregano	
1 piece (2") cinnamon stick	Finely chopped cilantro, for garnish
1 teaspoon cracked black peppercorns	Chopped red onion, for garnish
1 cup lower-sodium beef broth	
2 cans (14 ounces each) red kidney beans, rinsed and drained, or 2 cups dried red kidney beans, soaked, cooked, and drained (see Basic Beans Variation, page 236)	Roasted red pepper strips, for garnish
	Light sour cream, for garnish

1. In a medium dry skillet over medium heat, toast cumin seeds, stirring, until fragrant and just beginning to brown, about 3 minutes. Immediately transfer to a mortar or spice grinder and grind. Set aside.

2. In a large zip-top plastic bag, combine flour and salt. Add beef and toss until evenly coated, discarding excess flour mixture.

This dish can be partially prepared in advance. Follow Step 1, then heat 1 tablespoon of the oil and complete Step 4. Cover and refrigerate the onion mixture overnight or for up to 2 days. When you're ready to finish the recipe, follow the beef as outlined in Steps 2 and 3. Stir well and continue with Step 5.

3. In a large skillet, heat 1 tablespoon of the oil over medium-high heat for 30 seconds. Add beef in batches and cook, stirring, adding more oil as necessary, until browned, about 4 minutes per batch. Transfer to the slow cooker stoneware.

4. Reduce the heat to medium. Add 1 tablespoon oil and onions; cook, stirring, until softened, about 4 minutes. Add garlic, oregano, cinnamon stick, peppercorns, and reserved cumin; cook, stirring, for 1 minute. Add broth and bring to a boil. Transfer to the slow cooker. Add beans and beer; stir well.

5. Cover and cook on Low for 8 to 10 hours or on High for 4 to 5 hours, or until beef is tender. Add chili powder, chiles, and jalapeño; stir well. Cover and cook on High for 20 minutes, or until peppers are tender. Discard cinnamon stick. Serve with garnishes of your choice.

MINDFUL MORSELS

You can reduce the amount of sodium in this dish by using canned beans with no salt added, cooking dried beans from scratch, or reducing the quantity of salt used to flavor the beef.

Amazing Chili

• The flavor of the chili hinges on the quality of the chili powder used. Most powders are a blend of dried, ground mild chiles, as well as cumin, oregano, garlic, and salt. Read the list of ingredients to be sure you're not buying one with starch and sugar fillers. Chili powder should not be confused with powdered or ground chiles of the cayenne pepper variety.

Every cook has a special version of chili. Maybe this one will become yours. It's meaty and nicely spiced with just the right amount of beans. Not everyone agrees that beans belong in a chili—consider the Texas version dubbed bowl of red—but the beans deliciously absorb the spices and rich tomato flavor.

1½ pounds lean ground beef	1 can (28 ounces) tomatoes, including juice, chopped
2 onions, chopped	1 cup reduced-sodium beef broth
1 large green bell pepper, chopped	1 can (19 ounces) pinto or red kidney beans, drained and rinsed
2 stalks celery, chopped	¼ cup chopped fresh parsley or cilantro
3 cloves garlic, minced	
2 tablespoons chili powder	
1½ teaspoons ground cumin	
1½ teaspoons dried oregano	
½ teaspoon red pepper flakes, or to taste	

1. In a Dutch oven or large saucepan, cook beef over medium-high heat, breaking it up with a wooden spoon, until no longer pink, about 7 minutes. Transfer beef to a strainer and drain fat. Return beef to the pan.

2. Reduce the heat to medium. Add onions, bell pepper, celery, garlic, chili powder, cumin, oregano, and red pepper flakes; cook, stirring often, until vegetables are softened, about 5 minutes.

3. Stir in tomatoes and their juice and broth; bring to a boil. Reduce the heat, cover, and simmer, stirring occasionally, for 1 hour.

4. Add beans and parsley; cover and simmer for 10 minutes longer. Serve warm.

NUTRIENTS PER SERVING

Calories	263
Carbohydrate	24 g
Fiber	6 g
Protein	22 g
Fat, total	9 g
Fat, saturated	3 g
Sodium	500 mg
Cholesterol	45 mg

EXCHANGES PER SERVING

2	Vegetable
1	Other Carbohydrate
3	Lean Meat
1	Fat

Two-Bean Turkey Chili

Makes 10 servings

This delicious chili, which has just a hint of heat, is perfect for family get-togethers. Add a tossed green salad sprinkled with shredded carrots, plus some whole grain rolls.

● **Works in slow cookers from 3½ to 6 quarts**

1 tablespoon cumin seeds	2 pounds bone-in turkey breast, skin removed, cut into ½" cubes (about 3 cups)
1 tablespoon olive oil	
2 onions, finely chopped	2 cans (14 ounces each) pinto beans, drained and rinsed
4 stalks celery, diced	
6 cloves garlic, minced	2 cups frozen sliced green beans
2 teaspoons dried oregano	
½ teaspoon cracked black peppercorns	1 tablespoon New Mexico or ancho chili powder dissolved in 2 tablespoons fresh lime juice
Zest of 1 lime	
2 tablespoons fine cornmeal	1 green bell pepper, diced
1 cup lower-sodium chicken broth	1 red bell pepper, diced
1 can (28 ounces) diced tomatoes, including juice	1 can (4½ ounces) diced mild green chiles

1. In a large dry skillet over medium heat, toast cumin seeds, stirring, until fragrant and just beginning to brown, about 3 minutes. Immediately transfer to a mortar or spice grinder and grind. Set aside.

2. In the same skillet, heat oil over medium heat for 30 seconds. Add onions and celery; cook, stirring, until celery is softened, about 5 minutes. Add garlic and cook, stirring, for 1 minute. Add oregano, peppercorns, reserved cumin, and zest; cook, stirring, for 1 minute. Add cornmeal and toss to coat. Add broth and cook, stirring, until mixture boils, about 1 minute. Add tomatoes and their juice and return to a boil. Transfer to the slow cooker stoneware.

3. Add turkey, pinto beans, and green beans; stir well. Cover and cook on Low for 8 hours or on High for 4 hours, or until turkey is tender and mixture is bubbly.

4. Add chili powder solution, green and red bell peppers, and chiles. Cover and cook on High for 30 minutes, or until bell peppers are tender.

White Chicken Chili

Makes 10 servings

Chili makes a great weekday meal. This version, featuring chicken and white beans, is lighter than traditional meat chilies. If you prefer more color, use 1 red and 1 green bell pepper. Complete the meal with a shredded carrot or sliced tomato salad, in season, and some whole grain bread.

• **Works best in a large (minimum 5-quart) slow cooker**

1 tablespoon cumin seeds	2 teaspoons dried ancho or New Mexico chili powder dissolved in 1 tablespoon fresh lime juice
1 tablespoon olive oil	
2 onions, finely chopped	
4 cloves garlic, minced	2 green bell peppers, finely chopped
2 teaspoons dried oregano	
1 piece (2") cinnamon stick	1 can (4½ ounces) diced mild green chiles, drained
1 teaspoon cracked black peppercorns	1 jalapeño pepper, finely chopped (see Tip, left)
2 cups lower-sodium chicken broth	1 cup shredded light Monterey Jack cheese
2 pounds boneless, skinless chicken thighs, quartered (about 12 thighs)	Finely chopped cilantro, for garnish
	Lime wedges (optional)
2 cups cooked dried or canned white kidney beans, drained and rinsed (see Basic Beans Variation, page 236)	

1. In a large dry skillet over medium heat, toast cumin seeds, stirring, until fragrant and just beginning to brown, about 3 minutes. Immediately transfer to a mortar or spice grinder and grind. Set aside.

2. In the same skillet, heat oil over medium heat for 30 seconds. Add onions and cook, stirring, until softened, about 3 minutes. Add garlic, reserved cumin, oregano, cinnamon stick, and peppercorns; cook, stirring, for 1 minute. Add broth and bring to a boil.

NUTRIENTS PER SERVING

Calories	233
Carbohydrate	15 g
Fiber	5 g
Protein	24 g
Fat, total	9 g
Fat, saturated	3 g
Sodium	372 mg
Cholesterol	69 mg

EXCHANGES PER SERVING

1	Starch
3	Lean Meat

This dish can be partially prepared in advance. Complete Steps 1 and 2. Cover and refrigerate the onion mixture for up to 2 days. When you're ready to finish the recipe, continue with Steps 3 and 4.

Note: *The suggested accompaniments for this recipe are not included in the nutrients or exchanges per serving. Whether you keep track of exchanges or count carbohydrates, remember to account for what these additional foods contribute.*

3. Transfer to the slow cooker stoneware. Add chicken and beans and stir well. Cover and cook on Low for 6 hours or on High for 3 hours, or until juices run clear when chicken is pierced with a fork.

4. Stir in chili powder solution. Add bell peppers, chiles, and jalapeño; stir well. Cover and cook on High for 20 to 30 minutes, or until peppers are tender. Add cheese and cook, stirring, until melted, about 1 minute. Ladle into bowls and garnish with cilantro. Pass lime wedges at the table, if using.

MINDFUL MORSELS

Look for canned dried legumes, such as kidney beans, prepared without salt. If you're using regular beans, be sure to rinse them thoroughly and drain before use. When you have the time, prepare your own (see Basic Beans, page 236).

Pork and Black Bean Chili

Makes 12 servings

TIPS

● A chipotle pepper in adobo sauce lends a slightly smoky flavor to this recipe, but it's not to everyone's taste. If you're unfamiliar with the flavor, add just half a pepper and a bit of the sauce. If you're a heat seeker, use a whole one and increase the quantity of adobo sauce.

● Count 1 tablespoon light sour cream, if using, as a Free Food.

Here's a festive, stick-to-your-ribs chili that's a perfect finish to a day in the chilly outdoors. To complete the meal, serve it with hot cornbread, a crisp green salad, and a robust red wine or ice-cold beer. Olé!

● **Works best in a large (minimum 5-quart) slow cooker**

1 tablespoon cumin seeds	2 dried ancho chile peppers
1 tablespoon olive oil	2 cups boiling water
2 pounds trimmed boneless pork shoulder, cut into 1" cubes, patted dry	1 cup coarsely chopped cilantro, stems and leaves
2 onions, finely chopped	½ cup lower-sodium chicken broth
4 cloves garlic, minced	1 chipotle pepper in adobo sauce (see Tips, left)
1 tablespoon dried oregano	Light sour cream (optional)
1 teaspoon salt	Finely chopped red or green onion (optional)
½ teaspoon cracked black peppercorns	
1½ cups flat beer	
2 tablespoons tomato paste	
4 cups cooked dried black beans or canned black beans, drained and rinsed (see Basic Beans Variation, page 236)	

1. In a large dry skillet over medium heat, toast cumin seeds, stirring, until fragrant and just beginning to brown, about 3 minutes. Immediately transfer to a mortar or spice grinder and grind. Set aside.

2. In the same skillet, heat half the oil over medium-high heat for 30 seconds. Add pork in batches and cook, stirring, adding remaining oil as necessary, until browned, about 4 minutes per batch. Using a slotted spoon, transfer to the slow cooker stoneware.

NUTRIENTS PER SERVING

Calories	225
Carbohydrate	19 g
Fiber	5 g
Protein	21 g
Fat, total	8 g
Fat, saturated	2 g
Sodium	483 mg
Cholesterol	53 mg

EXCHANGES PER SERVING

1	Starch
2½	Lean Meat

This dish can be partially prepared in advance. Complete Steps 1, 3, and 5, heating 1 tablespoon oil in the pan before softening the onions. Cover and refrigerate the onion and chile mixtures separately for up to 2 days, being aware that the chile mixture will lose some of its vibrancy if held for this long. (For best results, rehydrate the chiles while the chili is cooking, or no sooner than the night before you plan to cook.) When you're ready to finish the recipe, brown the pork (Step 2), or, if you're pressed for time, omit this step and continue with Steps 4 and 6.

Note: *The suggested accompaniments for this recipe are not included in the nutrients or exchanges per serving. Whether you keep track of exchanges or count carbohydrates, remember to account for what these additional foods contribute.*

3. Reduce the heat under the pan to medium. Add onions and cook, stirring, until softened, about 3 minutes. Add garlic, reserved cumin, oregano, salt, and peppercorns; cook, stirring, for 1 minute. Stir in beer and tomato paste.

4. Pour mixture over meat in the slow cooker. Add beans and stir to combine. Cover and cook on Low for 8 hours or on High for 4 hours, or until pork is tender.

5. Half an hour before the recipe has finished cooking, in a heatproof bowl, soak chiles in boiling water for 30 minutes, weighing them down with a cup to ensure they remain submerged. Drain, discarding soaking liquid and stems, and chop coarsely. Transfer to a blender. Add cilantro, broth, and chipotle pepper; purée until smooth.

6. Add chile mixture to pork and stir well. Cover and cook on High for 30 minutes, or until flavors meld. Ladle into bowls, dollop each with 1 tablespoon sour cream, and sprinkle with chopped onion, if using.

MINDFUL MORSELS

Oregano, like many herbs, contains flavonoids, which act as antioxidants. Consumption of these antioxidants has been linked with reduced rates of heart disease and stroke. Although many culinary herbs act as antioxidants, USDA researchers have found oregano to have the most powerful antioxidant activity of the herbs they have studied.

Barley and Sweet Potato Chili

Makes 6 servings

This unusual chili has great flavor, and with the addition of optional toppings, such as sliced roasted pepper strips (either jarred or freshly roasted) and cilantro, it can be enhanced and varied to suit many tastes. Serve it with a simple green salad topped with sliced avocado.

NUTRIENTS PER SERVING

Calories	217
Carbohydrate	43 g
Fiber	7 g
Protein	7 g
Fat, total	3 g
Fat, saturated	1 g
Sodium	636 mg
Cholesterol	0 mg

EXCHANGES PER SERVING

2	Starch
2	Vegetable

• **Large (minimum 5-quart) slow cooker**

1 tablespoon cumin seeds	1 cup lower-sodium vegetable broth
1 tablespoon olive oil	
2 onions, finely chopped	1 tablespoon chili powder dissolved in 2 tablespoons fresh lime juice (see Tips, left)
2 cloves garlic, minced	
1 teaspoon dried oregano	
½ teaspoon salt	1 green bell pepper, diced (optional)
½ teaspoon cracked black peppercorns	
½ cup whole (hulled) or pot barley	1 jalapeño pepper, minced, or ½ to 1 chipotle pepper in adobo sauce, minced (see Tips, left)
1 can (28 ounces) tomatoes, including juice, coarsely crushed	Sliced roasted bell peppers (optional), for garnish
2 medium sweet potatoes, peeled and cut into 1" cubes	Finely chopped cilantro, for garnish
1 can (14 ounces) red kidney or black beans, drained and rinsed, or ½ cup dried red kidney or black beans, soaked, cooked, and drained (see Basic Beans Variation, page 236)	

1. In a large dry skillet over medium heat, toast cumin seeds, stirring, until fragrant and just beginning to brown, about 3 minutes. Immediately transfer to a mortar or spice grinder and grind. Set aside.

This dish can be partially prepared in advance. Complete Steps 1 and 2. Cover and refrigerate the tomato mixture overnight or for up to 2 days. When you're ready to finish the recipe, continue with Step 3.

Note: *The suggested accompaniments for this recipe are not included in the nutrients or exchanges per serving. Whether you keep track of exchanges or count carbohydrates, remember to account for what these additional foods contribute.*

2. In the same skillet, heat oil over medium heat for 30 seconds. Add onions and cook, stirring, until softened, about 3 minutes. Add garlic, reserved cumin, oregano, salt, and peppercorns; cook, stirring, for 1 minute. Add barley and stir well. Add tomatoes and their juice; bring to a boil. Transfer to the slow cooker stoneware. Add sweet potatoes, beans, and broth.

3. Cover and cook on Low for 6 to 8 hours or on High for 3 to 4 hours, or until barley and sweet potatoes are tender. Stir in chili powder solution, bell pepper (if using), and jalapeño. Cover and cook on High for 20 to 30 minutes, or until flavors meld and green pepper is tender. To serve, ladle into bowls and garnish with sliced roasted peppers, if using, and cilantro.

MINDFUL MORSELS

The nutrient analysis on this recipe was done using pearl barley. For added fiber and nutrients, look for whole (also known as hulled) barley.

Tamale Pie with Chili Millet Crust

Makes 10 servings

TIPS

● If you don't care for much heat, use the jalapeño pepper. Heat seekers may prefer a whole chipotle in adobo sauce.

● When handling hot peppers, wear rubber gloves to avoid skin irritation.

This tasty pie is a great dish for après ski or to come home to after a brisk day outdoors. Add a tossed green salad, and pass the salsa at the table.

● **Large (minimum 6-quart) slow cooker**

TAMALE PIE

- 1 tablespoon cumin seeds
- 1 tablespoon olive oil
- 2 onions, finely chopped
- 4 stalks celery, thinly sliced
- 4 cloves garlic, minced
- 2 teaspoons dried oregano
- 1 teaspoon salt
- ½ teaspoon cracked black peppercorns
- 2 cans (14 ounces each) black or pinto beans, drained and rinsed
- 1 can (28 ounces) diced tomatoes, drained
- 2 cups frozen corn kernels
- 1 green bell pepper, diced
- 1 jalapeño pepper or 1 chipotle pepper in adobo sauce, diced (see Tips, left)

  Salsa (optional)

TOPPING

- 1 cup millet
- 3 cups water

  Freshly ground black pepper
- 1 cup shredded light Monterey Jack cheese
- 1 can (4½ ounces) chopped mild green chiles, including juice

1. **Make the pie:** In a large dry skillet over medium heat, toast cumin seeds, stirring, until fragrant and just beginning to brown, about 3 minutes. Immediately transfer to a mortar or spice grinder and grind. Set aside.

2. In the same skillet, heat oil over medium heat for 30 seconds. Add onions and celery; cook, stirring, until celery is softened, about 5 minutes. Add garlic, reserved cumin, oregano, salt, and peppercorns; cook, stirring, for 1 minute. Add beans and tomatoes; bring to a boil. Transfer to the slow cooker stoneware.

NUTRIENTS PER SERVING

Calories	235
Carbohydrate	39 g
Fiber	8 g
Protein	12 g
Fat, total	5 g
Fat, saturated	1 g
Sodium	665 mg
Cholesterol	6 mg

EXCHANGES PER SERVING

2	Starch
2	Vegetable
1	Very Lean Meat
1	Fat

This dish can be partially prepared in advance. Complete Steps 1 and 2. Cover and refrigerate overnight or for up to 2 days. When you're ready to cook, continue with Steps 3 through 5.

Note: *The suggested accompaniments for this recipe are not included in the nutrients or exchanges per serving. Whether you keep track of exchanges or count carbohydrates, remember to account for what these additional foods contribute.*

3. Add corn and stir well. Cover and cook on Low for 3 hours or on High for 1½ hours.

4. **Make the topping:** About half an hour before filling is done, in a large saucepan, toast millet over medium heat, stirring constantly, until it crackles and releases its aroma, about 5 minutes. Add water and pepper to taste; bring to a boil. Reduce the heat to low, cover, and cook until millet is tender and all of the water is absorbed, about 20 minutes. Stir in cheese and chiles and their juice; set aside.

5. Add bell pepper and jalapeño pepper to the slow cooker; stir well. Spread millet topping evenly over pie. Place 2 clean tea towels, each folded in half (so you will have 4 layers), over the top of the stoneware to absorb moisture. Cover and cook on High for 1½ to 2 hours, or until topping is set.

MINDFUL MORSELS

A serving of this recipe provides folate, a B vitamin essential for the proper development of all the cells in the body. Good sources of naturally occurring folate are dried peas and beans, orange juice, and vegetables such as broccoli, asparagus, green beans, and tomatoes.

Brown Rice Chili

Makes 10 servings

• Large cans of tomatoes come in 28-ounce and 35-ounce sizes. For convenience, this recipe calls for the 28-ounce size. If you happen to have the 35-ounce size, drain off 1 cup of the juice before adding to the recipe.

• When handling hot peppers, wear rubber gloves to avoid skin irritation.

This tasty chili is an ideal dish for vegetarians because the combination of rice and beans produces a complete protein. The flavor is outstanding when it's made using reconstituted dried chiles. Just be aware that New Mexico chiles can range widely in heat. If you are using these chiles in this recipe, check to make certain that they are not described as "hot."

• **Works best in a large (minimum 5-quart) slow cooker**

1 tablespoon olive oil	2 cups lower-sodium vegetable broth
2 onions, chopped	2 dried ancho, mild New Mexico, or guajillo chile peppers (see Tips, left)
4 stalks celery, chopped	
1 cup brown rice, rinsed	
4 cloves garlic, minced	2 cups boiling water
1 tablespoon dried oregano	½ cup chopped cilantro stems and leaves
1 teaspoon ground cumin	
½ teaspoon salt	2 cups corn kernels, thawed if frozen
½ teaspoon cracked black peppercorns	
	1 green bell pepper, diced
1 can (28 ounces) diced tomatoes, including juice (see Tips, left)	1 jalapeño pepper, seeded and diced, optional (see Tips, left)
2 cups cooked dried or canned red kidney beans, drained and rinsed	

1. In a large skillet, heat oil over medium heat for 30 seconds. Add onions and celery; cook, stirring, until celery is softened, about 5 minutes. Add rice, garlic, oregano, cumin, salt, and peppercorns; cook, stirring, for 1 minute. Add tomatoes and their juice and bring to a boil. Transfer to the slow cooker stoneware. Add beans and 1½ cups of the broth; stir well.

NUTRIENTS PER SERVING

Calories	206
Carbohydrate	40 g
Fiber	8 g
Protein	8 g
Fat, total	3 g
Fat, saturated	0 g
Sodium	479 mg
Cholesterol	0 mg

EXCHANGES PER SERVING

2½	Starch

This dish can be partially prepared in advance. Complete Steps 1 and 3. Cover and refrigerate the onion and chile mixtures separately overnight. (For best results, rehydrate the chiles while the chili is cooking.) When you're ready to finish the recipe, continue with Steps 2 and 4.

2. Place 2 clean tea towels, each folded in half (so you will have 4 layers), over the top of the stoneware. Cover and cook on Low for 8 hours or on High for 4 hours, or until hot and bubbly.

3. Half an hour before recipe is finished cooking, in a heatproof bowl, soak chile peppers in boiling water for 30 minutes, weighing them down with a cup to ensure they remain submerged. Drain, discarding soaking water and stems, and chop coarsely. Transfer to a blender. Add remaining ½ cup broth and cilantro. Purée until smooth.

4. Add chile mixture, corn, bell pepper, and jalapeño, if using, to the slow cooker; stir well. Cover and cook on High for 30 minutes, or until bell pepper is tender and flavors meld.

MINDFUL MORSELS

Low in calories, tomatoes are extremely nutritious. They contain vitamins A and C, potassium, and folate and are loaded with phytonutrients such as lycopene, a powerful antioxidant that may have cancer-fighting properties.

Vegetable Chili

Makes 8 servings

TIPS

● If you don't have leeks, substitute 2 yellow onions, finely chopped.

● If you prefer a more peppery chili, use up to 1 teaspoon of cracked black peppercorns in this recipe.

● You can substitute your favorite chili powder blend for the ancho or New Mexico chili powder.

● When handling hot peppers, wear rubber gloves to avoid skin irritation.

● Count 1 tablespoon light sour cream, if using, as a Free Food.

Here's a chili that is loaded with flavor and nutrients. Garnish with any combination of roasted red peppers, diced avocado, finely chopped red onions, and cilantro. Add a simple green salad and some whole grain bread for a great weekday meal.

● **Large (minimum 5-quart) slow cooker**

1 tablespoon cumin seeds

4 cups thinly sliced zucchini (about 1 pound)

½ teaspoon salt

2 tablespoons olive oil, divided

4 cloves garlic, minced

4 carrots, diced

4 stalks celery, diced

2 large leeks, white and green parts only, cleaned and thinly sliced (see Tips, left and page 42)

2 teaspoons dried oregano

½ teaspoon cracked black peppercorns (see Tips, left)

1 can (28 ounces) diced tomatoes, including juice

1 can (14 ounces) kidney or pinto beans, drained and rinsed

1 cup bulgur

1 cup boiling water

1 tablespoon ancho or New Mexico chili powder dissolved in 2 tablespoons fresh lemon juice (see Tips, left)

2 green bell peppers, diced

1 jalapeño pepper or chipotle pepper in adobo sauce, diced (see Tips, left)

Light sour cream (optional)

NUTRIENTS PER SERVING

Calories	204
Carbohydrate	38 g
Fiber	9 g
Protein	7 g
Fat, total	5 g
Fat, saturated	1 g
Sodium	480 mg
Cholesterol	0 mg

EXCHANGES PER SERVING

2	Starch
2	Vegetable
½	Fat

1. In a large dry skillet over medium heat, toast cumin seeds, stirring, until fragrant and just beginning to brown, about 3 minutes. Immediately transfer to a mortar or spice grinder and grind. Set aside.

2. In a colander set in a sink, combine zucchini and salt. Set aside to sweat for 20 minutes. Rinse thoroughly under cold running water and pat dry with paper towels. Set aside.

3. In the same skillet, heat 1 tablespoon of the oil over medium heat for 30 seconds. Add zucchini and cook, stirring, for 3 minutes. Add garlic and cook, stirring, until zucchini softens and just begins to brown, about 4 minutes. Transfer to a medium bowl, cover, and refrigerate.

This dish can be partially prepared in advance. Complete Steps 1 through 4. Cover and refrigerate zucchini mixture and tomato mixture separately overnight or for up to 2 days. When you're ready to finish the recipe, continue with Steps 5 and 6.

Note: *The suggested accompaniments for this recipe are not included in the nutrients or exchanges per serving. Whether you keep track of exchanges or count carbohydrates, remember to account for what these additional foods contribute.*

4. In the same large skillet, heat remaining 1 tablespoon oil over medium heat. Add carrots, celery, and leeks; cook, stirring, until carrots are softened, about 7 minutes. Add reserved cumin, oregano, and peppercorns; cook, stirring, for 1 minute. Add tomatoes and their juice and bring to a boil. Transfer to the slow cooker stoneware.

5. Stir in beans. Cover and cook on Low for 6 hours or on High for 3 hours, or until vegetables are tender.

6. In a large bowl, combine bulgur and boiling water. Set aside until water is absorbed, about 30 minutes. Meanwhile, add chili pepper solution to the slow cooker and stir well. Add bell peppers, jalapeño, and reserved zucchini to the slow cooker; stir well. Cover and cook on High for 20 to 30 minutes, or until peppers are tender. Stir in reserved bulgur. Ladle chili into bowls and dollop each with 1 tablespoon sour cream, if using.

MINDFUL MORSELS

One serving of this delicious chili provides more than 100 percent of the recommended daily intake (RDI) of vitamin A. Although vitamin A is famous for keeping your eyes healthy, it has other important functions, such as contributing to your night-vision capabilities, supporting bone growth, and keeping cells functioning well.

Squash and Black Bean Chili

Makes 6 servings

TIP

• Be sure to add the optional chipotle pepper if you like heat and a bit of smoke.

MAKE AHEAD

This dish can be partially prepared in advance. Complete Steps 1 and 2. Cover and refrigerate the tomato mixture overnight or for up to 2 days. When you're ready to finish the recipe, continue with Step 3.

Note: *The suggested accompaniments for this recipe are not included in the nutrients or exchanges per serving. Whether you keep track of exchanges or count carbohydrates, remember to account for what these additional foods contribute.*

Flavored with cumin and chili powder and a hint of cinnamon, this luscious chili makes a fabulous weeknight meal. Add a tossed green salad and a whole grain roll, relax, and enjoy.

• **Works in slow cookers from 3½ to 6 quarts**

1 tablespoon cumin seeds	4 cups cubed (1") peeled butternut squash
1 tablespoon olive oil	2 green bell peppers, diced
2 onions, finely chopped	1 can (4½ ounces) chopped mild green chiles
4 cloves garlic, minced	1 finely chopped chipotle pepper in adobo sauce (optional)
2 teaspoons chili powder	Finely chopped cilantro, for garnish
1 teaspoon dried oregano	
1 piece (3") cinnamon stick	
1 can (28 ounces) diced tomatoes, including juice	
1 can (14 ounces) black beans, drained and rinsed, or ½ cup dried black beans, soaked, cooked, and drained (see Basic Beans Variation, page 236)	

1. In a large dry skillet over medium heat, toast cumin seeds, stirring, until fragrant and just beginning to brown, about 3 minutes. Immediately transfer to a mortar or spice grinder and grind. Set aside.

2. In the same skillet, heat oil over medium heat for 30 seconds. Add onions and cook, stirring, until softened, about 3 minutes. Add garlic, chili powder, reserved cumin, oregano, and cinnamon stick; cook, stirring, for 1 minute. Add tomatoes and their juice; bring to a boil. Transfer to the slow cooker stoneware. Add beans and squash; stir well.

3. Cover and cook on Low for 8 hours or on High for 4 hours, or until squash is tender. Add bell peppers, chiles, and chipotle pepper, if using. Cover and cook on High for 20 minutes, or until bell pepper is tender. Discard cinnamon stick. When ready to serve, ladle into bowls and garnish with cilantro.

NUTRIENTS PER SERVING

Calories	171
Carbohydrate	34 g
Fiber	8 g
Protein	7 g
Fat, total	3 g
Fat, saturated	0 g
Sodium	589 mg
Cholesterol	0 mg

EXCHANGES PER SERVING

1½	Starch
2	Vegetable

Butternut Chili

Makes 8 servings

TIPS

● If you prefer, you can soak and purée the chiles while preparing the chili and refrigerate until you're ready to add to the recipe.

● To toast cumin seeds: Place the seeds in a dry skillet over medium heat and cook, stirring, until fragrant and the seeds are just beginning to brown, about 3 minutes. Transfer to a mortar or spice grinder and grind.

MAKE AHEAD

This dish can be partially prepared in advance. Complete Steps 1 and 3. Cover and refrigerate tomato and chile mixtures separately overnight. The next morning, continue with Step 2 and 4.

NUTRIENTS PER SERVING

Calories	270
Carbohydrate	28 g
Fiber	8 g
Protein	18 g
Fat, total	11 g
Fat, saturated	4 g
Sodium	654 mg
Cholesterol	34 mg

EXCHANGES PER SERVING

2	Starch
3	Lean Meat
1	Fat

The combination of beef, butternut squash, ancho chiles, and cilantro in this chili is a real winner. Don't be afraid to make extra, because it's great reheated.

● **Large (minimum 5-quart) slow cooker**

1 tablespoon olive oil	1 can (28 ounces) diced tomatoes, including juice
1 pound lean ground beef	
2 onions, finely chopped	3 cups cubed (1") peeled butternut squash
4 cloves garlic, minced	
1 tablespoon cumin seeds, toasted and ground (see Tips, left)	2 cups cooked dried or canned kidney beans, drained and rinsed
2 teaspoons dried oregano	2 dried New Mexico, ancho, or guajillo chiles
1 teaspoon salt	2 cups boiling water
½ teaspoon cracked black peppercorns	½ cup coarsely chopped cilantro
1 piece (2") cinnamon stick	

1. In a large skillet, heat oil over medium-high heat for 30 seconds. Add beef and onions; cook, stirring, until beef is no longer pink, about 5 minutes. Add garlic, toasted cumin, oregano, salt, peppercorns, and cinnamon stick; cook, stirring, for 1 minute. Add tomatoes and their juice and bring to a boil.

2. Place squash and beans in the slow cooker stoneware and cover with beef mixture sauce. Cover and cook on Low for 6 to 8 hours or on High for 3 to 4 hours, or until squash is tender.

3. Half an hour before recipe is finished cooking, in a heatproof bowl, soak dried chiles in boiling water for 30 minutes, weighing them down with a cup to ensure they are submerged. Drain, reserving ½ cup of the soaking liquid. Discard stems and chop coarsely. Transfer to a blender and add cilantro and reserved soaking liquid. Purée until smooth.

4. Add chile mixture to the slow cooker and stir well. Cover and cook on High for 30 minutes, or until hot and bubbly and flavors meld.

Light Chili

Makes 6 servings

TIPS

● Large cans of tomatoes come in 28-ounce and 35-ounce sizes. For convenience, this recipe calls for the 28-ounce size. If you happen to have the 35-ounce size, drain off 1 cup of the juice before adding to the recipe.

● When handling hot peppers, wear rubber gloves to avoid skin irritation.

● Count 1 tablespoon light sour cream, if using, as a Free Food.

Note: *The suggested accompaniments for this recipe are not included in the nutrients or exchanges per serving. Whether you keep track of exchanges or count carbohydrates, remember to account for what these additional foods contribute.*

Though this is a "light" chili, it has a rich, creamy sauce and robust flavor from the spices. Serve it with a dab of light sour cream, if you like, your favorite salsa, and a sprinkling of chopped cilantro.

● **Works in slow cookers from 3½ to 6 quarts**

1 tablespoon cumin seeds	8 ounces portobello mushrooms, stems removed, caps cut into 1" cubes
1 tablespoon olive oil	
2 onions, finely chopped	1½ cups shredded light Monterey Jack cheese
6 cloves garlic, minced	
1 tablespoon dried oregano	2 green bell peppers, diced
½ teaspoon salt	1 to 2 jalapeño peppers, finely chopped (see Tips, left)
1 teaspoon cracked black peppercorns	
1 can (28 ounces) diced tomatoes, including juice (see Tips, left)	1 can (4½ ounces) diced mild green chiles, drained
	Light sour cream (optional)
2 cups lower-sodium vegetable broth	Salsa
	Finely chopped cilantro
1 can (19 ounces) white kidney beans, drained and rinsed	

1. In a large dry skillet over medium heat, toast cumin seeds, stirring, until fragrant and just beginning to brown, about 3 minutes. Immediately transfer to a mortar or spice grinder and grind. Set aside.

2. In the same skillet, heat oil over medium heat for 30 seconds. Add onions and cook, stirring, until softened, about 3 minutes. Add garlic, reserved cumin, oregano, salt, and peppercorns; cook, stirring, for 1 minute. Add tomatoes and their juice and broth; bring to a boil. Cook, stirring, until liquid is reduced by one-third, about 5 minutes. Transfer to the slow cooker stoneware.

3. Add beans and mushrooms and stir to combine. Cover and cook on Low for 6 to 8 hours or on High for 3 to 4 hours, or until mixture is hot and bubbly. Stir in cheese, bell peppers, jalapeños, and green chiles. Cover and cook on High for 20 to 30 minutes, or until peppers are tender and cheese is melted. Ladle into bowls and dollop each with 1 tablespoon sour cream (if using), salsa, and chopped cilantro.

NUTRIENTS PER SERVING

Calories	274
Carbohydrate	33 g
Fiber	10 g
Protein	17 g
Fat, total	10 g
Fat, saturated	4 g
Sodium	586 mg
Cholesterol	18 mg

EXCHANGES PER SERVING

2	Starch
2	Lean Meat

VEGETABLE
SIDES

Asparagus with Parmesan and Toasted Almonds

Makes 6 servings

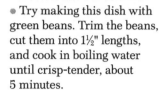
TIP

• Try making this dish with green beans. Trim the beans, cut them into 1½" lengths, and cook in boiling water until crisp-tender, about 5 minutes.

When locally grown asparagus appears at the market, it's a rite of spring. Here the cut spears are tossed with crunchy almonds and melting Parmesan—and it's every bit as pleasing as a buttery Hollandaise.

1½ pounds asparagus	2 cloves garlic, minced
½ cup water	¼ cup freshly grated Parmesan cheese
¼ cup sliced blanched almonds	
1 tablespoon butter	Freshly ground black pepper

1. Snap off asparagus ends; cut spears on the diagonal into 2" lengths. In a large nonstick skillet, bring water to a boil. Cook asparagus for 2 minutes (start timing when water returns to a boil), or until just crisp-tender. Run under cold water to chill; drain and set aside.

2. Dry the skillet and place over medium heat. Add almonds and toast, stirring often, until golden, 2 to 3 minutes. Transfer to a plate and reserve.

3. Increase the heat under the skillet to medium-high. Add butter, reserved asparagus, and garlic; cook, stirring, until asparagus is just tender, about 4 minutes.

4. Sprinkle with cheese and season with pepper to taste. Transfer to a serving bowl and top with reserved almonds.

NUTRIENTS PER SERVING

Calories	75
Carbohydrate	4 g
Fiber	1 g
Protein	4 g
Fat, total	5 g
Fat, saturated	2 g
Sodium	105 mg
Cholesterol	8 mg

EXCHANGES PER SERVING

½	Vegetable
½	High-fat Meat

Steamed Broccoli with Cheddar Cheese Sauce

Makes 6 servings (with 1¼ cups sauce)

TIP

• To prepare broccoli stems, cut off the woody ends and peel the stems. Cut into 2" × ½" pieces.

This simple vegetable side dish is always a highlight at family gatherings, including Christmas and Thanksgiving. You can also serve the cheese sauce with other vegetables, such as cauliflower or Brussels sprouts.

8 cups broccoli stems and florets (1 large bunch)	1 cup shredded light Cheddar cheese
1 tablespoon cornstarch	Ground nutmeg
1 cup low-fat milk	Cayenne pepper

1. Place a steamer basket in a large pot with 2" of water. Bring to a boil over high heat. Place the broccoli in the basket and steam until just crsip-tender, about 5 minutes. Drain well and place in an 8-cup casserole dish.

2. Meanwhile, in a small saucepan, combine cornstarch and milk; whisk until smooth. Cook over medium heat, whisking constantly, until mixture comes to a boil and thickens, 5 to 7 minutes. Remove the pan from the heat and whisk in cheese until melted. Season with nutmeg and cayenne to taste. Pour cheese sauce over broccoli and serve immediately.

NUTRIENTS PER SERVING

Calories	112
Carbohydrate	9 g
Fiber	3 g
Protein	9 g
Fat, total	5 g
Fat, saturated	3 g
Sodium	210 mg
Cholesterol	15 mg

EXCHANGES PER SERVING

1½	Vegetable
1	Medium-fat Meat

Cauliflower with Hazelnut Crumb Topping

Makes 6 servings

● You can sprinkle the garlic-crumb mixture over other vegetables, such as broccoli, Brussels sprouts, or spinach. Unblanched almonds, pecans, or walnuts can replace the hazelnuts.

Note: *The suggested accompaniments for this recipe are not included in the nutrients or exchanges per serving. Whether you keep track of exchanges or count carbohydrates, remember to account for what these additional foods contribute.*

Snowy cauliflower topped with cheese and nuts makes the perfect side dish for a Sunday roast. For vegetarians, it becomes a main course dish when served along with brown rice or another grain or a bowl of pasta.

1 tablespoon butter	2 tablespoons chopped fresh parsley
¼ cup hazelnuts, finely chopped	1 medium cauliflower, broken into florets
½ cup soft bread crumbs (see Tips, page 253)	
1 large clove garlic, minced	
½ cup finely shredded light Swiss or light Cheddar cheese	

1. Preheat the broiler. Coat a 12" × 8" shallow baking dish with cooking spray. Bring a large saucepan of water to a boil.

2. In a medium nonstick skillet, melt butter over medium heat. Add hazelnuts and cook, stirring, until lightly toasted, about 1 minute. Add bread crumbs and garlic; cook, stirring, until crumbs are lightly browned, about 1 minute. Remove from the heat and let cool.

3. In a medium bowl, combine crumb mixture, cheese, and parsley; set aside.

4. Cook cauliflower in boiling water until crisp-tender, 3 to 5 minutes. Drain well. Place cauliflower in the prepared baking dish and sprinkle with crumb mixture. Broil for 1 to 2 minutes, or until topping is lightly browned.

NUTRIENTS PER SERVING

Calories	133
Carbohydrate	7 g
Fiber	2 g
Protein	8 g
Fat, total	9 g
Fat, saturated	4 g
Sodium	155 mg
Cholesterol	18 mg

EXCHANGES PER SERVING

1	Vegetable
1	High-fat Meat

Lemon-Glazed Baby Carrots

Makes 4 servings

TIPS

• If doubling the recipe, glaze the vegetables in a large nonstick skillet so the broth evaporates more quickly.

• Try adding rutabaga and parsnips, cut to match the size of the baby carrots, to this tasty dish.

This is a great choice for accompanying a holiday roast or turkey. Packages of ready-to-cook, peeled, whole baby carrots are widely available in supermarkets. They certainly make a cook's life easier—especially when you're preparing a mammoth family dinner and plan to serve several dishes.

1 pound baby carrots	½ teaspoon grated lemon zest
¼ cup reduced-sodium chicken broth or vegetable broth	¼ teaspoon salt
1 tablespoon fresh lemon juice	Freshly ground black pepper
1 tablespoon packed brown sugar	1 tablespoon finely chopped fresh parsley or chives
2 teaspoons butter	

1. Bring a medium saucepan of water to a boil.

2. Cook carrots in boiling water for 5 to 7 minutes (start timing when water returns to a boil), or until just crisp-tender; drain and return to the saucepan.

3. Add broth, lemon juice, brown sugar, butter, zest, salt, and pepper to taste. Cook over medium heat, stirring often, until liquid has evaporated and carrots are nicely glazed, 3 to 5 minutes.

4. Transfer carrots to a serving bowl and sprinkle with parsley.

NUTRIENTS PER SERVING

Calories	75
Carbohydrate	13 g
Fiber	2 g
Protein	1 g
Fat, total	3 g
Fat, saturated	1 g
Sodium	265 mg
Cholesterol	5 mg

EXCHANGES PER SERVING

1	Vegetable
½	Other Carbohydrate
½	Fat

Parsnip and Carrot Purée with Cumin

Makes 8 servings

TIP

• If you prefer not to use sugar, you may substitute your favorite granular sugar substitute.

MAKE AHEAD

Peel and cut the parsnips and carrots in advance. Cover and refrigerate overnight.

The cumin adds a slightly exotic note to this traditional dish, which makes a great accompaniment to chicken, beef, or fish.

• **Works in slow cookers from 3½ to 6 quarts**

1 teaspoon cumin seeds	1 tablespoon butter or butter substitute
4 cups cubed peeled parsnips (½" cubes)	1 teaspoon sugar
2 cups thinly sliced carrots	½ teaspoon salt
¼ cup water or lower-sodium vegetable broth	¼ teaspoon freshly ground black pepper

1. In a dry medium skillet over medium heat, toast cumin seeds, stirring, until fragrant and just beginning to brown, about 3 minutes. Immediately transfer to a mortar or spice grinder and grind. Set aside.

2. In the slow cooker stoneware, combine parsnips, carrots, water, butter, reserved cumin, sugar, salt, and pepper. Cover and cook on Low for 8 to 10 hours or on High for 4 to 5 hours, or until vegetables are tender.

3. Transfer mixture to a large bowl and mash with a potato masher until smooth or purée in a food processor. Serve immediately.

NUTRIENTS PER SERVING

Calories	85
Carbohydrate	17 g
Fiber	3 g
Protein	1 g
Fat, total	2 g
Fat, saturated	1 g
Sodium	188 mg
Cholesterol	4 mg

EXCHANGES PER SERVING

2	Vegetable
½	Other Carbohydrate

Saffron-Scented Fennel Gratin

Makes 8 servings

This dish can be partially prepared in advance. Complete Step 1. Cover and refrigerate the fennel mixture overnight. The next morning, continue with steps 2 and 3.

This flavorful gratin is a great accompaniment to roast chicken or beef.

● **Works in slow cookers from 3½ to 6 quarts**

2 tablespoons olive oil	Freshly ground black pepper (optional)
3 fennel bulbs, trimmed, cored, and thinly sliced vertically	½ teaspoon saffron threads
2 cups lower-sodium vegetable broth	½ cup coarsely grated Parmesan cheese

1. In a large skillet, heat the oil over medium-high heat for 30 seconds. Add fennel in batches, adding more oil as necessary, and cook, stirring, just until the fennel begins to brown, about 5 minutes per batch. Transfer to the slow cooker stoneware and add broth. Season to taste with pepper, if using.

2. Place a clean tea towel, folded in half (so you will have 2 layers), over the top of the stoneware to absorb moisture. Cover and cook on Low for 6 hours or on High for 3 hours, or until fennel is tender.

3. Preheat the broiler. Using a slotted spoon, transfer fennel to a heatproof serving dish and cover. Pour liquid from the slow cooker into a medium saucepan and add saffron. Bring to a boil over medium heat and cook until reduced by half, about 6 minutes. Pour reduced liquid over fennel. Sprinkle with cheese and place under the broiler until cheese is melted and lightly browned.

NUTRIENTS PER SERVING

Calories	93
Carbohydrate	8 g
Fiber	3 g
Protein	4 g
Fat, total	6 g
Fat, saturated	2 g
Sodium	277 mg
Cholesterol	5 mg

EXCHANGES PER SERVING

1½	Vegetable
1	Fat

Ratatouille

Makes 8 servings

Ratatouille makes a great accompaniment to roast meat; if you're a vegetarian, enjoy it over baked tofu.

• **Large (minimum 5-quart) slow cooker**

2 medium eggplants (about 12 ounces each), peeled and cut into 1" cubes	½ teaspoon salt
2 tablespoons kosher or coarse sea salt	½ teaspoon cracked black peppercorns
3 tablespoons olive oil	8 ounces mushrooms, sliced
4 zucchini (about 1½ pounds), peeled and thinly sliced	1 can (28 ounces) diced tomatoes, including juices
2 cloves garlic, minced	2 green bell peppers, cut into ½" cubes
2 onions, thinly sliced	½ cup chopped parsley or basil
1 teaspoon herbes de Provence (see Tips, page 84)	

1. Preheat the oven to 400°F.

2. In a colander placed in the sink, combine eggplant and salt. Toss to ensure eggplant is well coated and let stand for 30 minutes to 1 hour. Rinse thoroughly under cold running water. Lay a clean tea towel on a work surface. Working in batches over the sink and using your hands, squeeze liquid out of eggplant. Transfer to the tea towel. When batches are complete, roll the towel up and press down to remove any remaining liquid.

3. Transfer eggplant to an ungreased rimmed baking sheet and toss with 1 tablespoon of the oil. Spread the eggplant evenly on the baking sheet. Cover with foil and bake for 15 minutes, or until soft and fragrant. Remove from the oven and transfer to the slow cooker stoneware.

NUTRIENTS PER SERVING

Calories	121
Carbohydrate	18 g
Fiber	5 g
Protein	3 g
Fat, total	6 g
Fat, saturated	1 g
Sodium	300 mg
Cholesterol	0 mg

EXCHANGES PER SERVING

1	Carbohydrate
1	Fat

This dish can be partially prepared in advance. Complete Steps 1 through 4. Cover and refrigerate the eggplant and zucchini mixtures separately overnight. The next day, continue with Steps 5 and 6.

4. While eggplant is cooking, heat 1 tablespoon of the oil over medium-high heat. Add zucchini and cook, stirring, for 6 minutes. Add garlic and cook, stirring, until zucchini is soft and browned, about 1 minute. Transfer to a medium bowl, cover, and refrigerate.

5. Reduce the heat under the pan to medium. Add remaining 1 tablespoon oil. Add onions and cook, stirring, until softened, about 3 minutes. Add herbes de Provence, salt, and peppercorns; cook, stirring, about 1 minute. Add mushrooms and toss until coated. Stir in tomatoes and bring to a boil. Transfer to the slow cooker.

6. Cover and cook on Low for 6 to 8 hours or on High for 3 to 4 hours, or until vegetables are tender. Add bell peppers, reserved zucchini mixture, and parsley; stir well. Cover and cook on High for 25 minutes, or until peppers are tender and zucchini is heated through.

MINDFUL MORSELS

Zucchini is a member of the summer squash family. While not a nutrient-dense vegetable, it does contain small amounts of a variety of nutrients, such as manganese, vitamin C, magnesium, and potassium.

Peas and Greens

Makes 4 servings

TIP

• Use any kind of paprika you prefer in this recipe. Hot paprika will add the zest heat seekers prefer. Smoked paprika will enhance the flavor with a pleasant smokiness.

MAKE AHEAD

This dish can be partially prepared in advance. Complete Steps 1 and 2. Cover and refrigerate the tomato mixture for up to 2 days. When you're ready to finish the recipe, continue with Steps 3 and 4.

NUTRIENTS PER SERVING

Calories	210
Carbohydrate	35 g
Fiber	8 g
Protein	11 g
Fat, total	5 g
Fat, saturated	1 g
Sodium	542 mg
Cholesterol	0 mg

EXCHANGES PER SERVING

2	Starch
1	Vegetable
½	Lean Meat

This delicious combination of black-eyed peas and greens, which is a Greek tradition, is a great dish for busy weeknights. It also makes a wonderful side dish for roasted meats, particularly lamb.

• **Works in slow cookers from 3½ to 6 quarts**

¼ teaspoon fennel seeds	2 cups cooked dried or canned black-eyed peas, drained and rinsed (see Basic Beans Variation, page 236)
1 tablespoon olive oil	
2 onions, finely chopped	
1 fennel bulb, cored, leafy stems discarded, and sliced vertically	2 tablespoons fresh lemon juice
4 cloves garlic, minced	1 teaspoon paprika (see Tip, left)
½ teaspoon salt	
½ teaspoon cracked black peppercorns	4 cups trimmed chopped spinach or Swiss chard (about 1 bunch)
1 can (14.5 ounces) diced tomatoes, including juice	

1. In large dry skillet over medium heat, toast fennel seeds, stirring, until fragrant, about 3 minutes. Immediately transfer to a mortar or spice grinder and grind. Set aside.

2. In the same skillet, heat oil over medium heat for 30 seconds. Add onions and sliced fennel; cook, stirring, until fennel is softened, about 5 minutes. Add garlic, salt, peppercorns, and reserved fennel seeds; cook, stirring, for 1 minute. Add tomatoes and their juice; bring to a boil. Transfer to the slow cooker stoneware.

3. Add peas and stir well. Cover and cook on Low for 8 hours or on High for 4 hours, or until peas are tender.

4. In a small bowl, whisk together lemon juice and paprika until paprika dissolves. Add to the slow cooker; stir well. Add spinach and stir until submerged. Cover and cook on High for 20 minutes, or until spinach is tender.

Creamy Mashed Potato Casserole

Makes 6 servings

Everyone's favorite do-ahead mashed potato casserole is perfect for a roast turkey or roast beef family dinner. For lump-free mashed potatoes, use a food mill or ricer instead of a potato masher.

6 large russet potatoes (about 3 pounds), peeled and quartered (see Tips, left)	Freshly grated nutmeg
	½ cup shredded light Cheddar cheese
¾ cup hot low-fat milk (approximately)	¼ cup fine dried bread crumbs (see Tip, page 81)
4 ounces light cream cheese, softened and cubed	½ teaspoon paprika

1. Preheat the oven to 350°F. Coat an 8-cup casserole dish with cooking spray. Bring a large saucepan of water to a boil.

2. Cook potatoes in boiling water until fork-tender, about 20 minutes. (Yukon Golds take a few minutes longer.) Drain well and return to the saucepan. Place the pan over low heat and dry the potatoes for 1 to 2 minutes.

3. Press potatoes through a food mill or ricer, mash with a potato masher, or beat with an electric mixer at low speed until very smooth. (Do not use a food processor or the potatoes will turn to glue.) Add milk and cream cheese; beat until smooth. Season with nutmeg to taste. Spoon the potatoes into the prepared casserole dish.

4. In a small bowl, combine Cheddar, bread crumbs, and paprika. Sprinkle evenly over potatoes.

5. Bake, uncovered, for 40 to 50 minutes, or until top is golden and a knife inserted in center is hot to the touch.

NUTRIENTS PER SERVING

Calories	239
Carbohydrate	36 g
Fiber	2 g
Protein	9 g
Fat, total	7 g
Fat, saturated	4 g
Sodium	285 mg
Cholesterol	21 mg

EXCHANGES PER SERVING

2	Starch
½	Other Carbohydrate
½	Lean Meat
½	Fat

Classic Scalloped Potatoes

Makes 6 servings

MAKE AHEAD

The casserole can be prepared ahead, covered, and refrigerated for up to 1 day. The baking time may need to be increased slightly

VARIATION

Scalloped Potatoes with Ham and Swiss Cheese
Add 4 ounces of smoked ham, cut into 1" strips, along with the potatoes to the sauce. Substitute light Swiss cheese for the Cheddar.

This side dish is an ideal accompaniment to baked him. Use your food processor to quickly slice the potatoes.

6 potatoes (about 2 pounds), peeled and thinly sliced	2 teaspoons Dijon mustard
1 tablespoon butter	½ teaspoon salt
1 large onion, halved lengthwise and thinly sliced	Pinch of freshly grated nutmeg
2 tablespoons all-purpose flour	1 cup shredded light Cheddar cheese
1½ cups low-fat milk	

1. Preheat the oven to 350°F. Coat an 11" × 9" baking dish with cooking spray.

2. Place potato slices in a colander and rinse under cold running water. Drain; wrap in a dry clean towel to dry.

3. In a large saucepan, melt butter over medium heat. Add onion and cook, stirring often, for 3 minutes, or until softened.

4. Meanwhile, place flour in a medium bowl. Stir in ¼ cup of the milk to make a smooth paste, then stir in remaining 1¼ cups milk until smooth. Stir in mustard, salt, and nutmeg. Add milk mixture to saucepan and bring to a boil over medium heat, stirring, until sauce thickens.

5. Add potatoes to sauce and bring to a boil over medium heat. Spoon into the prepared baking dish and sprinkle with cheese. Bake for 45 to 50 minutes, or until potatoes are tender and top is golden.

NUTRIENTS PER SERVING

Calories	211
Carbohydrate	28 g
Fiber	2 g
Protein	9 g
Fat, total	7 g
Fat, saturated	4 g
Sodium	450 mg
Cholesterol	21 mg

EXCHANGES PER SERVING

1½	Starch
½	Vegetable
½	High-fat Meat
½	Fat

Potato Pudding

Makes 4 servings

TIP

Make sure to grate the potatoes just before using because they discolor quickly.

This classic comfort food, also known as kugel, *is a staple in Jewish cooking. It's a delicious accompaniment to roasted meats and chicken.*

2 large eggs
2 tablespoons all-purpose flour
1 tablespoon chopped fresh parsley
1 large clove garlic, minced
½ teaspoon salt
¼ teaspoon freshly ground black pepper
1 onion
6 potatoes (about 2 pounds), peeled and quartered

1. Preheat the oven to 350°F. Coat an 8"-square baking dish with cooking spray.

2. In a large bowl, beat eggs. Stir in flour, parsley, garlic, salt, and pepper.

3. Using a food processor, grate onion. Fold onion into egg mixture.

4. Rinse potatoes and pat dry. Grate potatoes in a food processor or with a hand grater. Wrap in a large clean kitchen towel and squeeze out excess moisture. Stir potatoes into onion mixture until combined. (Do this quickly before potatoes discolor.)

5. Spread potato mixture evenly in the prepared baking dish. Bake for about 1 hour, or until top is nicely browned. Cut into 4 squares and serve.

NUTRIENTS PER SERVING

Calories	194
Carbohydrate	36 g
Fiber	3 g
Protein	7 g
Fat, total	3 g
Fat, saturated	1 g
Sodium	330 mg
Cholesterol	93 mg

EXCHANGES PER SERVING

2	Starch
½	Other Carbohydrate

Easy Parmesan Potato Bake

Makes 6 servings

VARIATION

Quick Microwave-Broiler Method Preheat the broiler. Layer the potatoes in the baking dish; pour the broth mixture over the top. Cover with a lid, or use microwave-safe plastic wrap and turn back 1 corner to vent. Microwave on High for 8 minutes. Rearrange the potato slices. Cover and microwave on High for another 6 to 8 minutes, or until potatoes are tender when pierced with a fork. Sprinkle with Parmesan cheese. Place under the broiler, about 5" from the heat; broil for 2 to 3 minutes, or until cheese is nicely browned. Sprinkle with parsley just before serving.

With the shortcut microwave method, you'll find this versatile dish a breeze to make for quick family suppers.

- 6 potatoes (about 2 pounds), peeled and thinly sliced
- 1 cup reduced-sodium chicken broth or vegetable broth
- 1 tablespoon melted butter or olive oil
- 1 large clove garlic, minced
- ¼ teaspoon salt
- ¼ teaspoon freshly ground black pepper
- ⅓ cup freshly grated Parmesan cheese
- 1 tablespoon chopped fresh parsley

1. Preheat the oven to 375°F. Coat an 11" × 9" baking dish with cooking spray.

2. Layer potatoes in the prepared baking dish. In a large glass measuring cup, combine broth, butter, garlic, salt, and pepper; pour over potatoes. Sprinkle with cheese and parsley.

3. Bake for 50 to 60 minutes, or until potatoes are tender and top is golden brown.

NUTRIENTS PER SERVING

Calories	134
Carbohydrate	21 g
Fiber	2 g
Protein	5 g
Fat, total	4 g
Fat, saturated	2 g
Sodium	305 mg
Cholesterol	10 mg

EXCHANGES PER SERVING

1½	Starch
½	Fat

Oven French Fries

Makes 4 servings

● Dark rimmed baking sheets attract the oven heat and will cook the potatoes faster, giving them a more intense color than shiny aluminum ones.

● One serving of these french fries contains 30 grams of carbohydrate and just 5 grams of fat. A comparable quantity of fast-food fries contains the same amount of carbohydrate but about 14 grams of fat and 80 additional calories.

If you love french fries (and who doesn't?) but are concerned about calories, here's the next best thing to deep-frying.

4 large or 6 medium russet potatoes (about 2 pounds), peeled and cut into 2" × ½" fries	4 teaspoons olive or vegetable oil

1. Preheat the oven to 450°F. Coat 2 baking sheets with cooking spray.

2. Rinse fries in several changes cold water to remove surface starch. Cover with cold water until ready to cook. Drain well, then wrap in a clean dry kitchen towel to dry potatoes thoroughly.

3. Place the potatoes on the prepared baking sheets, drizzle with oil, and toss to coat evenly. Arrange in a single layer. Bake for 25 to 30 minutes, stirring occasionally, or until tender and golden brown.

NUTRIENTS PER SERVING

Calories	171
Carbohydrate	30 g
Fiber	2 g
Protein	3 g
Fat, total	5 g
Fat, saturated	1 g
Sodium	5 mg
Cholesterol	0 mg

EXCHANGES PER SERVING

2	Starch
½	Fat

Broccoli and Cheese–Stuffed Potatoes

Makes 4 servings

> ### TIPS
>
> ● Cheddar and broccoli is a classic combo, but feel free to get adventurous with whatever cheese and vegetables are in the fridge. For example, you might try part-skim mozzarella cheese and lightly sautéed mushrooms, diced red peppers, or seasoned with basil.
>
> ● To microwave potatoes: Arrange the potatoes in a circle 1" apart on a paper towel. Microwave on High, turning halfway through cooking, until the potatoes are just tender when pierced with a fork. Microwave cooking times: 1 potato, 4 to 5 minutes; 2 potatoes, 6 to 8 minutes; 4 potatoes, 10 to 12 minutes.

These delicious baked potatoes are great to take along to work if you have the use of a microwave for reheating.

4 large baking potatoes (8 ounces each)	¾ cup shredded light Cheddar or light Swiss cheese
3 cups small broccoli florets with chopped peeled stems	2 scallions, chopped
½ cup low-fat plain yogurt or buttermilk (approximately)	Cayenne pepper

1. Preheat the oven to 400°F. Scrub potatoes well and pierce skins with a fork in several places to allow steam to escape. Bake for 1 hour, or until potatoes give slightly when squeezed. Do not turn off the oven. Or microwave potatoes (see Tips, left).

2. Place a steamer basket in a large pot with 2" of water. Bring to a boil over high heat. Place broccoli in the basket and steam until just crisp-tender, about 5 minutes. Drain well.

3. Cut a thin slice from tops of warm potatoes. Scoop out potatoes and transfer to a large bowl, leaving a ¼" shell, being careful not to tear the skins.

4. Mash potato with a potato masher or fork, beating in enough yogurt until smooth. Add broccoli, ½ cup of the cheese, and scallions. Season with cayenne to taste.

5. Spoon filling into potato shells, mounding the tops. Arrange in a shallow 13" × 9" baking dish; sprinkle with remaining cheese. Bake for 20 minutes, or until cheese melts. Or microwave on Medium-high for 5 to 7 minutes, or until heated through and cheese melts.

NUTRIENTS PER SERVING

Calories	295
Carbohydrate	51 g
Fiber	6 g
Protein	13 g
Fat, total	5 g
Fat, saturated	3 g
Sodium	230 mg
Cholesterol	16 mg

EXCHANGES PER SERVING

3	Starch
½	Other Carbohydrate
½	Lean meat

Butternut Squash with Snow Peas and Red Pepper

Makes 6 servings

● To prepare squash for this recipe, peel using a vegetable peeler or paring knife. Cut into lengthwise quarters and seed. Cut into thin ¼" × 1½" pieces.

If the soft texture of a squash purée doesn't appeal to you, try this easy stir-fry instead.

1 tablespoon vegetable oil	1 tablespoon packed brown sugar
5 cups prepared butternut squash (see Tip, left)	1½ teaspoons grated fresh ginger
1 red bell pepper, cut into thin strips	Freshly ground black pepper
4 ounces snow peas, ends trimmed	

1. In a large nonstick skillet, heat oil over medium-high heat. Add squash and cook, stirring, until almost tender, 3 to 4 minutes.

2. Add bell pepper, snow peas, brown sugar, and ginger. Cook, stirring often, until vegetables are crisp-tender, about 2 minutes. Season with pepper to taste.

NUTRIENTS PER SERVING

Calories	95
Carbohydrate	19 g
Fiber	3 g
Protein	2 g
Fat, total	2 g
Fat, saturated	0 g
Sodium	5 mg
Cholesterol	0 mg

EXCHANGES PER SERVING

1	Starch
½	Fat

Cherry Tomato and Zucchini Sauté with Basil

Makes 4 servings

Stir 2 tablespoons pine nuts in a dry skillet over medium heat until lightly golden, about 2 minutes. Add with the basil. The nuts will add ½ Fat Exchange.

This colorful vegetable medley is a great summer side dish.

2 teaspoons olive oil
3 small zucchini, halved lengthwise and thinly sliced
2 cups cherry tomatoes, halved
2 scallions, sliced
2 teaspoons balsamic vinegar
½ teaspoon ground cumin (optional)
Freshly ground black pepper
2 tablespoons chopped fresh basil or mint leaves

In a large nonstick skillet, heat oil over medium-high heat. Add zucchini and cook, stirring, for 1 minute. Add tomatoes, scallions, vinegar, and cumin, if using. Cook, stirring, until zucchini is crisp-tender and tomatoes are heated through, 1 to 2 minutes. Season with pepper to taste. Sprinkle with basil and serve immediately.

NUTRIENTS PER SERVING

Calories	52
Carbohydrate	7 g
Fiber	2 g
Protein	1 g
Fat, total	3 g
Fat, saturated	0 g
Sodium	10 mg
Cholesterol	0 mg

EXCHANGES PER SERVING

1½	Vegetable
½	Fat

Teriyaki Vegetable Stir-Fry

Makes 4 servings

● Vegetables that take longer to cook, such as carrots, broccoli, and cauliflower, should be added to the pan first, before adding quicker-cooking ones like peppers and zucchini.

● You can also toss the cooked vegetables with 4 ounces of cooked spaghettini for an easy pasta supper.

Use this recipe as a guideline, and then get creative with whatever vegetables you have in the fridge. You'll need about 5 cups in total.

2 tablespoons light teriyaki sauce or reduced-sodium soy sauce	1 large clove garlic, minced
2 tablespoons water	2 teaspoons vegetable oil
1 tablespoon unseasoned rice vinegar	2 cups small cauliflower or broccoli florets
2 teaspoons packed brown sugar	2 small zucchini, halved lengthwise and thinly sliced
1 teaspoon cornstarch	1 red bell pepper, cut into 2" strips

1. In a glass measuring cup, combine teriyaki sauce, water, vinegar, brown sugar, cornstarch, and garlic; set aside.

2. In a wok or large skillet, heat oil over high heat. Add cauliflower and cook, stirring, for 1 minute. Add zucchini and bell pepper; cook, stirring, for 2 minutes.

3. Reduce the heat to medium. Stir teriyaki mixture and add to pan. Cook, stirring, until sauce is slightly thickened. Cover and cook for 1 minute, or until vegetables are crisp-tender.

NUTRIENTS PER SERVING

Calories	66
Carbohydrate	10 g
Fiber	2 g
Protein	2 g
Fat, total	3 g
Fat, saturated	0 g
Sodium	140 mg
Cholesterol	0 mg

EXCHANGES PER SERVING

1½	Vegetable
½	Fat

Oven-Roasted Root Vegetables

Makes 6 servings

Oven-roasting sweetens and concentrates the flavors of these sturdy root vegetables. This dish is a natural with steak or chicken.

3 carrots, peeled and cut into 2" × ½" pieces

2 parsnips, peeled and cut into 2" × ½" pieces

½ small rutabaga (about 8 ounces), peeled and cut into 2" × ½" pieces

1 red onion, cut into wedges

2 cloves garlic, cut into slivers

¼ cup dry sherry or reduced-sodium chicken broth

1 tablespoon butter, melted

½ teaspoon salt

¼ teaspoon freshly ground black pepper

2 tablespoons finely chopped fresh parsley

1. Preheat the oven to 400°F. Coat a 13" × 9" baking dish with cooking spray.

2. Place the carrots, parsnips, rutabaga, onion, and garlic in the prepared baking dish.

3. In a small bowl, combine sherry and butter; drizzle over vegetables. Sprinkle with salt and pepper.

4. Cover the dish with foil and bake for 30 minutes. Remove the foil and bake for 25 to 30 minutes longer, stirring occasionally, or until vegetables are tender and light golden. Sprinkle with parsley before serving.

TIP

• Most of us are used to roasting potatoes, so moving on to other vegetables isn't that much of a shift in our cooking style. Try this treatment with other vegetables such as peppers, winter squash, beets, cauliflower, and even asparagus. You'll be amazed with the results. Use oil instead of butter and add a sprinkling of dried herbs, if you like. Reduce the cooking time according to the size and type of vegetables.

NUTRIENTS PER SERVING

Calories	101
Carbohydrate	19 g
Fiber	4 g
Protein	2 g
Fat, total	2 g
Fat, saturated	1 g
Sodium	245 mg
Cholesterol	5 mg

EXCHANGES PER SERVING

1	Vegetable
1	Other Carbohydrate
½	Fat

SENSATIONAL
SIDE SALADS

Layered Greek Salad

Makes 10 servings

- To serve, spoon down through the vegetable layers so each serving has a little bit of everything.

- If tomatoes aren't fully ripened when you buy them, place them in a paper bag on your counter for a day or two. The ethylene gas given off by the tomatoes speeds up the ripening process. Never store tomatoes in the fridge—the cold temperature numbs their sweet flavor. A sunny windowsill may seem like a good place to ripen tomatoes, but a hot sun often bakes rather than ripens them.

NUTRIENTS PER SERVING

Calories	172
Carbohydrate	15 g
Fiber	2 g
Protein	11 g
Fat, total	9 g
Fat, saturated	4 g
Sodium	695 mg
Cholesterol	12 mg

EXCHANGES PER SERVING

½	Milk, Fat-free/Low-fat
2	Vegetable
½	Medium-fat Meat
1	Fat

Remember the layered salads of the 1950s—the ones made with shredded iceberg lettuce, sliced cooked eggs, and frozen peas, all crowned with heavy mayonnaise? This updated version layers colorful vegetables that accent the flavors of Greece with a garlic-yogurt dressing and feta cheese topping.

DRESSING

- 4 cups low-fat plain yogurt
- 2 cloves garlic, minced
- 2 tablespoons olive oil
- 2 tablespoons red wine vinegar
- 1 teaspoon salt
- 1 teaspoon sugar
- 1 teaspoon dried oregano
- ¼ teaspoon freshly ground black pepper

SALAD

- 1 small head romaine lettuce, shredded (about 8 cups, packed)
- 1 small Spanish onion, diced
- 1 red bell pepper, diced
- 1 green bell pepper, diced
- ½ seedless cucumber, cubed
- 1½ cups crumbled light feta cheese (about 6 ounces)
- ¼ cup chopped fresh parsley
- 2 ripe tomatoes, cut into wedges, for garnish (see Tips, left)
- 12 kalamata olives, for garnish

1. **Make the dressing:** Place yogurt in a cheesecloth-lined strainer set over a bowl. Cover and refrigerate for 4 hours, or until reduced to about 2½ cups. Transfer to a medium bowl; discard liquid whey. Stir in garlic, oil, vinegar, salt, sugar, oregano, and black pepper.

2. **Make the salad:** Line the bottom of an 8" or 9" round glass salad bowl with lettuce. Next, layer separately the onion, red bell pepper, green bell pepper, and cucumber.

3. Spread top with yogurt mixture. Refrigerate, loosely covered, for 8 hours or overnight. Sprinkle with feta and parsley. Garnish with tomato wedges and olives.

Spinach, Mushroom, and Carrot Salad

Makes 8 servings

This party salad is not complicated to make, nor is it expensive to prepare. But the flavors make it special enough to serve for company—with tangy lime juice, mustard, and cumin balancing the sweetness of raisins and carrots.

SALAD

- 1 package (10 ounces) fresh baby spinach, stemmed and coarsely chopped (about 8 cups)
- 1½ cups sliced mushrooms
- 2 cups shredded carrots
- 1½ cups seedless cucumber, halved lengthwise and sliced
- 1 small red onion, thinly sliced
- ⅓ cup dark raisins

DRESSING

- ¼ cup extra virgin olive oil
- 2 tablespoons fresh lime juice
- 1 tablespoon honey
- 2 teaspoons Dijon mustard
- ¾ teaspoon ground cumin
- 1 clove garlic, minced
- ½ teaspoon salt
- ¼ teaspoon freshly ground black pepper

1. **Make the salad:** In a serving bowl, layer one-third of the spinach, all of the mushrooms, another third of the spinach, all of the carrots, then remaining spinach. Layer cucumber, onion, and raisins on top. Cover and refrigerate for up to 4 hours.

2. **Make the dressing:** In a medium bowl, whisk together oil, lime juice, honey, mustard, cumin, garlic, salt, and pepper. Just before serving, drizzle over salad and toss gently.

NUTRIENTS PER SERVING

Calories	122
Carbohydrate	14 g
Fiber	2 g
Protein	2 g
Fat, total	7 g
Fat, saturated	1 g
Sodium	220 mg
Cholesterol	0 mg

EXCHANGES PER SERVING

½	Fruit
1	Vegetable
1½	Fat

Warm Mushroom and Goat Cheese Salad

Makes 4 servings

● Most produce stores sell mixes of greens, but you can make your own mixture using radicchio, arugula, and oak leaf lettuces, or other greens you prefer.

● Toast walnuts on a baking sheet in a 350°F oven for 7 to 9 minutes.

VARIATION

Instead of goat cheese in this recipe, use light Brie or light Camembert.

There are so many wonderful mushroom varieties in the supermarket these days—feel free to use any combination, depending on what's available when you decide to make this earthy starter or luncheon salad. Select apple varieties such as Cortland or Granny Smith, which resist browning when sliced.

6 cups mesclun or mixed salad greens (see Tips, left)	½ cup sliced scallions
1 large apple, quartered and cored	¼ cup honey
	¼ cup cider vinegar
1 light goat cheese log (3½ ounces), cut into 8 slices	¼ teaspoon salt
	¼ teaspoon freshly ground black pepper
2 tablespoons olive oil	⅓ cup coarsely chopped toasted walnuts (see Tips, left)
8 ounces cremini mushrooms, thickly sliced	
4 ounces assorted mushrooms, such as oyster, shiitake, and porcini, thickly sliced	

1. Divide salad greens among 4 plates. Cut apple quarters into 8 thin slices; arrange slices in a circle in the middle of each of 8 plates. Place 2 slices goat cheese in the center of each circle. (This can be done shortly before serving, covered, and refrigerated.)

2. In a large nonstick skillet, heat oil over medium-high heat. Add cremini and assorted mushrooms; cook, stirring, until tender, 3 to 5 minutes.

3. Add scallions, honey, vinegar, salt, and pepper; cook, stirring, until hot, about 15 seconds. Remove the pan from the heat. Spoon warm mushroom mixture over salad greens. Sprinkle with walnuts and serve.

NUTRIENTS PER SERVING

Calories	260
Carbohydrate	35 g
Fiber	5 g
Protein	9 g
Fat, total	12 g
Fat, saturated	4 g
Sodium	280 mg
Cholesterol	12 mg

EXCHANGES PER SERVING

1	Vegetable
2	Other Carbohydrate
1	Medium-fat Meat
1	Fat

Creamy Coleslaw

Makes 6 servings

VARIATION

Waldorf Coleslaw
Substitute 2 chopped large stalks celery for the carrots, and add 2 diced apples and ¾ cup chopped walnuts.

A family barbecue and picnic calls for a generous bowl of old-fashioned cabbage slaw with a creamy mayonnaise-mustard dressing.

8 cups finely shredded green cabbage	2 tablespoons cider vinegar
2 carrots, shredded	1 tablespoon Dijon mustard
5 scallions, sliced	½ teaspoon celery seeds (optional)
2 tablespoons chopped fresh parsley	½ teaspoon salt
½ cup light mayonnaise	¼ teaspoon freshly ground black pepper
2 tablespoons honey	

1. In a serving bowl, combine cabbage, carrots, scallions, and parsley.

2. In a small bowl, stir together mayonnaise, honey, vinegar, mustard, celery seeds (if using), salt, and pepper. Pour over cabbage mixture and toss to coat well. Refrigerate until ready to serve.

NUTRIENTS PER SERVING

Calories	123
Carbohydrate	16 g
Fiber	3 g
Protein	2 g
Fat, total	7 g
Fat, saturated	1 g
Sodium	335 mg
Cholesterol	6 mg

EXCHANGES PER SERVING

1	Vegetable
½	Other Carbohydrate
1½	Fat

Caesar Salad with Garlic Croutons

Makes 8 servings

● The traditional dressing for Caesar salad contains coddled (slightly cooked) eggs. Mayonnaise is used here instead because there is a small chance that raw eggs may contain salmonella bacteria.

● Make sure salad greens are washed and dried thoroughly, preferably in a salad spinner, for best results.

The king of tossed salads was named after a Tijuana restaurateur by the name of Caesar Cardini. Here, mayonnaise gives this classic salad an even creamier texture than the original. The Nutrients per Serving and the Exchanges per Serving include the Garlic Croutons (opposite).

¼ cup extra virgin olive oil

2 tablespoons light mayonnaise

2 tablespoons fresh lemon juice

2 tablespoons water

1 teaspoon Dijon mustard

2 cloves garlic, minced

3 anchovy fillets, chopped, or 1 tablespoon anchovy paste

¼ teaspoon freshly ground black pepper

1 large head Romaine lettuce, torn into bite-size pieces (about 12 cups)

Garlic croutons (opposite)

⅓ cup freshly grated Parmesan cheese

1. In a food processor, combine oil, mayonnaise, lemon juice, water, mustard, garlic, anchovy fillets, and pepper; process until smooth and creamy.

2. Arrange lettuce in salad bowl; pour dressing over and toss lightly. Add croutons and sprinkle with cheese. Toss again. Taste and season with additional pepper, if desired. Serve immediately.

NUTRIENTS PER SERVING

Calories	177
Carbohydrate	12 g
Fiber	2 g
Protein	6 g
Fat, total	12 g
Fat, saturated	3 g
Sodium	305 mg
Cholesterol	7 mg

EXCHANGES PER SERVING

½	Starch
½	Vegetable
½	Medium-fat Meat
2	Fat

Garlic Croutons

Homemade croutons make a definite flavor difference, but 4 cups of store-bought croutons will work in a pinch.

1 tablespoon olive oil

1 clove garlic, minced

4 cups cubed crusty bread, cut into ½-inch pieces

2 tablespoons freshly grated Parmesan cheese

1. Preheat the oven to 375°F.
2. In a small bowl, combine oil and garlic; drizzle over bread cubes and toss. Sprinkle with cheese and toss again.
3. Arrange bread cubes on a baking sheet in a single layer. Toast in the oven, stirring once, for about 10 minutes or until golden.

Grilled Vegetable Salad

Makes 4 servings

• Soak bamboo skewers in cold water for 15 minutes to prevent them from burning when grilling the vegetables.

This delectable grilled salad can be made with whatever vegetables you have on hand. You might also try sliced baby eggplant, thickly sliced fennel, or thick asparagus spears.

VEGETABLES

1 Vidalia or other sweet onion
1 red bell pepper
1 yellow bell pepper
3 small zucchini

DRESSING

2 tablespoons extra virgin olive oil
1 tablespoon finely chopped fresh parsley

1 tablespoon balsamic vinegar
1 tablespoon red wine vinegar
1 teaspoon Dijon mustard
1 large clove garlic, minced
2 teaspoons finely chopped fresh rosemary or thyme
½ teaspoon salt
½ teaspoon freshly ground black pepper

1. Coat a barbecue grill with cooking spray and preheat to medium-high. Soak 4 bamboo skewers in water (see Tips, left).
2. **Make the vegetables:** Slice onion into 4 rounds. Insert small soaked bamboo skewers through slices to prevent them from falling apart when grilling. Cut red and yellow bell peppers into quarters; remove ribs and seeds. Cut zucchini crosswise into halves, then cut each piece in half lengthwise. Arrange vegetables on a baking sheet.
3. **Make the vinaigrette:** In a bowl, combine oil, parsley, balsamic and red wine vinegars, mustard, garlic, rosemary, salt, and pepper. Brush vegetables with all of the vinaigrette and let marinate at room temperature for 30 minutes, or for up to 4 hours.
4. Grill vegetables for 12 to 15 minutes, turning occasionally (remove vegetables gradually as they become crisp-tender). Transfer to a serving platter and serve warm or at room temperature.

NUTRIENTS PER SERVING

Calories	72
Carbohydrate	10 g
Fiber	2 g
Protein	1 g
Fat, total	4 g
Fat, saturated	0 g
Sodium	165 mg
Cholesterol	0 mg

EXCHANGES PER SERVING

2	Vegetable
½	Fat

Bean Salad with Mustard-Dill Dressing

Makes 6 servings

Bean salad is another staple most of us grew up with. Originally, this salad used canned string beans, but fresh beans give it a new lease on taste, as does the addition of fiber-packed chickpeas.

TIP

● Some bean salad recipes call for canned green beans, which contain added salt. It's better to use fresh or frozen. One-half cup of fresh green beans cooked without salt contains 2 milligrams of sodium; the same amount of canned beans contains 180 milligrams.

VARIATION

Instead of chickpeas, you can try canned mixed beans, which usually include chickpeas, red and white kidney beans, and black-eyed peas and are available in most supermarkets.

SALAD

- 1 pound green beans, trimmed and cut into 1" pieces
- 1 can (19 ounces) chickpeas, drained and rinsed
- ⅓ cup chopped red onion

DRESSING

- 2 tablespoons extra virgin olive oil
- 2 tablespoons red wine vinegar
- 1 tablespoon Dijon mustard
- 1 tablespoon sugar
- ¼ teaspoon salt
- ¼ teaspoon freshly ground black pepper
- 2 tablespoons finely chopped fresh dill

1. Bring a large pot of water to a boil.

2. **Make the salad:** Cook beans in boiling water for 3 to 5 minutes (start timing when water returns to a boil), or until crisp-tender. Drain and rinse under cold running water to chill. Drain again. Pat dry with paper towels.

3. In a serving bowl, combine beans, chickpeas, and onion.

4. **Make the dressing:** In a small bowl, whisk together oil, vinegar, mustard, sugar, salt, and pepper until smooth. Stir in dill.

5. Pour dressing over beans and toss well. Refrigerate until serving time.

NUTRIENTS PER SERVING

Calories	161
Carbohydrate	23 g
Fiber	4 g
Protein	6 g
Fat, total	6 g
Fat, saturated	1 g
Sodium	325 mg
Cholesterol	0 mg

EXCHANGES PER SERVING

1	Vegetable
1	Other Carbohydrate
½	Medium-fat Meat
1	Fat

Green Bean and Plum Tomato Salad

Makes 6 servings

TIP

● Use this terrific mustardy dressing with other favorite vegetable salad mixtures and crisp greens.

When preparing this dish ahead of time, keep the blanched green beans, tomatoes, and dressing separate, and combine them just before serving to prevent the salad from getting soggy.

SALAD

1 pound young green beans, trimmed

8 small plum tomatoes (about 1 pound)

2 scallions, sliced

DRESSING

¼ cup olive oil

4 teaspoons red wine vinegar

1 tablespoon grainy mustard

1 clove garlic, minced

½ teaspoon sugar

¼ teaspoon salt

¼ teaspoon freshly ground black pepper

¼ cup chopped fresh parsley

1. Bring a medium saucepan of water to a boil.

2. **Make the salad:** Cook beans in boiling water for 3 to 5 minutes (start timing when water returns to a boil), or until crisp-tender. Drain and rinse under cold running water to chill; drain again. Pat dry with paper towels or wrap in a clean dry towel.

3. Cut plum tomatoes in half lengthwise; using a small spoon, scoop out centers. Cut each piece in half lengthwise again; place in a bowl.

4. **Make the dressing:** In a small bowl, whisk together oil, vinegar, mustard, garlic, sugar, salt, and pepper. Stir in parsley.

5. Just before serving, combine beans, tomatoes, and scallions in a serving bowl. Pour dressing over salad and toss well.

NUTRIENTS PER SERVING

Calories	128
Carbohydrate	10 g
Fiber	3 g
Protein	2 g
Fat, total	10 g
Fat, saturated	1 g
Sodium	150 mg
Cholesterol	0 mg

EXCHANGES PER SERVING

2	Vegetable
2	Fat

Best-Ever Potato Salad

Makes 8 servings

If anything signals the arrival of summer days and backyard barbecues, it's a trusty potato salad. This version goes beyond tossing potatoes with mayonnaise. Here, warm potatoes are steeped in a tasty marinade before the mayonnaise is introduced. The result: a summertime family favorite.

6 new potatoes (about 2 pounds), left whole

¾ cup frozen peas

2 tablespoons red wine vinegar

1 tablespoon Dijon mustard

1 clove garlic, minced

2 stalks celery, diced

4 scallions, sliced

¼ cup chopped fresh parsley or dill

3 hard-cooked eggs, chopped

½ cup light mayonnaise

¼ cup low-fat plain yogurt or light sour cream

Salt

Freshly ground black pepper

1. Bring a medium saucepan of water to a boil.

2. Cook potatoes until just tender, 20 to 25 minutes. Drain and when cool enough to handle, peel and cut into ½" cubes. Place in a serving bowl.

3. Bring a small saucepan of water to a boil. Place frozen peas in a strainer and pour boiling water over them; drain well.

4. In a small bowl, stir together vinegar, mustard, and garlic; pour mixture over warm potatoes and toss gently. Let cool to room temperature. Stir in celery, scallions, and parsley. Add chopped eggs and peas.

5. In another small bowl, combine mayonnaise, yogurt, and salt and pepper to taste. Fold into potato mixture until evenly coated. Refrigerate until serving time.

NUTRIENTS PER SERVING

Calories	162
Carbohydrate	20 g
Fiber	2 g
Protein	5 g
Fat, total	7 g
Fat, saturated	1 g
Sodium	395 mg
Cholesterol	75 mg

EXCHANGES PER SERVING

1	Starch
½	Medium-fat Meat
1	Fat

Speedy Mexicali Rice and Black Bean Salad

Makes 8 servings

TIP

● To cook the rice, rinse ¾ cup basmati rice under cold running water; drain. In a medium saucepan, bring 1½ cups water to a boil. Add rice and ¼ teaspoon salt; cover and simmer until tender, about 15 minutes. Spread hot rice on a baking sheet to cool.

Your turn to bring the salad to the next reunion or neighborhood get-together? Here's a surefire winner that can be easily doubled to feed as many folks as the occasion demands. Even better, it can be made a day ahead.

SALAD

2½ cups cooked basmati rice (see Tip, left)

1 can (19 ounces) black beans, drained and rinsed

1 cup cooked corn kernels

1 red bell pepper, diced

4 scallions, sliced

DRESSING

½ cup light sour cream

2 tablespoons extra virgin olive oil

4 teaspoons fresh lime or lemon juice

1 teaspoon ground cumin

1 teaspoon dried oregano

½ teaspoon hot pepper sauce

½ cup chopped fresh cilantro or parsley

1. **Make the salad:** In a large serving bowl, combine rice, beans, corn, pepper, and scallions.

2. **Make the dressing:** In a small bowl, combine sour cream, oil, lime juice, cumin, oregano, and hot pepper sauce.

3. Pour dressing over rice mixture and toss well. Cover and refrigerate for up to 8 hours. Stir in cilantro just before serving.

NUTRIENTS PER SERVING

Calories	185
Carbohydrate	31 g
Fiber	4 g
Protein	6 g
Fat, total	5 g
Fat, saturated	1 g
Sodium	230 mg
Cholesterol	0 mg

EXCHANGES PER SERVING

1	Starch
1	Other Carbohydrate
½	Medium-fat Meat

Tabbouleh

Makes 8 servings

● Bulgur is precooked cracked wheat that has been dried; it needs only to be soaked in water before using.

● This salad keeps well for several days. It's better to add the tomatoes as a garnish just before serving to prevent the salad from becoming soggy.

The Lebanese salad tabbouleh, made with nutty-tasting bulgur, is a good example of the vibrant comfort foods from the Mediterranean that have become so popular in recent years. This refreshing salad is often displayed next to traditional favorites, such as potato salad and coleslaw, in the deli section of supermarkets. But you'll find it very inexpensive and easy to make in your home kitchen.

¾ cup fine bulgur	¼ cup extra virgin olive oil
2 cups finely chopped fresh parsley, preferably flat-leaf	1 teaspoon salt
4 scallions, finely chopped	½ teaspoon paprika
¼ cup finely chopped fresh mint or 2 tablespoons dried (optional)	¼ teaspoon freshly ground black pepper
¼ cup fresh lemon juice	2 tomatoes, seeded and diced

1. In a large bowl, combine bulgur and cold water to cover. Let stand for 30 minutes. Drain in a fine strainer. Using the back of a spoon or with your hands, squeeze out as much water as possible.

2. In a serving bowl, combine softened bulgur, parsley, scallions, and mint, if using.

3. In a small bowl, stir together lemon juice, oil, salt, paprika, and pepper. Pour over bulgur mixture and toss well. Cover and refrigerate until serving time. Just before serving, sprinkle with tomatoes.

NUTRIENTS PER SERVING

Calories	119
Carbohydrate	13 g
Fiber	3 g
Protein	2 g
Fat, total	7 g
Fat, saturated	1 g
Sodium	0 mg
Cholesterol	305 mg

EXCHANGES PER SERVING

½	Starch
½	Vegetable
1½	Fat

Basil-Garlic Vinaigrette

Makes 1 cup (2 tablespoons per serving)

● Store the dressing in an airtight container in the refrigerator for up to 1 week.

Instead of fresh basil, use ½ cup packed fresh parsley and 1 teaspoon dried basil.

A simple way to trim fat in salad dressings is to replace part of the oil called for with low-sodium chicken broth and fresh herbs to give the dressing body and a boost of fresh flavor.

½ cup packed fresh basil leaves	1 tablespoon Dijon mustard
⅓ cup reduced-sodium chicken broth	1 large clove garlic
¼ cup extra virgin olive oil	¼ teaspoon freshly ground black pepper
¼ cup white wine vinegar	
1 tablespoon balsamic vinegar	

In a food processor or blender, purée basil, broth, oil, wine vinegar, balsamic vinegar, mustard, garlic, and pepper until smooth.

NUTRIENTS PER SERVING

Calories	67
Carbohydrate	1 g
Fiber	0 g
Protein	0 g
Fat, total	7 g
Fat, saturated	1 g
Sodium	70 mg
Cholesterol	0 mg

EXCHANGES PER SERVING

1½	Fat

DELECTABLE
DESSERTS

Peach Almond Cake

Makes 12 servings

● To peel peaches, plunge them into boiling water for 15 to 30 seconds to loosen the skins.

● Replace your supplies of baking powder and baking soda every 6 months; once opened, they oxidize and lose their leavening power.

● For perfect cakes, loaves, bars, and squares, it's essential to use the correct size of baking pan specified in each recipe.

This coffee cake is welcome at brunch, afternoon tea, or dessert. Make it year-round with other seasonal fruits such as pears, apples, pitted cherries, or plums.

1½ cups all-purpose flour	¼ cup butter, melted
¾ cup plus 2 tablespoons sugar	½ teaspoon almond extract
1½ teaspoons baking powder	3 peaches, peeled and sliced
½ teaspoon baking soda	3 tablespoons sliced blanched almonds
¼ teaspoon salt	½ teaspoon ground cinnamon
2 large eggs	
⅔ cup low-fat plain yogurt	

1. Preheat the oven to 350°F. Spray a 9" springform pan or cake pan with cooking spray.

2. In a large bowl, stir together flour, ¾ cup sugar, baking powder, baking soda, and salt.

3. In a medium bowl, beat eggs, yogurt, butter, and almond extract until smooth. Stir into dry ingredients to make a smooth thick batter. Spread in the prepared pan. Arrange peaches on top in a circular fashion.

4. In a small bowl, combine almonds, 2 tablespoons sugar, and cinnamon. Sprinkle over peaches. Bake for 50 to 60 minutes, or until a tester inserted in the center comes out clean. Transfer to a rack to cool.

NUTRIENTS PER SERVING

Calories	191
Carbohydrate	31 g
Fiber	1 g
Protein	4 g
Fat, total	6 g
Fat, saturated	3 g
Sodium	195 mg
Cholesterol	42 mg

EXCHANGES PER SERVING

1	Starch
1	Other Carbohydrate
1	Fat

Raspberry Coffee Cake

Makes 12 servings

TIPS

● Quick-frozen berries do not need to be defrosted before they are added to the batter.

● Incorrect measurement is a major cause of baking failures. Use a liquid cup measure for fluids and a dry measure for dry ingredients such as flour. Spoon the dry ingredient into the dry measure and level off using a knife. Do not pack the dry measure down by tapping it on the countertop instead of spooning; this removes the air and allows you to increase the amount of flour.

Keep bags of quick-frozen berries stocked in your freezer to make this delectable cake in any season. It's best served the same day it's baked, warm or at room temperature.

COFFEE CAKE

1½ cups all-purpose flour
¾ cup granulated sugar
½ cup sweetened shredded coconut
2 teaspoons baking powder
½ teaspoon baking soda
¼ teaspoon salt
¾ cup light sour cream
¼ cup canola oil
2 large eggs
1 teaspoon vanilla extract
1 cup fresh or frozen unsweetened raspberries or blueberries

CRUMB TOPPING

3 tablespoons packed brown sugar
2 tablespoons quick-cooking rolled oats
2 tablespoons sweetened shredded coconut
2 tablespoons all-purpose flour
½ teaspoon ground cinnamon
2 tablespoons butter, cut into pieces

1. Preheat the oven to 350°F. Spray a 9" springform pan or cake pan with cooking spray.

2. **Make the cake:** In a large bowl, combine flour, sugar, coconut, baking powder, baking soda, and salt.

3. In another large bowl, beat sour cream with oil, eggs, and vanilla. Stir in flour mixture; mix well. Gently fold in raspberries. Spread batter in the prepared pan.

4. **Make the topping:** In a large bowl, combine brown sugar, oats, coconut, flour, and cinnamon. Cut in butter using a pastry blender or 2 knives to make coarse crumbs. Sprinkle evenly over batter.

5. Bake on the middle rack of the oven for 55 to 60 minutes, or until a tester inserted in the center come out clean. Transfer cake in pan to a rack to completely cool.

NUTRIENTS PER SERVING

Calories	241
Carbohydrate	34 g
Fiber	1 g
Protein	4 g
Fat, total	10 g
Fat, saturated	3 g
Sodium	185 mg
Cholesterol	36 mg

EXCHANGES PER SERVING

1	Starch
1½	Other Carbohydrate
1½	Fat

Frozen Strawberry Cake

Makes 12 servings

TIP

● Instead of using orange-flavored liqueur, substitute the same quantity of undiluted frozen orange juice concentrate.

Surprisingly easy to prepare, this impressive frozen dessert is sublime when fresh berries are in season.

1 frozen pound cake (10 ounces)	4 tablespoons fresh lime juice
6 cups fresh strawberries, hulled	⅓ cup sugar
6 tablespoons orange-flavored liqueur (see Tip, left)	4 cups low-fat strawberry frozen yogurt, softened slightly

1. Line a 9" × 5" loaf pan with plastic wrap, with the ends hanging generously over the sides of the pan.

2. Slightly defrost pound cake. Trim dark crusts from top and sides of cake; cut into 24 slices, each ¼" thick.

3. Quarter and slice 2 cups of the berries. Place in a medium bowl and add 3 tablespoons of the liqueur and 2 tablespoons of the lime juice. Set aside.

4. In a food processor, purée sugar and remaining 4 cups berries, 3 tablespoons liqueur, and 2 tablespoons lime juice; pour into a large bowl.

5. Spread scant ¼ cup strawberry purée in the prepared pan. Layer with 8 slices of cake, arranged lengthwise with slightly overlapping edges. Spread cake with scant ¼ cup purée, then top with 2 cups frozen yogurt and another scant ¼ cup purée. Repeat layers of cake, purée, frozen yogurt, and purée. Arrange remaining cake slices on top and spread with ¼ cup purée; reserve remaining purée. Fold plastic wrap over top, pressing gently down on cake. Freeze for 8 hours.

6. Stir reserved purée into sliced strawberry mixture. Cover and refrigerate.

7. To serve, place cake in refrigerator for 30 minutes to soften slightly. Lift out of the pan and remove the plastic wrap. Cut cake into slices and arrange on serving plates. Top with a generous spoonful of strawberry mixture.

NUTRIENTS PER SERVING

Calories	269
Carbohydrate	45 g
Fiber	2 g
Protein	4 g
Fat, total	7 g
Fat, saturated	4 g
Sodium	40 mg
Cholesterol	45 mg

EXCHANGES PER SERVING

1	Starch
½	Fruit
1½	Other Carbohydrate
1½	Fat

Strawberry-Rhubarb Cobbler

Makes 8 servings

TIP

● If you're using frozen fruit, there's no need to defrost first.

MAKE AHEAD

If you prefer to bake the cobbler earlier in the day, reheat it in a 350°F oven for about 15 minutes.

Indulge in this old-fashioned dessert when local berries and rhubarb are in season. It's also good in winter, when you turn to your freezer for your stash of summer fruits.

FRUIT	BISCUIT TOPPING
4 cups chopped fresh rhubarb	1 cup all-purpose flour
2 cups sliced strawberries	¼ cup sugar
¾ cup sugar	1½ teaspoons baking powder
2 tablespoons cornstarch	¼ teaspoon salt
1 teaspoon grated orange zest	¼ cup cold butter, cut into pieces
	½ cup low-fat milk
	1 teaspoon vanilla extract

1. Preheat the oven to 400°F.

2. **Make the fruit:** Place rhubarb and strawberries in a 9" round or square baking dish.

3. In a small bowl, combine sugar, cornstarch, and zest; sprinkle over fruit and toss gently.

4. Bake for 20 to 25 minutes (increase to 30 minutes if using frozen fruit), or until hot and bubbles appear around edges.

5. **Make the topping:** When fruit is almost done baking, in a large bowl, combine flour, sugar, baking powder, and salt. Cut in butter using a pastry blender or fork to make coarse crumbs.

6. In a glass measure, combine milk and vanilla; stir into dry ingredients to make a soft, sticky dough.

7. Using a large spoon, drop 8 separate spoonfuls of dough onto hot fruit.

8. Bake for 25 to 30 minutes, or until top is golden and fruit is bubbly.

NUTRIENTS PER SERVING

Calories	245
Carbohydrate	45 g
Fiber	2 g
Protein	3 g
Fat, total	6 g
Fat, saturated	4 g
Sodium	190 mg
Cholesterol	16 mg

EXCHANGES PER SERVING

1	Starch
½	Fruit
1½	Other Carbohydrate
1	Fat

Irresistible Peach Almond Crumble

Makes 9 servings

TIP

- Fresh peaches work best, but in a pinch, substitute 1 can (28 ounces) peaches, drained and sliced. Omit the cornstarch.

Note: *The suggested accompaniment for this recipe is not included in the nutrients or exchanges per serving. Whether you keep track of exchanges or count carbohydrates, remember to account for what these additional foods contribute.*

When you pair fresh, ripe peaches with a crumbly nut topping, it's a juicy, sweet treat. For a special occasion, serve the crumble warm with low-fat frozen yogurt. It's the ultimate comfort-food dessert.

FRUIT

- 4 cups sliced peeled peaches or nectarines
- ¼ cup peach or apricot preserves
- 2 teaspoons cornstarch

TOPPING

- ½ cup all-purpose flour
- ½ cup old-fashioned rolled oats
- ¼ cup packed brown sugar
- ¼ teaspoon ground ginger
- ¼ cup butter, melted
- 2 tablespoons sliced almonds

1. Preheat the oven to 375°F. Coat an 8" baking dish with cooking spray.

2. **Make the fruit:** In a large bowl, toss peaches with preserves and cornstarch. Spread in the prepared baking dish.

3. **Make the topping:** In a small bowl, combine flour, oats, brown sugar, and ginger. Pour in butter and stir to make coarse crumbs. Sprinkle over fruit and top with almonds.

4. Bake for 30 to 35 minutes, or until topping is golden and filling is bubbly. Serve warm or at room temperature.

NUTRIENTS PER SERVING

Calories	197
Carbohydrate	34 g
Fiber	2 g
Protein	3 g
Fat, total	6 g
Fat, saturated	3 g
Sodium	60 mg
Cholesterol	14 mg

EXCHANGES PER SERVING

½	Starch
½	Fruit
1	Other Carbohydrate
1	Fat

Lemon Fool with Fresh Berries

Makes 8 servings

TIPS

● Whipped cream is a delicious traditional ingredient in many desserts, but it's high in fat, so combine small amounts with lower-fat ingredients, such as the fresh fruit and low-fat yogurt in this recipe.

● Instead of individual serving dishes, layer the berries and lemon fool in a 6-cup deep glass serving bowl.

MAKE AHEAD

You can prepare the recipe through Step 1 a day in advance. On the day you plan to serve it, you can prepare the recipe up to the point of garnishing in Step 4 and refrigerate it for up to 4 hours.

NUTRIENTS PER SERVING

Calories	186
Carbohydrate	29 g
Fiber	2 g
Protein	3 g
Fat, total	7 g
Fat, saturated	4 g
Sodium	30 mg
Cholesterol	68 mg

EXCHANGES PER SERVING

½	Fruit
1½	Other Carbohydrate
1½	Fat

Here's an updated version of the traditional "fool"—an old-fashioned dessert with fruit or berries folded into whipped cream or custard. This dessert is ideal for entertaining because it can be assembled earlier in the day.

½ cup cold water
2 tablespoons cornstarch
⅔ cup sugar
⅓ cup fresh lemon juice
1 tablespoon finely grated lemon zest
2 large egg yolks
1 cup low-fat plain yogurt

½ cup heavy cream
4 cups fresh berries, such as sliced strawberries, raspberries, or blueberries
Additional berries, fresh mint sprigs, and grated lemon zest, for garnish

1. In a small saucepan, whisk together water and cornstarch until smooth. Add sugar, lemon juice, zest, and egg yolks; cook over medium heat, whisking constantly, until mixture comes to a full boil. Boil for 15 seconds. Remove the pan from the heat and pour lemon mixture into a large bowl. Let cool slightly. Cover surface with plastic wrap and refrigerate for 2 hours, or until chilled.

2. When chilled, whisk lemon mixture until smooth. Whisk in yogurt.

3. In the bowl of an electric mixer, beat cream on medium speed until stiff peaks form. Gently fold into lemon-yogurt mixture.

4. Arrange half of the berries in 6 parfait glasses or large wine glasses. Top with half of the lemon fool, then layer with remaining berries and lemon fool. To serve, garnish with whole berries, mint sprigs, and grated lemon zest.

Warm Maple Apple Pudding

Makes 9 servings

Saucy fruit topped with cake batter makes one of the most soothing desserts ever created. This version uses sweet, snappy Macintosh apples and pure maple syrup.

4 cups peeled, sliced, and cored Macintosh apples	½ teaspoon baking soda
½ cup pure maple syrup	¼ cup butter, cut into pieces
1 cup all-purpose flour	½ cup buttermilk
¼ cup sugar	1 large egg
1½ teaspoons baking powder	1 teaspoon vanilla extract

1. Preheat the oven to 350°F. Coat an 8" square baking dish with cooking spray.

2. In a large saucepan, bring apples and syrup to a boil. Reduce the heat and simmer until softened, about 3 minutes. Pour into the prepared baking dish.

3. In a large bowl, combine flour, sugar, baking powder, and baking soda. Cut in butter, using a pastry blender or 2 knives, to make fine crumbs.

4. In a small bowl, combine buttermilk, egg, and vanilla. Pour over flour mixture and stir just until combined. Drop batter by large spoonfuls onto warm apple slices.

5. Bake for 30 minutes, or until top is golden and a tester inserted in the center comes out clean. Serve warm.

NUTRIENTS PER SERVING

Calories	207
Carbohydrate	36 g
Fiber	1 g
Protein	3 g
Fat, total	6 g
Fat, saturated	3 g
Sodium	190 mg
Cholesterol	35 mg

EXCHANGES PER SERVING

½	Starch
½	Fruit
1½	Other Carbohydrate
1	Fat

Creamy Rice Pudding

Makes 8 servings

TIPS

● If short-grain rice is unavailable, use long-grain (not converted) instead. Long-grain rice is not as starchy, so reduce the amount of milk to 4 cups total. Combine the long-grain rice with 3½ cups of the milk and continue with the recipe as directed.

● Be careful of spillovers and pudding sticking to the pan: Be sure to turn the heat down so the mixture just simmers gently.

● Instead of using vanilla for flavoring, add a 3" strip of lemon peel to the milk-rice mixture when cooking. Remove it before serving.

When it comes to comfort food, rice pudding tops a lot of people's lists. It's creamy, luscious, and oh-so-satisfying.

5 cups whole milk	1 large egg yolk
½ cup short-grain rice, such as Arborio	¼ cup golden raisins
⅓ cup sugar	1 teaspoon vanilla extract
½ teaspoon salt	Ground cinnamon (optional)

1. In a large saucepan, combine 4½ cups of the milk, the rice, sugar, and salt; bring to a boil. Reduce the heat to medium-low and simmer, partially covered, stirring occasionally, for about 45 to 50 minutes, or until rice is tender and mixture has thickened.

2. In a small bowl, beat together egg yolk and remaining ½ cup milk. Add to rice mixture and cook, stirring, until creamy, about 1 minute. Remove the pan from the heat. Stir in raisins and vanilla.

3. Serve either warm or at room temperature (pudding thickens slightly as it cools). Sprinkle with cinnamon, if desired.

NUTRIENTS PER SERVING

Calories	194
Carbohydrate	29 g
Fiber	0 g
Protein	6 g
Fat, total	6 g
Fat, saturated	3 g
Sodium	220 mg
Cholesterol	44 mg

EXCHANGES PER SERVING

½	Starch
½	Milk, Whole
1	Other Carbohydrate
½	Fat

Basmati Rice Pudding

Makes 10 servings

TIPS

● Demerara sugar, named for the colony in Guyana where it was originally found, is a type of raw, coarse-textured cane sugar, often used in baking. It is brown in color.

● Although brown rice is more nutritious than white rice, it's also more perishable because the germ layer contains healthful oils. Like most whole grains, it turns rancid if not properly stored. That means it's important to buy from a source with high turnover.

Note: *The suggested accompaniment for this recipe is not included in the nutrients or exchanges per serving. Whether you keep track of exchanges or count carbohydrates, remember to account for what these additional foods contribute.*

NUTRIENTS PER SERVING

Calories	138
Carbohydrate	22 g
Fiber	1 g
Protein	5 g
Fat, total	4 g
Fat, saturated	2 g
Sodium	50 mg
Cholesterol	14 mg

EXCHANGES PER SERVING

½	Starch
½	Other Carbohydrate
½	Whole Milk

The cardamom in this pudding imparts an irresistible Indian flavor. It's delicious served at room temperature, but it also works well warm or cold. If you're feeling indulgent, add a little cream.

● **Works best in a small (3½-quart) slow cooker**

4 cups whole milk or enriched rice milk	2 teaspoons ground cardamom
⅓ cup Demerara sugar or brown sugar (see Tips, left)	¾ cup brown basmati rice, rinsed

1. Lightly coat the slow cooker stoneware with cooking spray.

2. In a large saucepan, bring milk to a boil over medium heat, stirring often. Add sugar and cardamom. Remove from the heat and stir in rice. Transfer to the prepared slow cooker.

3. Place a tea towel, folded in half (so you will have 2 layers), over the top of the stoneware to absorb moisture. Cover and cook on High for 3 hours, or until rice is tender and pudding is creamy. Transfer to a serving bowl and cool to room temperature.

Pumpkin Rice Pudding

Makes 10 servings

TIPS

● Cook ⅔ cup raw rice to get the 2 cups of cooked rice required for this recipe.

● If you prefer, use 1½ teaspoons pumpkin pie spice instead of the cinnamon, nutmeg, and cloves.

The combination of flavors and the chewy but crunchy texture of this luscious pudding make it hard to resist.

● **Works best in a small (3½-quart) slow cooker**

2 cups cooked brown rice (see Tips, left)	1 teaspoon ground cinnamon (see Tips, left)
1½ cups pumpkin purée (not pie filling)	½ teaspoon grated nutmeg
1 cup dried cranberries or dried cherries	¼ teaspoon ground cloves
1 cup fat-free evaporated milk	Low-fat vanilla-flavored yogurt, whipped cream, or whipped topping (optional)
½ cup packed dark brown sugar	
2 large eggs	

1. Coat the slow cooker stoneware with cooking spray.

2. In the prepared slow cooker, combine rice, pumpkin purée, and cranberries.

3. In a medium bowl, whisk together milk, brown sugar, eggs, cinnamon, nutmeg, and cloves until smooth and blended. Stir into pumpkin mixture. Cover and cook on High for 3 hours, or until pudding is set. Garnish each serving with 1 tablespoon yogurt, if using, and serve warm.

NUTRIENTS PER SERVING

Calories	179
Carbohydrate	38 g
Fiber	3 g
Protein	5 g
Fat, total	2 g
Fat, saturated	1 g
Sodium	54 mg
Cholesterol	38 mg

EXCHANGES PER SERVING

½	Starch
1	Fruit
1	Other Carbohydrate

Cinnamon Raisin Bread Pudding

Makes 9 servings

On a comfort scale, bread puddings, with their old-fashioned appeal, rate as one of the most-loved desserts. This simple bread pudding, featuring cinnamon bread in a custard base, takes no time to put together.

12 slices cinnamon raisin swirl bread (1 pound loaf)
2 cups whole milk
1 cup half-and-half
¾ cup plus 2 tablespoons sugar
6 large eggs
2 teaspoons vanilla extract
½ teaspoon ground cinnamon

1. Preheat the oven to 375°F. Coat a 12" × 8" baking dish with cooking spray.

2. Place bread slices in a single layer on 2 baking sheets and lightly toast in the oven for 10 to 12 minutes. Remove from the oven and let cool. Leave the oven on.

3. When cool, cut bread into cubes and place in the prepared baking dish.

4. In a medium bowl, whisk together milk, half-and-half, ¾ cup sugar, eggs, and vanilla. Pour over bread. Let soak for 10 minutes, pressing down gently with a spatula.

5. In a small bowl, combine cinnamon and 2 tablespoons sugar. Sprinkle over bread.

6. Place the baking dish in a large shallow roasting pan or deep broiler pan. Carefully add enough boiling water to come halfway up the sides of the dish. Bake for 45 to 50 minutes, or until top is puffed and custard is set in the center. Transfer pan to a rack to cool. Serve warm or at room temperature.

NUTRIENTS PER SERVING

Calories	329
Carbohydrate	50 g
Fiber	2 g
Protein	11 g
Fat, total	10 g
Fat, saturated	4 g
Sodium	275 mg
Cholesterol	140 mg

EXCHANGES PER SERVING

2	Starch
1½	Milk, Whole
½	Other Carbohydrate
1	Fat

Bread Pudding with Caramelized Pears

Makes 8 servings

TIPS

● Bartlett pears work particularly well in this recipe.

● Can't figure out the volume of a baking dish? Look for the measurements on the bottom of the dish, or measure by pouring in enough water to fill it completely.

● When a recipe calls for a baking pan, it refers to a metal pan, while a baking dish refers to glass.

In the old days, bread puddings were an economy dish, simply made with stale bread and custard. But there's nothing humble about this recipe. The golden pear topping flecked with raisins transforms it into a special dessert fit for company. Serve it either warm or at room temperature.

6 slices whole wheat sandwich bread	2 tablespoons water
2 tablespoons butter, softened	4 pears, peeled, cored, and sliced
4 large eggs	½ teaspoon freshly grated nutmeg
⅔ cup sugar	⅓ cup raisins
2 teaspoons vanilla extract	¼ cup sliced blanched almonds
2 cups hot low-fat milk	

1. Preheat the oven to 350°F. Coat an 8-cup baking dish with cooking spray.

2. Trim crusts from bread; butter 1 side of each slice. Cut each slice into 4 triangles. Layer in the prepared baking dish, overlapping the triangles.

3. In a large bowl, whisk together eggs, ⅓ cup of the sugar, and the vanilla. Whisk in hot milk in a stream, stirring constantly. Pour over bread.

4. In a large nonstick skillet, combine water and remaining ⅓ cup sugar. Cook over medium heat, stirring occasionally, until mixture turns a deep caramel color. Immediately add pears and nutmeg (be careful of spatters). Cook, stirring often, until pears are tender and sauce is smooth, about 5 minutes. Stir in raisins. Spoon evenly over bread. Sprinkle almonds on top.

5. Place the baking dish in a shallow roasting pan. Carefully add enough boiling water to come halfway up the sides of the dish. Bake for 40 to 45 minutes, or until custard is set in the center. Remove the dish from the water bath and transfer to a rack to cool.

NUTRIENTS PER SERVING

Calories	247
Carbohydrate	41 g
Fiber	3 g
Protein	7 g
Fat, total	7 g
Fat, saturated	3 g
Sodium	150 mg
Cholesterol	103 mg

EXCHANGES PER SERVING

½	Starch
1	Fruit
1	Other Carbohydrate
½	Medium-fat Meat
1	Fat

Crème Caramel

Makes 6 servings

MAKE AHEAD

The crème caramel can be made up to 2 days ahead of serving.

NUTRIENTS PER SERVING

Calories	196
Carbohydrate	28 g
Fiber	0 g
Protein	6 g
Fat, total	7 g
Fat, saturated	3 g
Sodium	75 mg
Cholesterol	139 mg

EXCHANGES PER SERVING

½	Milk, Whole
1½	Other Carbohydrate
½	Medium-fat Meat

This self-saucing French custard was the rage in the '70s. Now that French cuisine is back in vogue, so too is this appealing dessert that is surprisingly easy to make and serve.

CARAMEL

½ cup sugar
¼ cup water

CUSTARD

½ cup sugar
2 large eggs
2 egg yolks
1 teaspoon vanilla extract
2½ cups whole milk

1. Preheat the oven to 325°F.

2. **Make the caramel:** In a heavy-bottomed medium saucepan, combine sugar and water. Place the pan over medium heat until sugar melts. Increase the heat to medium-high and cook until sugar mixture boils (do not stir). When syrup has turned a rich caramel color, remove the pan from the heat. Pour caramel into 6 individual ramekins or 6-ounce custard cups. Quickly rotate the dishes to spread caramel evenly over bottom.

3. **Make the custard:** In a medium bowl, whisk together sugar, eggs, egg yolks, and vanilla.

4. In another medium saucepan, heat milk over medium heat until almost boiling. Pour hot milk mixture in a thin stream into egg mixture, whisking constantly. Pour through a strainer into the prepared ramekins.

5. Arrange the ramekins in a 13" × 9" baking pan. Carefully add enough boiling water to come 1" up the sides of the dish. Bake for 25 minutes, or until a tester inserted in the center comes out clean. Let cool to room temperature, then refrigerate until ready to serve. To serve, run a knife around the edges to loosen custards. Invert onto serving plates.

Peach Raspberry Betty

Makes 8 servings

● To make dried bread crumbs for this recipe, toast 4 slices of whole wheat bread. Tear the bread into pieces and process in a food processor until finely ground.

● Use a light-flavored whole wheat loaf for this recipe. Bread with heavy molasses content will overpower the fruit.

The combination of peaches and raspberries is a universal favorite. Although this dessert is best made in summer when fresh fruit is in season, it's also delicious made with canned or frozen fruit, making it a year-round treat.

● **Works in slow cookers from 3½ to 6 quarts**

2 cups dried whole wheat bread crumbs (see Tips, left)	2 cups raspberries
¼ cup chopped toasted almonds	½ cup packed brown sugar
	1 tablespoon all-purpose flour
2 tablespoons extra virgin olive or coconut oil or almond butter	½ teaspoon almond extract
	¼ cup cranberry-raspberry or cranberry juice (no sugar added)
5 cups sliced peaches (about 4 or 5)	

1. Lightly coat the slow cooker stoneware with cooking spray.

2. In a large bowl, combine bread crumbs, almonds, and oil; set aside.

3. In a separate large bowl, combine peaches, raspberries, brown sugar, flour, and almond extract.

4. In the prepared stoneware, layer one-third of the bread crumb mixture, then half of the peach mixture. Repeat, then finish with a layer of bread crumbs on top. Drizzle juice over the top. Cover and cook on High for 2½ to 3 hours, or until hot and bubbly.

NUTRIENTS PER SERVING

Calories	200
Carbohydrate	37 g
Fiber	5 g
Protein	3 g
Fat, total	6 g
Fat, saturated	1 g
Sodium	65 mg
Cholesterol	0 mg

EXCHANGES PER SERVING

1	Starch
1	Fruit
½	Other Carbohydrate
1	Fat

Cranberry Pear Brown Betty

Makes 8 servings

The combination of textures and flavors in this old-fashioned favorite is what makes it special. When cranberries are in season, freeze a bag or two so you can make this wholesome dessert year-round. It's a great way to use up day-old bread.

● **Works best in a small (3½-quart) slow cooker**

2 cups dry coarse whole wheat bread crumbs (see Tip, page 331)	1 cup fresh or frozen cranberries
2 tablespoons butter, melted, or extra virgin olive oil	¼ cup packed brown sugar
6 pears, peeled, cored, and sliced	1 tablespoon fresh lemon juice
	½ cup cranberry juice (no sugar added)

1. Coat the slow cooker stoneware with cooking spray.

2. In a medium bowl, combine bread crumbs and butter. Set aside.

3. In a large bowl, combine pears, cranberries, brown sugar, and lemon juice.

4. In the prepared stoneware, spread one-third of the bread crumb mixture. Layer half of the pear mixture over the top. Repeat. Finish with a layer of crumbs, and pour juice over the top. Cover and cook on High for 4 hours, or until fruit is tender and mixture is hot and bubbly.

NUTRIENTS PER SERVING

Calories	150
Carbohydrate	30 g
Fiber	4 g
Protein	2 g
Fat, total	4 g
Fat, saturated	2 g
Sodium	85 mg
Cholesterol	8 mg

EXCHANGES PER SERVING

1	Starch
1	Fruit
½	Fat

Scrumptious Oatmeal Cookies

Makes 36 cookies (1 cookie per serving)

● Use whatever combination of dried fruits and nuts appeals to your family or whatever you happen to have on hand. Just add 1½ cups in total to the batter.

● Let the baking sheets cool completely before using them again to prevent the dough from melting and spreading out too much during baking.

Kids love home-baked cookies, especially moist and chewy ones like these, made with wholesome oatmeal.

¾ cup butter, softened	1½ cups old-fashioned rolled oats
1¼ cups packed brown sugar	¾ cup sliced almonds or chopped pecans
1 large egg	
1 teaspoon vanilla extract	¾ cup dried cranberries, dried cherries, or raisins
1¼ cups whole wheat flour	
½ teaspoon baking soda	
¼ teaspoon salt	

1. Preheat the oven to 350°F. Line 2 baking sheets with parchment paper.

2. In a large bowl, cream butter and brown sugar with a wooden spoon until fluffy. Beat in egg and vanilla.

3. In another large bowl, stir together flour, baking soda, and salt. Stir into butter mixture, mixing well. Stir in oats, almonds, and dried cranberries.

4. Drop by heaping tablespoonfuls, about 2" apart, onto the prepared baking sheets, and flatten with a fork.

5. Bake one sheet at a time on the middle rack of the oven for 12 to 14 minutes, or until edges of cookies are golden. Remove from the oven and let stand for 5 minutes on the baking sheet before transferring with a spatula to a rack to cool.

NUTRIENTS PER SERVING

Calories	113
Carbohydrate	16 g
Fiber	1 g
Protein	2 g
Fat, total	5 g
Fat, saturated	3 g
Sodium	80 mg
Cholesterol	16 mg

EXCHANGES PER SERVING

½	Starch
½	Other Carbohydrate
1	Fat

Scottish Shortbread

Makes 48 cookies (2 cookies per serving)

The secret to this tender, easy-to-make shortbread is to have a light touch and not overhandle the dough.

1 cup unsalted butter, softened	2 cups all-purpose flour
½ cup superfine sugar	½ teaspoon salt

1. Preheat the oven to 300°F.

2. In a large bowl, cream butter with a wooden spoon until fluffy. Beat in sugar a spoonful at time, until well blended. Stir in flour and salt. Gather dough into a ball.

3. On a lightly floured work surface, gently knead the dough 4 or 5 times, or until smooth. Roll out a portion of the dough on a lightly floured surface to ⅓" thickness. Cut out shapes using cooking cutters and place on 2 ungreased baking sheets.

4. Bake one sheet at a time on the middle rack of the oven for 25 to 30 minutes, or until edges of cookies are light golden. Transfer cookies to a rack to cool.

NUTRIENTS PER SERVING

Calories	122
Carbohydrate	12 g
Fiber	0 g
Protein	1 g
Fat, total	8 g
Fat, saturated	5 g
Sodium	50 mg
Cholesterol	21 mg

EXCHANGES PER SERVING

½	Starch
½	Other Carbohydrate
1½	Fat

Hazelnut and Dried Cranberry Biscotti

Makes 48 biscotti (1 cookie per serving)

TIPS

● To toast and skin hazelnuts, place on a rimmed baking sheet in a preheated 350°F oven until lightly browned, 8 to 10 minutes. Place in a clean, dry towel, and rub off most of the skins.

● Be sure to replenish your spices regularly and buy the freshest dried fruits and nuts.

VARIATION

Dried cranberries add a sweet-tart flavor; substitute golden raisins or chopped dried apricots, if you prefer.

NUTRIENTS PER SERVING

Calories	76
Carbohydrate	11 g
Fiber	0 g
Protein	1 g
Fat, total	3 g
Fat, saturated	1 g
Sodium	45 mg
Cholesterol	13 mg

EXCHANGES PER SERVING

½	Other Carbohydrate
1	Fat

These crunchy morsels make wonderful gifts for friends and family. Pack the biscotti in fancy containers or tins, or wrap them in clear cellophane and add a bright ribbon.

½ cup butter, softened	¼ teaspoon ground cloves
1 cup packed brown sugar	¼ teaspoon salt
2 large eggs	½ cup dried cranberries
2⅓ cups all-purpose flour	¾ cup hazelnuts, toasted, skinned, and coarsely chopped (see Tips, left)
1½ teaspoons baking powder	
1½ teaspoons ground cinnamon	
¼ teaspoon ground allspice	

1. Preheat the oven to 325°F. Line 2 baking sheets with parchment paper.

2. In the bowl of an electric mixer, cream butter with brown sugar on medium speed until light and fluffy. Add eggs and beat until incorporated.

3. In a large bowl, combine flour, baking powder, cinnamon, allspice, cloves, and salt. Add to butter mixture and stir to make a soft dough. Fold in cranberries and hazelnuts.

4. Turn dough out onto a lightly floured surface. With floured hands, shape into a ball and divide in half. Pat into 2 logs, each about 2" wide and 12" long. Place the logs on one of the prepared baking sheets, about 2" apart.

5. Bake on the middle rack of the oven for 20 to 25 minutes, or until firm to the touch. Remove from the oven and let cool on the pan for 10 minutes. Do not turn off the oven. Using a long spatula, transfer the logs to a cutting board. With a serrated knife, cut diagonally into ½"-thick slices.

6. Place biscotti upright on the baking sheet, ½" apart, using 2 baking sheets, if necessary. Return to the oven and bake for 15 to 20 minutes, or until dry and lightly brown. Transfer biscotti to a rack to cool.

Fudgy Chocolate Brownies

Makes 32 brownies (1 brownie per serving)

These brownies are so moist and chewy, they will disappear in no time. Luckily, this recipe makes a big batch, so you can stash half in the freezer.

BROWNIES

- 1 cup butter, softened
- 1½ cups granulated sugar
- 4 large eggs
- 2 teaspoons vanilla extract
- 1 cup unsweetened cocoa powder
- 1 cup all-purpose flour
- ¾ teaspoon baking powder
- ½ teaspoon salt
- 1 cup walnuts, chopped

FROSTING

- 1 cup confectioner's sugar
- ⅓ cup unsweetened cocoa powder
- 2 tablespoons butter, softened
- 2 tablespoons low-fat milk

1. Preheat the oven to 350°F. Coat a 13" × 9" foil-lined baking pan lined with cooking spray.

2. **Make the brownies:** In the bowl of an electric mixer, cream butter with sugar on medium speed until light and fluffy. Add eggs one at a time, and beat until incorporated. Add vanilla and beat until incorporated.

3. In a large bowl, sift together cocoa powder, flour, baking powder, and salt. Add to butter mixture and beat to make a smooth batter. Fold in walnuts.

4. Spread batter in the prepared baking pan. Bake on the middle rack of the oven for 25 to 30 minutes, or until a tester inserted in the center comes out clean. Transfer the pan to a rack to cool until slightly warm.

5. **Make the frosting:** In the bowl of an electric mixer, beat confectioner's sugar, cocoa powder, butter, and milk until smooth. Spread frosting over slightly warm brownies.

6. When frosting is set, cut into 32 brownies.

NUTRIENTS PER SERVING

Calories	164
Carbohydrate	19 g
Fiber	1 g
Protein	2 g
Fat, total	10 g
Fat, saturated	5 g
Sodium	120 mg
Cholesterol	41 mg

EXCHANGES PER SERVING

½	Starch
½	Other Carbohydrate
2	Fat

Luscious Lemon Squares

Makes 36 squares (1 square per serving)

These classy lemon treats with a shortbread crust are always appreciated when friends are invited for a fresh-brewed cup of tea or coffee.

CRUST

1 cup all-purpose flour
¼ cup granulated sugar
½ cup butter, cut into pieces

FILLING

1 cup granulated sugar
¼ cup fresh lemon juice

2 large eggs
2 tablespoons all-purpose flour
½ teaspoon baking powder
1 tablespoon grated lemon zest
Pinch of salt
2 tablespoons confectioner's sugar

1. Preheat the oven to 350°F.

2. **Make the crust:** In a large bowl, combine flour and sugar. Cut in butter with a pastry blender or 2 knives to make coarse crumbs. Press the mixture into the bottom of an 8"-square baking pan. Bake for 18 to 20 minutes, or until light golden. Transfer the pan to a rack to cool.

3. **Make the filling:** In a medium bowl, combine granulated sugar, lemon juice, eggs, flour, baking powder, zest, and salt. Pour over crust.

4. Bake for 25 to 30 minutes, or until filling is set and light golden. Transfer the pan to a rack to cool. When cool, dust with confectioner's sugar and cut into 36 squares.

NUTRIENTS PER SERVING

Calories	70
Carbohydrate	11 g
Fiber	0 g
Protein	1 g
Fat, total	3 g
Fat, saturated	2 g
Sodium	35 mg
Cholesterol	17 mg

EXCHANGES PER SERVING

½	Other Carbohydrate
½	Fat

Lunch Box Oatmeal-Raisin Bars

Makes 32 bars (1 bar per serving)

Ideal for school lunches, these chewy bars travel well. Package them individually in plastic wrap, place in a covered container, and freeze. It's so easy to pop a bar from the freezer into lunch bags or grab them for on-the-go snacks.

⅔ cup packed brown sugar

⅓ cup butter

⅓ cup golden corn syrup

2½ cups quick-cooking rolled oats

½ cup raisins or chopped dried apricots

¼ cup all-purpose flour

1 large egg

1 teaspoon vanilla extract

1. Preheat the oven to 350°F. Coat a 13" × 9" foil-lined baking pan with cooking spray.

2. In a large glass bowl, combine brown sugar, butter, and corn syrup. Microwave on High for 2 minutes; stir until smooth. Microwave for 1 minute longer, or until sugar dissolves and mixture comes to a full boil. Stir in oats, raisins, and flour.

3. In a small bowl, beat egg with vanilla. Stir into oat mixture.

4. Spread oat mixture evenly in the prepared pan. Bake for 20 to 25 minutes, or until golden around the edges. Remove from the oven and let cool for 10 minutes in the pan. Lift off the foil and cut into 32 bars. Transfer to a rack to cool completely.

NUTRIENTS PER SERVING

Calories	87
Carbohydrate	15 g
Fiber	1 g
Protein	2 g
Fat, total	3 g
Fat, saturated	1 g
Sodium	30 mg
Cholesterol	11 mg

EXCHANGES PER SERVING

½	Starch
½	Other Carbohydrate
½	Fat

Peanutty Cereal Snacking Bars

Makes 24 bars (1 bar per serving)

TIP

● Wrap the bars individually in plastic wrap and freeze. Then, when making school lunches, just pop a wrapped bar into each lunch bag.

Peanut butter fans will love these no-bake bars. They're a breeze to make and taste so much better than the expensive packaged snack bars sold in supermarkets.

1 cup smooth or chunky light peanut butter	4 cups toasted rice cereal
⅔ cup honey or golden corn syrup	2 cups muesli-type cereal with fruit and nuts

1. Coat a 13" × 9" foil-lined baking pan with cooking spray.

2. In a large saucepan, combine peanut butter and honey. Cook over medium heat, stirring constantly, until smooth. (Or place in a large glass bowl, and microwave on High for 2 minutes or until smooth, stirring once.)

3. Fold in both cereals until evenly coated. Press firmly into the prepared baking pan. Let cool, then cut into 3" × 1½" bars.

NUTRIENTS PER SERVING

Calories	121
Carbohydrate	19 g
Fiber	1 g
Protein	4 g
Fat, total	4 g
Fat, saturated	1 g
Sodium	110 mg
Cholesterol	0 mg

EXCHANGES PER SERVING

½	Starch
½	Other Carbohydrate
½	High-fat Meat

Classic Chocolate Chip Cookies

Makes 40 cookies (1 cookie per serving)

VARIATION

Double Chocolate Chunk Cookies Decrease the flour to 1½ cups. Sift the flour with ½ cup unsweetened cocoa powder and ½ teaspoon baking soda. Replace the chocolate chips with white chocolate chunks.

You'll never be short of taste testers when the first batch of these cookies comes out of the oven. Served with a cold glass of low-fat milk, they're pure heaven.

¾ cup butter, softened
¾ cup granulated sugar
½ cup packed brown sugar
2 large eggs
2 teaspoons vanilla extract

1¾ cups all-purpose flour
½ teaspoon baking soda
½ teaspoon salt
1½ cups semi-sweet chocolate chips

1. Preheat the oven to 350°F. Line 2 baking sheets with parchment paper.

2. In the bowl of an electric mixer, cream butter with granulated and brown sugars on medium speed until fluffy; beat in eggs and vanilla until smooth.

3. In a large bowl, stir together flour, baking soda, and salt. Beat into sugar mixture until combined; stir in chocolate chips.

4. Drop batter by tablespoonfuls, about 2" apart, onto prepared baking sheets.

5. Bake one sheet at time on the middle rack of the oven for 10 to 12 minutes, or until edges of cookies are firm. (Bake for the shorter time if you prefer cookies with a soft chewy center.) Cool for 2 minutes on the baking sheet, then transfer cookies to a wire rack to cool completely.

NUTRIENTS PER SERVING

Calories	110
Carbohydrate	15 g
Fiber	1 g
Protein	1 g
Fat, total	6 g
Fat, saturated	3 g
Sodium	85 mg
Cholesterol	19 mg

EXCHANGES PER SERVING

½	Starch
½	Other Carbohydrate
1	Fat

Brown Sugar Apple Slices with Dried Cranberries

Makes 6 servings

TIP

● Use apples that hold their shape after cooking, such as Cortland, Granny Smith, or Golden Delicious.

This quick dessert sauce is great on its own or over low-fat yogurt. It tastes like old-fashioned apple pie—but without all the effort and calories.

⅓ cup orange juice	¼ cup dried cranberries
¼ cup packed brown sugar	½ teaspoon ground cinnamon
1 teaspoon cornstarch	
4 apples, peeled, cored, and sliced	

In a large saucepan, combine orange juice, brown sugar, and cornstarch; stir until smooth. Stir in apples, cranberries, and cinnamon. Cook over medium heat, stirring occasionally, until apples are just tender and sauce is slightly thickened, 7 to 9 minutes. Serve warm or at room temperature.

NUTRIENTS PER SERVING

Calories	111
Carbohydrate	29 g
Fiber	2 g
Protein	0 g
Fat, total	0 g
Fat, saturated	0 g
Sodium	5 mg
Cholesterol	0 mg

EXCHANGES PER SERVING

1	Fruit
1	Other Carbohydrate

Ultimate Baked Apples

Makes 8 servings

TIP

• Buy nuts from a store with high turnover. They are high in fat and tend to become rancid very quickly. This is especially true of walnuts. If you're buying in bulk, taste before you buy; if not, taste one from the package before using. If they're not sweet, substitute an equal quantity of pecans.

These luscious apples, simple to make yet delicious, are the definitive autumn dessert. Serve them with a dollop of whipped cream. They're equally appealing (and healthier) accompanied by yogurt or even served plain.

• **Large (minimum 5-quart) oval slow cooker**

½ cup dried cranberries	8 apples, cored
½ cup chopped toasted walnuts (see Tip, left)	1 cup cranberry juice (no sugar added)
2 tablespoons packed brown sugar	Low-fat vanilla-flavored yogurt or whipped cream (optional)
1 teaspoon grated orange zest	

1. In a medium bowl, combine cranberries, walnuts, brown sugar, and zest. To stuff the apples, hold your hand over the bottom of the apple and, using your fingers, tightly pack the core space with filling. One at a time, place filled apples in the slow cooker stoneware. Drizzle cranberry juice evenly over tops.

2. Cover and cook on Low for 8 hours or on High for 4 hours, or until apples are tender. Transfer to a serving dish and spoon cooking juices over them. Serve hot with a dollop of yogurt, if using.

NUTRIENTS PER SERVING

Calories	180
Carbohydrate	36 g
Fiber	4 g
Protein	1 g
Fat, total	6 g
Fat, saturated	1 g
Sodium	2 mg
Cholesterol	0 mg

EXCHANGES PER SERVING

2½	Fruit
1	Fat

Bananas in Spiced Rum Sauce

Makes 6 servings

A splash of spirits turns bananas into a special-occasion dessert in a matter of minutes, using your microwave oven.

¼ cup packed brown sugar

2 tablespoons orange juice

1 tablespoon fresh lime juice

¼ teaspoon ground cinnamon

¼ teaspoon freshly grated nutmeg

2 tablespoons dark rum

4 firm but ripe bananas

Low-fat plain yogurt (optional)

1. In a glass measure, combine brown sugar, orange juice, lime juice, cinnamon, and nutmeg. Microwave on High for 1½ to 2 minutes, or until sauce boils and reduces slightly. Add rum.

2. Peel bananas, halve lengthwise, and cut each half into 3 pieces. Arrange banana pieces in a single layer in an 8" or 9" round or square shallow baking dish and pour sauce over top. Cover loosely with waxed paper and microwave on High for 2½ to 4 minutes, or until bananas are softened.

3. Serve warm, topped with a dollop of yogurt, if using.

NUTRIENTS PER SERVING

Calories	129
Carbohydrate	31 g
Fiber	2 g
Protein	1 g
Fat, total	1 g
Fat, saturated	0 g
Sodium	5 mg
Cholesterol	0 mg

EXCHANGES PER SERVING

1	Fruit
1	Other Carbohydrate

Gingery Pears Poached in Green Tea

Makes 8 servings

You'll love the combination of ginger and pears in this light but delicious dessert. Sprinkle with toasted almonds and top with a dollop of vanilla yogurt for a perfect finish to a substantial meal.

TIPS

● There's a strong taste of ginger in these pears, which some might feel overpowers the pears. Vary the amount of ginger to suit your preference.

● When poaching, as in this recipe, use firmer pears (such as Bosc) for best results.

MAKE AHEAD

This dessert should be made early in the day or the night before so it can be well chilled before serving.

● **Works best in a small (3½-quart) slow cooker**

4 cups boiling water	8 firm pears, such as Bosc, peeled, cored, and cut lengthwise into quarters
2 tablespoons green tea leaves	
½ cup honey	Toasted sliced almonds (optional)
1 to 2 tablespoons grated ginger (see Tips, left)	Low-fat vanilla-flavored yogurt (optional)
1 teaspoon almond extract	
1 teaspoon grated lemon zest	

1. In a medium pot, combine boiling water and tea leaves. Cover and let steep for 5 minutes. Strain through a fine strainer into the slow cooker stoneware.

2. Add honey, ginger, almond extract, and zest; stir well. Add pears. Cover and cook on Low for 6 hours or on High for 3 hours, or until pears are tender. Transfer to a serving bowl, cover, and chill thoroughly. Serve garnished with toasted almonds and a dollop of yogurt, if using.

NUTRIENTS PER SERVING

Calories	131
Carbohydrate	35 g
Fiber	2 g
Protein	1 g
Fat, total	1 g
Fat, saturated	0 g
Sodium	1 mg
Cholesterol	0 mg

EXCHANGES PER SERVING

1	Fruit
1	Other Carbohydrate

INDEX

Underscored page references indicate boxed text. **Boldfaced** page references indicate photographs.

CONVERSION CHART

These equivalents have been slightly rounded to make measuring easier.

VOLUME MEASUREMENTS

U.S.	Imperial	Metric
¼ tsp	–	1 ml
½ tsp	–	2 ml
1 tsp	–	5 ml
1 Tbsp	–	15 ml
2 Tbsp (1 oz)	1 fl oz	30 ml
¼ cup (2 oz)	2 fl oz	60 ml
⅓ cup (3 oz)	3 fl oz	80 ml
½ cup (4 oz)	4 fl oz	120 ml
⅔ cup (5 oz)	5 fl oz	160 ml
¾ cup (6 oz)	6 fl oz	180 ml
1 cup (8 oz)	8 fl oz	240 ml

WEIGHT MEASUREMENTS

U.S.	Metric
1 oz	30 g
2 oz	60 g
4 oz (¼ lb)	115 g
5 oz (⅓ lb)	145 g
6 oz	170 g
7 oz	200 g
8 oz (½ lb)	230 g
10 oz	285 g
12 oz (¾ lb)	340 g
14 oz	400 g
16 oz (1 lb)	455 g
2.2 lb	1 kg

LENGTH MEASUREMENTS

U.S.	Metric
¼"	0.6 cm
½"	1.25 cm
1"	2.5 cm
2"	5 cm
4"	11 cm
6"	15 cm
8"	20 cm
10"	25 cm
12" (1')	30 cm

PAN SIZES

U.S.	Metric
8" cake pan	20 × 4 cm sandwich or cake tin
9" cake pan	23 × 3.5 cm sandwich or cake tin
11" × 7" baking pan	28 × 18 cm baking tin
13" × 9" baking pan	32.5 × 23 cm baking tin
15" × 10" baking pan	38 × 25.5 cm baking tin (Swiss roll tin)
1½ qt baking dish	1.5 liter baking dish
2 qt baking dish	2 liter baking dish
2 qt rectangular baking dish	30 × 19 cm baking dish
9" pie plate	22 × 4 or 23 × 4 cm pie plate
7" or 8" springform pan	18 or 20 cm springform or loose-bottom cake tin
9" × 5" loaf pan	23 × 13 cm or 2 lb narrow loaf tin or pâté tin

TEMPERATURES

Fahrenheit	Centigrade	Gas
140°	60°	–
160°	70°	–
180°	80°	–
225°	105°	¼
250°	120°	½
275°	135°	1
300°	150°	2
325°	160°	3
350°	180°	4
375°	190°	5
400°	200°	6
425°	220°	7
450°	230°	8
475°	245°	9
500°	260°	–

ABOUT THE AUTHORS

An avid cook, **Johanna Burkhard** is a well-established food writer, public relations consultant, and author of five cookbooks, including *400 Best Comfort Food Recipes*. Living in Toronto, she combines her keen interest in food and wine with her passion for cooking and sharing a wonderful meal with friends and family.

Judith Finlayson is a food writer and journalist with a lifelong love of cooking. She is the author of numerous books, including five slow cooker books, and most recently *The Complete Whole Grains Cookbook*. Judith, her husband, and daughter live in Toronto.

Barbara Selley is a registered dietician working and living in Toronto. Her company, Food Intelligence, provides consulting services to publishers in the United States and Canada.